THE NATURAL HISTORY
OF MAN

THE
NATURAL HISTORY
OF MAN

J. S. Weiner

Anchor Books
Anchor Press / Doubleday
Garden City, New York
1973

THE NATURAL HISTORY OF MAN was originally published by Universe
Books in 1971.

Anchor Books edition: 1973

CONTENTS

LIST OF FIGURES

LIST OF PLATES

ACKNOWLEDGEMENTS

The author and publisher would like to thank the following for providing material for illustrations:

PLATES: Australian News and Information Bureau for jacket photo and 16A; Trustees of the British Museum (Natural History) for 1A and B, 6A, 7B and C, 8C, E and F, 9A and C, 10B, 15; Professor P.V. Tobias for 2B and C and 6C, from 'Early Man in East Africa', Science, vol. 149 (1965), pp. 22–33; Zoological Society of London for 3, from G.M. Vevers and J.S. Weiner, 'Use of a Tool by a Captive Capuchin Monkey', Symp. Zool. Soc. Lond., no. 10 (1963), pp. 115–17; Zoological Society and Dr A. Kortland for 4B, from A. Kortland and M. Kooij, 'Protohominid Behaviour in Primates', Symp. Zool. Soc. Lond., no. 10 (1963), pp. 61–88; Nature and Dr J.R. Napier for 5, from Nature (London), vol. 196, pp. 409–11; R. Hoffstetter for 6E; Dr Harrison for 7A; Smithsonian Institution Press for 7C, from Ales Hrdlicka, 'Skeletal Remains of Early Man', Smithsonian Miscellaneous Collections, vol. 83; Dr A. Thoma, Dr H.V. Vallois, and Magyar Némzeti Múseum, Budapest, for 7D (photo J. Karáth); Musée de l'Homme, Paris, for 7E and F, 8A and B, 9B, D and E, and 10A; Science Journal, London, for 10E, from 'Discovery' (June, 1963); Doubleday and Co., New York for 10D and 11B, from W. Howells, Mankind in the Making, © 1959, 1967 by W. Howells; K. Oakley for 11A; P.E.P. Deraniyagala for 12A; Professor Buchi and R. Oldenbourg-Verlag, Munich, for 12B and C, from 'Rassengeschichte des indopakistanischen Subkontinentes' in Rassengeschichte der Menscheit; Current Anthropology and Edmund D. Gill for 14B; Professor Andrew Abbie and Frederick Muller, Ltd for 14C; Professor Andrew Abbie and Oceania for 16B; United States Information Service for 18A; Novosti Press Agency for 18B; The Wenner-Gren Foundation for Anthropological Research, Incorporated for 19B from Tepexman Man by Helmut de Terva, Javier Romero and T.D. Stewart; University of Minnesota Press for 19A, from Jenks and Thiel, Pleistocene Man in Minnesota; Mainichi Press Co. for 22C; Yoshobi Nakamura for 22B; Harcourt Brace Jovanovich for 22A, © 1960 by Leonardo da Vinci Editrice, reproduced from The Island of the Fisherwomen; the Press Association for 13, 17A and 20; and Professor David Maybury-Lewis, Department of Anthropology, Harvard University, for 21. Also Human Biology for 4A.

FIGURES: Dr Josef Biegert and the Aldine Publishing Co. for 4A and B, reprinted from Sherwood L. Washburn, ed., Classification and Human Evolution (Chicago, Aldine, 1963), copyright © 1963 by Wenner-Gren Foundation for Anthropological Research, Inc.; Wilder Penfield and the Royal Society of Medicine for 5, originally published in 'Engrams in the Human Brain', Proc. R. Soc. Med.,

1963, 61, 831, drawing by Dr Stanley Cobb; Prof. A.H. Schultz, Dr Gabriel W. Lasker, and the Wenner-Gren Foundation for Anthropological Research for 7, 8 and 9, originally printed in 'Ontogenetic Specialisations of Man', *Archiv der Julius Klaus Stiftung*, 24, 197–216; Edinburgh University Press for 10A and 23B; Elwyn L. Simons and *Nature* for 10B, originally from *Nature*, 205, 1967, 137; University of Chicago Press for 10C, from A.S. Romer, *Vertebrate Palaeontology*, 3rd edition, University of Chicago Press, 1966; W.H. Freeman and Company, with Elwyn L. Simons for 12 and 15 from Simons, 'The Early Relatives of Man', *Scientific American*, 211, July 1964, 58 and 59, and for 19, from J. Napier, 'The Evolution of the Hand', *ibid.*, 217 (December 1962) figs. 56 and 61, copyright © 1964, 1962 by Scientific American, Inc. All rights reserved; The Clarendon Press for 17D, E and F from Harrison *et al.*, *Human Biology;* Dr C.K. Brain for 20C, from 'The Transvaal Museum's Fossil Project at Swartkrans, *S. Afr. J. Sci.*, 63, no. 3, p. 383; John Wiley and Sons Limited for 21A from Stevens, ed., *Handbook of Experimental Psychology*, p. 155 The Macmillan Co. (New York) for 21B from Penrose and Rasmussen, *The Cerebral Cortex of Man*, 1960; Oxford University Press, London, for 23A from Samson Wright, *Applied Physiology;* J.M. Tanner and Pergamon Press Ltd for 25, from Symposium on Human Growth, 1960; Dr Kenneth P. Oakley for 30A–E, 31B, 37D and E, and part of 50; Professor Grahame Clark for part of 50; Professor François Bordes for 30F, 31A, 37A, B and F and 39, from *The Old Stone Age* (London, World University Library 1968); Royal Anthropological Institute for 34; Dr R. Tregear and Academic Press for 40 from Tregear, *Physical Functions of the Skin;* Dr G. Malcolm Brown and the American Physiological Society for 43A from *Journal of Applied Physiology*, 5, 221 (1952), p. 22; The Royal Society for 43B from *Proc. Roy. Soc.*, 143B, 392, p. 401; Loren D. Carlson and Academic Press for 44, from Edholm and Bacharach, eds, *The Physiology of Human Survival*, 1965, p. 45; D.F. Roberts and the Wistar Press for 45: A is from 'The Geographical Distribution of the Physical Characters of Man', D.Phil. thesis, Oxford (1953), B is from 'Body, Race and Climate', *American Journal of Physical Anthropology*, 11, no. 4, pp. 533–58; *South African Medical Journal* for 46, from article by T. Schrire, 32 (11 Oct. 1958), p. 998; Blackwell Scientific Publications Ltd for 47, from W.C. Boyd, *Genetics and the Races of Man*, p. 145; J. & A. Churchill for 49, from Penrose, *Recent Advances in Human Genetics*, p. 67; Methuen and Co., Holle Verlag GmbH, and Irene Lhote for 51A, B and D from 'The Rock Art of the Maghreb and Sahara', in *The Art of the Stone Age* (1961); Thomas Nelson & Sons (South Africa) Ltd for 51C, from A.R. Wilcox, *Rock Art of South Africa;* Dr Teuku Jacob for 52; Dr A.C. Allison for 55; *Human Biology* for 27; and the *Journal of Comparative Neurology* for 28.

CHAPTER 1

PERSPECTIVE

The pattern in time and space

The natural history of man is a pattern woven in time and space by the shaping processes of evolution. To trace out in detail this complex of pattern and process has been the task pursued by anthropologists with special intensity since Darwin's day. With the advance of evolutionary theory and the many splendid discoveries of fossils over the last hundred years we can now present a reasonably coherent and convincing account of the course of man's biological evolution, and to some extent of its causes.

To do this satisfactorily demands the ecological approach. We must examine the evolving populations of man and his precursors in the setting of the total environment; for it is the interaction between the biological needs of the organism and the stresses of the physical and organic environment which engenders the struggle for adaptation and survival and thereby the selection of new and more favourable characters. This intense, never-ceasing ecological interaction is responsible for the natural history of man and ultimately for his technological and cultural history also. For the intensity of the struggle with the environment will force man at last to a self-conscious awareness of his situation in nature; with this realisation will begin that quest for reconciliation with natural forces and the control of the world and human society which emerges as religion, philosophy, technology and science.

Emerging from the obscurity of its anthropoid origin to the final ascendancy over the animal kingdom, the human stock has traversed four great ecological epochs. The first—the most critical and the most prolonged—came to its end with the 'break-out' from the restricted anthropoid arboreal and forest covered environment. The second epoch was notable for the progressive development of a terrestrial hunting mode of life in a warm sunny terrain; from it there emerged the hominid, a creature biologically adaptable and resourceful. As a direct consequence, the third epoch was one of enormous ecological expansion and population differentiation. A wide variety of habitats was successfully colonised. This required the full exercise of adaptive powers; at the same time it brought about some degree of regional variation since the still meagre hunting and gathering technology could do relatively little to counter the biological selection imposed by the harsh exigencies of the many new environments. In due course this struggle forced man to a new ecological relationship; and in the fourth epoch, our own epoch, man entered into the phase of deliberate control and modification of the environment, beginning with the manipulation of primary food sources, plant and animal, and ending with the man-made urbanised habitat and energy-harnessed machine systems of the present day.

Each of these four epochs represented more than the achievement of a successful ecological adjustment; in each era adaptability, partly biological but increasingly technological, underwent a continued enhancement; the species found itself capable of transcending the bounds of its native habitat and erupting into that of the new epoch. Thus, at the end of the long anthropoid phase, the arboreal habitat could be abandoned in favour of the open, terrestrial life of the first hominids; by the end of this australopithecine phase, the bipedal hominid framework was perfected in essentials and a highly adaptable and resourceful creature of the genus *Homo* was able to move out of the African equatorial homeland into a varied range of climate and habitat on a world scale. The ecological understanding so acquired led at the end of this third stage to the abandonment of a life based on wild food, nomadism and casual shelter and to its substitution by a settled existence and the managed ecology of the fourth phase. In this fourth era, still continuing at the present time, the control of the natural world of matter, energy and living forms, seems near to completion. Already the ecological challenge of the future is clear—it is surely the

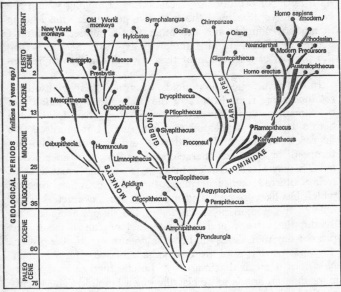

1 Time scale and epochs of the cenozoic era showing the evolutionary radiation of the Anthropoidea

achievement of that social self-control that will ensure the survival of a secure and harmonious world society.

The succession of animal forms leading to the precursors of man can be traced far back into geological time. But here we begin with that critical phase at about twenty million years ago that marks the beginning of the gradual change from the ape-like stage to the human.

The transition occupied nearly all those twenty million years, if we trace it from the first appearance of the ancestral arboreal ape-like Dryopithecines, their diversification in southeast Europe, India and east Africa and up to the emergence of the first African hominids, the Australopithecinae. During this same long period there took place the concurrent evolutionary emergence and diversification of the pongid or ape family. This first long phase witnessed the gradual development of tool-using powers, a gradual familiarisation with the forest floor and finally the advance beyond the forest's edge.

As a result of evolutionary radiation or branching within the earliest Dryopithecines, the two divergent lines, one leading to modern pongids and the other to the modern hominids, became established. This radiation expresses no more than the process of adaptation of these two lineages to their contrasting habitats.

In this divergence the pongids, despite their specialisations, retained some reminiscence of the prehominid potentiality of the common dryopithecine ancestry they shared with the hominids. They developed to some small but unmistakable degree in the hominid direction. There came about the 'anthropoid' or man-like characters of present day apes which led Thomas Henry Huxley in 1863 to call the great apes of today 'blurred copies of man'. It is this common ancestry which has likewise endowed man with some characters traceable to the pongid potentialities of the dryopithecines. This overlapping of ape and man does not of course mean that present day men descended from a creature at all like present day apes or that apes are descendants of some form of man. Nor does it mean that man is to be classified as an ape any more than an ape is to be classified as a hominid. The twenty or thirty million years of separate development have produced an enormous divergence without totally erasing some marks of their distant common origins.

Anthropogenesis—the establishment of the human stock—did not come about in one small circumscribed area. The new hominid populations were gradually built up by the continuous selection of favourable characters from a whole range of existing diversified populations and remoulded into more successful combinations. The dryopithecine populations that served as this ancestral matrix were located in the forested regions of India, Europe and east Africa during Miocene times from thirty till thirteen million years ago. In the next ten million years or so, till the end of the Pliocene, the record, though scanty, clearly reveals the existence of hominid precursors.

Under the influence of the selective pressures responsible for the successful transfer from an arboreal and herbivorous mode of life to a bipedal terrestrial and carnivorous existence, the dryopithecine morphological structure underwent a large overall modification of the cranium and dentition, of the post-cranial skeleton and especially the limb structure, to assume the basic hominid plan first clearly identifiable as a whole in the Australopithecines. At the same time there gradually became manifest in rudimentary form the essential hominid properties of close co-operative social relationships, of communication, and basic to all, of deliberate tool handling; underlying all of these was the progressive enhancement of brain function and of mental capacity; developments in behaviour rested on the evolutionary advance of the nervous system.

The australopithecine era lasted several million years—the exact period remains uncertain, but less than one million years ago their supersession by their descendants, the first members of the genus *Homo*, *Homo erectus*, was an accomplished fact.

Perhaps one of the most outstanding properties bequeathed by the australopithecine precursors of *Homo* can be described simply as that of a generalised adaptability. This is evidenced not only in the enhanced mobility of bipedalism, in manual dexterity and the exploitation of a variety of materials for toolmaking, in communication, and in flexible social groupings, but as we shall see in detail, in such characters as the ability to exist on the most varied of diets, to withstand wide variations and combinations of climate, to utilise energy at a high rate during work, and the possession of a highly efficient immunological system. With these we should take note of such a basic property as the pigment-making and relatively hairless skin.

All these seem explicable as the outcome of the restricted equatorial hunting australopithecine phase, perfected no doubt in important respects in the earliest phases of *Homo erectus*. Only in this way can we understand the remarkable similarities, as well as the peculiarities, of the physiological, developmental, metabolic, immunological and social characteristics evinced by the present day world wide human species, characteristics overriding all the variability of its constituent populations.

Crucial as was the australopithecine heritage, the fossil record testifies to further modifications in the phase of *Homo*, notably in the continued expansion of the brain with remodelling of the cranium, jaws and teeth. Along with these, steady progress in tool-making was maintained as new habitats were occupied. From *Homo erectus* there emerged the first 'archaic' varieties of *Homo sapiens* and these in turn provided the genetic matrix for the development of 'modern' varieties of *sapiens* man.

Because each hominid stage moves into the next by a continual replacement—a graded transformation—the record exhibits a spectrum or continuum of populations exhibiting a mosaic of more or less advanced features, of generalised and specialised characters, each stage presaging the next.

The Australopithecines, the first hominids, were able to establish themselves in the lightly wooded savannahs first of eastern and then of southern Africa; the *erectus* form of *Homo* developed not only in Africa (*Atlanthropus*) but far beyond; representatives are found in Europe (Heidelberg man) and as far away as Java (*Pithecanthropus*) and later on in China. The morphological as well as the spatial spectrum of the genus now expands to reveal the 'archaic' large-brained *sapiens* populations of *Homo*—those varieties which will in time replace *Homo erectus* and give rise to the continuum of neanderthaloid, rhodesioid and the first true 'modern' forms. These later, archaic varieties of *Homo sapiens*, occupied a still larger area than did *Homo erectus*—southern Africa, most of Europe, the Middle East and southeast Asia. Finally, out of this welter, modern *sapiens* man emerges as the sole surviving hominid species—a network of hunting groups slowly multiplying over a wide extent of Africa, Europe and Asia, moving in due course into the peripheral areas of these continents and finally erupting into North and South America, southeast Asia, Australia and Oceania.

Ecological adaptability and variability are clearly the hallmarks of a species capable of occupying, with ever-increasing success, so varied a network of habitats. But the evolutionary history of man remained bound up for a long time with the small ecological unit exposed to the rigour of natural selection under the conditions of stress and danger in the very variable environments of the late Pleistocene. The basis of man's diversity, or what is called 'racial differentiation' today, must have become evident at that time.

In the late Pleistocene men in Europe and Africa began to show themselves aware of the natural world around them; on cave walls they paint their food animals with extreme accuracy and depict them in the hunt. Man now explicitly recognises the outside world as a source of food and other materials, and also of danger. That intellectual process of deliberately distinguishing the world of man from the world of nature has begun. These pleistocene hunters, like the non-literate hunter-gatherers of today, possessed without doubt a highly detailed body of ecological knowledge of the plants, animals and topography of their surroundings.

The interaction between men and their environments, natural or artificial, will always invoke biological change, as immediate responses through developmental and physiological adjustment and as long term responses through selection and other agencies. But after the end of the pleistocene epoch it is on the technological and cultural level that the spectacular developments occur. Side by side with the remaining hunters, gatherers and fishermen there arise the first agriculturalists, pastoralists and nomadic farmers. Domestication of animals and crops is the first sign of the new era of man's mastery of the natural world. In this neolithic era the biological constitution of man is closely bound up with the way of life pursued by populations of varying degrees of social complexity and ecological mastery. The small isolate still remains, tribal bands of hunters are still widespread, but larger agglomerations of farming villages are forming. Geographically separate entities are increasingly eroded by migration and intermixture as we enter the historical and literate period. The natural environment is more and more supplemented and superseded by the new social environment. The selective and adaptive forces still contrive to operate but new biological responses are demanded in the more crowded conditions of urbanised life and the total dependence on cultivated food.

This deliberate exploitation of the environment becomes the main preoccupation of neolithic farmers and herdsmen; and this is greatly intensified and institutionalised as settlements become larger and permanent, and when crop cultivation becomes more technically exacting. As the neolithic settlements grow into villages and towns, as farming becomes dependent on elaborate systems of irrigation and complex water allocation, as trade develops and metal working begins, the time comes when the unaided human brain proves inadequate for recording and storing the mass of social data; the invention of writing is the logical solution. Civilisation as the phase of human history characterised by conscious and deliberate ecological and social control reaches its full expression with the industrial and scientific revolution. The climax is reached with the establishment of a complex social and ecological system on a world scale.

Not for long will simple communities, the 'savage survivals' such as the Australian, African or Indian hunter gatherers, continue to exist alongside the metropolitan conurbations of industrial societies. Soon the last remains of the palaeolithic and neolithic worlds will be buried forever.

Rate of hominid evolution

We have sketched out the pattern of hominid phylogeny* (Fig. 1) extending over the miocene, pliocene, pleistocene and post-pleistocene epochs, a period of some thirty million years. This rate of evolutionary change is not very different from that among mammals generally.

We can distinguish some five major phylogenetic steps—not as a simple linear series but as a progressive overlapping sequence. Putting this sequence in approximate stages, we may say that the separation from the common dryopithecine ape-like stock involved five noteworthy grades as denoted by (1) *Ramapithecus* (in several varieties, e.g. *Kenyapithecus*); (2) *Australopithecus* in two or three varieties, (3) *Homo erectus* showing geographical diversity and leading to (4) archaic varieties of *Homo sapiens*—Rhodesian, Solo and Neanderthaloid and the 'intermediate' varieties and (5) finally the 'modern' form of *Homo sapiens*. We have thus an apparent taxonomic rate of five or six major taxa and perhaps fifteen lesser taxa appearing in twenty-five million years. How do

---

* For the definition of this and other technical terms, see Glossary.

these generic or species rates compare with those of other animal lineages? In the evolutionary line of the horses, from *Hyracotherium* (*Eohippus*) to *Equus* some eight successive genera appear from Eocene to Pleistocene, about sixty million years (one in eight million years). This rate is not widely different from that characterising hominid phylogeny (one in five million years). Zeuner and Rensch both think that half a million years serve to establish a 'good' species and this is borne out in the hominoid-hominid line.

Climatic change in the hominid era

The 'anthropoid era' commenced about sixty million years ago, in the Eocene. By the beginning of the Miocene, about thirty million years later, the hominoid (dryopithecine) apes were well-established. For some two hundred million years previously (throughout the preceding mezozoic era and up to the Eocene) temperatures far to the north (and south) of the equator had remained high and subtropical; warm-temperate conditions extended into regions which to-day suffer extremely cold winters. The tropical character of the Eocene at the latitude of London (50°N) is attested by the existence of a flora of a kind now to be found in the Indo-Malayan rainforest. The eocene forests of Spitzbergen included species such as beech, sycamore, linden and oak, which now live much further south. Far north of present limits the marine waters of western Europe in the Eocene contained alligators, crocodiles, the pearly nautilus. From the Eocene onwards and during the ensuing Oligocene these warm mid-latitudes steadily cooled down and by pliocene times conditions were substantially similar to the cool climates of the present day. The annual mean temperature of western Europe dropped about 15°C from the Eocene to the end of the Pliocene.

For a good deal of the Miocene, the whole of the Pliocene and the first stages of the Pleistocene, a period of the order of twenty million years, the northern latitudes imposed conditions only possible to plants and animals successfully selected for arctic or cold climates. Indeed, the spread of ice sheets southward in Eurasia from Greenland and from Scandinavia, not once but at least three times in the Pleistocene, obliterated all plant and animal life beneath the ice; at the same time the glacial climate produced a southward shift of the forest regions. Pleistocene remains of both sub-arctic plants and animals are found far to the south in North America and central Europe.

The main stages of the slow establishment of the hominids were thus confined to warmer and indeed tropical regions of the Old World. The world into which the descendants of *Australopithecus* finally emerged offered a far greater variety of biotopes than that of his remote miocene and pliocene ancestors. The further stages of evolution of human communities took place against a background of the successive cold glacial and warmer interglacial phases of the Pleistocene. Today the world is in one of the warmer interglacial stages, the retreat of the ice margins of Scandinavia, the Alps and the Himalayas having begun some 15–20,000 years ago, marking the ending of the fourth or Würm Glaciation. The first evidences of settled life based on a productive agricultural economy are *c.* 9500 BP (Middle East), *c.* 5500 BP (north Africa), *c.* 3000 BP (east Africa), *c.* 3000 BP (Burma).

Agencies of evolution

Since Darwin's day the majority of human biologists have accepted that the theory of natural selection leading to the 'survival of the fittest' provides an adequate causal explanation for all the major phases of hominid differentiation, even though we shall never be able to do more than offer plausible reconstructions of the likely factors involved at any particular stage. Modern population genetics has greatly strengthened the selectionist theory and indeed has given for a number of cases in man a clear insight into natural selection at work, as will be discussed in detail later. There is now a widespread belief that heritable variations must in the majority of instances carry an adaptive significance as a consequence of natural selection. The factors or agents of evolutionary change are: 'the struggle for existence', meaning that more young are produced than can survive and reproduce, that there exists considerable *heritable variation* in each population, that some heritable characteristics impart *survival value* (in that such characteristics will appear more frequently in the next generation). Thus differential survival and fertility produce a genetic change in the next generation. The extent and rapidity of the genetic change will depend on such variables as population *size* and degree of *isolation* in time and space.

Genetic variation is essentially particulate; entirely novel variants of a character are brought into being by gene mutation; changes in the prevalence of particular variants of a character correspond to the predominance of particular combinations of genes. But small changes can accumulate if they are favourable, so that the result is a replacement in the range or frequency of a character by one with a different range or frequency. It is the biological value, the survival value, which gives rate and direction to the accumulation of favourable genes and the elimination of unfavourable ones.

These 'Darwinian' factors are in principle believed to be operative both at the supraspecific and the infraspecific levels; they explain the evolutionary changes responsible for diversification between populations as well as those that may effect, given enough time, the appearance of new species and eventually of new genera. As inference from a great mass of data we may take it that 'Darwinian' principles apply fully to anthropogenesis—the emergence of man, to hominisation—the establishment of man, and to the population diversity of modern man.

The evolutionary and palaeontological picture we have sketched presents hominid evolution as a long continuous series of relatively small and gradual changes within a network of connected populations; certain changes appearing in one population slowly pervading the whole network (for example, the disappearance of eyebrow ridges, the appearance of a chin eminence or the expansion of the brain case); some characteristics remain restricted to a group of populations which consequently are left outside the main front of the evolutionary advance (for example, the neanderthal facies). A progression of this kind exhibited by the hominid palaeontological record (designated as the successive stages

—*Australopithecus, Homo erectus, Homo sapiens*) is fully in accord with the Darwinian argument.

As Jepson has put it: 'To the palaeontologist, accustomed to seeing the minute morphological fluctuations in a population of one species slowly change, as the group rises through geological time to become a different species (in terms of any definition), the one certain fact about the two species is that they are genetically connected.'

Julian Huxley has discussed in detail the interpretation of palaeontological data in the light of modern genetics and the natural selection theory. He writes

. . . evolution, as revealed in fossil trends, is an essentially continuous process. The building-blocks of evolution, in the shape of mutations, are, to be sure, discrete quanta of change. But firstly, the majority of them (and the very great majority of those which survive to become incorporated in the genetic constitution of living things) appear to be of small extent; secondly, the effect of a given mutation will be different according to the combinations of modifying genes present; thirdly, its effect may be masked or modified by environmental modification. The net result will be that, for all practical purposes, most of the variability of a species at any given moment will be continuous, however accurate are the measurements made; and that most evolutionary change will be gradual, to be detected by a progressive shifting of a mean value from generation to generation.

And again, 'It is highly probable that it is by means of small mutations, notably in the form of series of multiple allelic steps, each adjusted for viability and efficiency by recombinations and further small mutations, that progressive and adaptive evolution has occurred.'

It may be objected that the gradual transformation of species during anthropogenesis or later within a continuous network of the *sapiens* species is difficult to visualise as occurring over the vast geographical areas from which the scattered remains of australopithecines or *Homo erectus* have come. Yet the palaeontological record testifies abundantly to the unbroken spread (with gradual change) of many genera and species over great distances. A clear and far reaching instance of this is provided by the palaeo-geography of the beginning of the Tertiary—the time of emergence of the first primates. In the Paleocene and early Eocene there was no connection between Europe and Asia—the Turgai Strait was an effective barrier to cross-migration. Between Europe and North America a direct landbridge across the Turgai Strait existed and this allowed a considerable intermigration—the faunas of the two continents formed 'geographically a single region' (Simpson). A number of genera, including the early primate *Paromomys* species, were identical in the two regions (Kurten). In tracing distributions over these great territories, the term 'migration' should not be understood as 'movement' nor should 'landbridges' be thought of as 'highways'. As Kurten points out, we are really dealing over very long periods with ordinary population spread and with areas that became populated by various mammal species as the land emerged from the water and became covered with vegetation. This consideration applies also to the evolutionary transformation which affected the hominids over great geographical areas.

When tracing the pattern of evolution over the immense period that takes us from *Dryopithecus* and *Ramapithecus* to modern *Homo sapiens*, we will become forcibly aware at every stage of selection showing itself capable of acting either to sustain or to stimulate the evolutionary succession.

In its sustaining role selection acts to produce gradually those adaptations necessary for survival in the given environment. Selection keeping the organism in equilibrium with its environment can be readily appreciated where the relative fitness or selective pressures of particular characters can be assessed. Quite clear examples are provided by the maintenance of the frequency of particular genes in small human breeding isolates as we shall see. At the same time some functional or morphological characteristics carry properties fitting the organism in advance, for a different environment or mode of life. These properties are properly termed 'pre-adaptations'—they can hasten the transition to new and challenging conditions, enabling the organism to get a foothold in an unfamiliar habitat.

Pre-adaptations are by their nature dramatic since, as already remarked, they help to carry the organism over from one habitat to a strange one. The change from an arboreal to a terrestrial way of life was based, as will be described in detail, on the utilisation and refinement of particular characters developed for tree-life but suitable also for ground-life. The brain of *Homo* was evolved for survival by hunting and food gathering but has served also for existence in the utterly new habitat of villages and towns.

The pattern of evolution of man in his hominid phase, as presented here as a network of transformation, differs radically from that postulated by the 'divergence–convergence' school. On this view (more recently propounded by Carleton Coon), it is supposed that at least over half a million years or so ago a number of separate ancestral hominid groups or lineages had come into being quite independently. Eventually these 'lines' led to the 'subspecies' of modern man—precisely five in Coon's view. At this point it is sufficient to say that this theory cannot be reconciled with general neo-Darwinian principles of evolution, especially over the relatively short period of time involved, nor is it consistent with the genetic, morphological and breeding structure of modern man. More detailed consideration will be given to reasons for rejecting such 'polyphyletic' views and accepting the 'monophyletic-spectrum' hypothesis sketched out above and to be described in detail later.

CHAPTER 2

ANTHROPOGENESIS

The transformation, as we picture it today, of ape-like, early hominid populations through a series of stages into a hominid or human form does not constitute, within the animal kingdom, an exceptional series of evolutionary events. Most present day mammalian species (as far as the record is available) can boast as spectacular a history of structural change over the last ten or thirty million years. Again there is little to choose between man, monkey or mouse in complexity of anatomical transformation such as characterises embryonic and postnatal development. In anthropogenesis, however, there is much more than the physical remoulding of an ape-like into a hominid anatomical structure. It involves also the emergence of quite new kinds of behaviour—the peculiarly 'human' attributes of speech and of tool-design and of family and suprafamily social cohesion. The distinctive evolutionary achievement of the hominids, in other words, lies in the capacity for the creation of a persistent culture, both of a material and social nature, to meet the challenges of the environment and to satisfy the needs of the social group.

It may fairly be claimed that the understanding of human evolution in terms of morphological and physiological modification has to a substantial degree been achieved. Today, it is the problem of the emergence of the cultural and behavioural attributes of mankind that occupies the attention of the human evolutionists.

The evidence which reveals the intrinsic pattern of anthropogenesis is quite substantial. It rests on a two-fold approach. In the first place there is the indirect evidence provided by the comparisons of living primates. This involves not only bodily characters such as locomotion, posture and brain size, as well as minutiae of anatomical make-up, but also social organisation and group behaviour. Using this comparative method T.H. Huxley in *Man's Place in Nature* (1863) arrived at his famous and far-reaching dictum 'whatever part of the animal fabric—whatever series of muscles, whatever viscera might be selected for comparison—the lower Apes (i.e. monkeys) and the Gorilla would differ more than the gorilla and man'. Basing himself likewise on the comparative approach, Darwin was able to make a conjectural reconstruction (as we shall see in detail later), of several of the major stages through which anthropogenesis passed. In the *Descent of Man* (1873) he postulated a basic common ancestry before the pongid and hominid divergence took effect and beyond this, at the root of the hominid branch, he postulated a stage which in essentials conforms to *Australopithecus*. Darwin painted a vivid picture of this, for him, entirely hypothetical creature, describing it in both anatomical and behavioural detail.

The second line of study is based on the direct evidence of the past history of human evolution as provided by actual fossils. Palaeontology has done much more than to confirm in substantial detail Darwin's projections or reconstructions of missing stages; it has revealed to us that hominid evolution presents a pattern of progressive transformation and diversification more complicated than the simple 'linear' schemes that served as 'family trees' for a long time.

These two lines of study mutually reinforce each other. Thus the evidence drawn from fossils serves to guide interpretations made from comparative studies of living forms. To the extent that fossil material supports deductions drawn from the comparison of living forms, we may gain confidence in the evolutionary judgements that we make on such intangible properties as social organisation or communication. We have, of course, in the fossil record, some vital indirect information on behaviour in the form of living floors, food debris and above all stone and bone implements.

Man's anthropoid ancestry

Every pre-human stage, in the course of some eighty million years of primate ancestry, has left its impression on man as we know him today. As we go back in time we find that the prehominid ape (hominoid) stage, the prehominoid monkey-like (cercopithecoid) stage and even the earlier prosimian (tarsioid and lemuroid) stages have all left their marks. This is the basic reason why man, past and present, is classified (Fig. 2) with the apes, past and present, in the family of the Hominoidea; and why man and these other hominoids are grouped with the monkeys, past and present, within the Anthropoidea; and why man, like other Anthropoidea, has enough in common with prosimians to be put into the one great mammalian order of the primates.

Commonplace as is this zoological evaluation of man, it still remains a remarkable judgement when we look at man as he is today. For in a major respect man differs utterly from all other primates. Man's mode of life is as no other primate's.

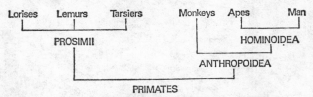

2 The Primate Order of mammals showing prosimians and anthropoids

The primate world is overwhelmingly the world of the forests and woodlands of tropical Africa and America, of the monsoon lands of India, Siam and Java. Every arboreal niche is the home of a primate group. The high canopies and slenderest branches are for the small, light and nimble, like the dwarf lemur or the marmoset. Not venturing so far out, but only a little below them are the jumping galago, the acrobatic spider monkeys and the gibbons; on the solid branches run the tree-shrews, the various species of *Cercopithecus* and, moving cautiously, the slow loris. In the forked trunks the young gorillas and chimpanzees make their nests. Under the trees the galago sometimes comes to the ground; here the adult gorilla keeps his permanent territory; only the baboon, who can still climb a tree easily enough, has left the wooded cover to live on rocky hillsides or in caves (Fig. 3).

3 The Anthropoidea in their habitats. Top layer:
spider monkey and gibbon; second layer:
guenon, tarsius, loris, colobus; third layer:
mangabey, tree-shrew, lemur, cercopithecus;
bottom layer: chimpanzee, gorilla, baboon, man

Yet urbanised modern man, living in his utterly different habitat, exhibits zoologically striking affinities in the structure and functioning of his body to all these varied, essentially arboreal, primates, and particularly to the monkeys and apes whose man-like resemblances obtain recognition in their group name—the Anthropoidea.

There are many detailed traits in the skeleton and skull, muscles, teeth, special senses and musculature and skin which link the Anthropoidea together. More immediately obvious are the external similarities. The characters which impart a 'man-like' impression to apes and monkeys are: the tendency to flattening of the face combined with enlargement of the brain case; the mobility of the facial musculature, especially of the lips; the presence of the rather fixed and relatively small external ear. The 'man-like' impression is further reinforced by the frequent holding of the trunk in a near vertical position, especially in the sitting posture, and the dextrous use of a 'free' hand which, like the foot, is equipped with flattened nails.

Amongst the prosimians these external features, if not altogether absent, are present in some cases only incipiently. Like many primitive mammals, most prosimians retain some claws on hand or foot, the posture is on the whole pronograde, the orbits are not yet rotated completely forward and the muzzle displays only the beginnings of recession. The prosimian hand possesses on the whole a lesser degree of prehensility. In particular contrast to the anthropoidea there is, as in lower animals, a naked and moist glandular skin, the rhinarium, surrounding the nostrils and the upper immobile lip is fixed to the underlying gum. *Tarsius* (which is put by some in a sub-order of its own) in a number of respects bridges the gaps between the prosimians and anthropoidea, e.g. in the lack of the rhinarium and the development of the visual system.

The classification shown in Fig. 2 summarises the taxonomic groupings amongst the primates. That the Anthropoidea, animals as variegated as monkeys, apes and man should yet be grouped together in the animal kingdom and separated off from the other primates—the *Prosimii*—is a taxonomic judge-

ment of such significance that some indication should be
given of the substantial accumulation of evidence on which
it rests. In the first place, the Anthropoidea are marked off
as 'advanced' primates, because they all exhibit to a height-
ened degree the development of various evolutionary trends
foreshadowed in the prosimians. Secondly—and this is denoted by their sub-ordinal name—they convey as we have
seen a strong impression of general 'man-like' quality. Thirdly,
detailed comparative investigation reveals a number of very
close resemblances between monkeys, apes and man, not
present in the lower primates. Fourthly, there are further
characters which, although distributed in different frequencies among the Anthropoidea, serve to reinforce the existence
of an 'overlap' between the main anthropoid sub-divisions.
Fifthly, there are certain particular similarities, while not
evident in the adult, which come to light when the foetus,
new born or infant are examined. Finally, there is the evidence of an underlying affinity as revealed by the sensitive
tests of immuno-genetics.

On this formidable body of evidence from comparative
studies of living anthropoids rests the case for arguing for
the earlier existence of a common anthropoid ancestral stage
which gave rise to a separate lineage leading to monkeys and
another stem, the hominoid stem, from which later on apes
and men diverged (Fig. 1). The lines of evidence listed
above can be dealt with here only in brief outline.

Anthropoids as advanced primates

Those primate features which become specially accentuated
among the anthropoidea—and which give them a phylogenetic unity—have been described in some detail by Le Gros
Clark in *The Antecedents of Man*, 1959. The features to be
noted specially are the following:

(a) The Anthropoidea, far more than the prosimians,
preserve a generalised structure of the limbs in the interests
of a highly mobile usage of the hands and feet, particularly
displayed in the grasping ability of the digits and in the opposability of thumb and big toe. In association with the highly

sensitive tactile properties of the finger-pads flattened nails replace sharp compressed claws throughout the Anthropoidea (with the interesting exception of the marmoset, in other ways also reminiscent of lower primates).

(b) Amongst the Anthropoidea the visual system has undergone a marked elaboration. For all (except the night monkey) day and night vision and colour vision is the rule, and this is based on the possession in the retina of both rods and cones. Moreover, there is in varying degree a develop-

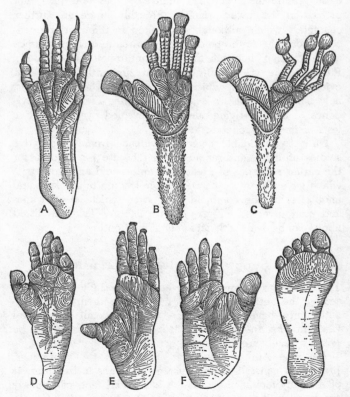

4a Feet of primates (after Biegert). A = tree shrew; B = galago; C = tarsius; D = baboon; E = orang; F = chimpanzee; G = man

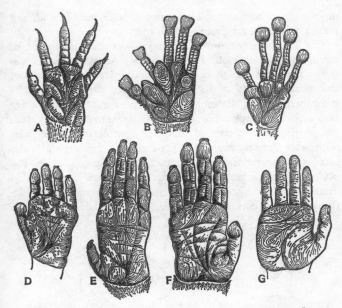

4b Hands of primates (after Biegert). A = tree shrew; B = galago;
C = tarsius; D = baboon; E = orang; F = chimpanzee; G = man

ment in the retina of those structures necessary for high visual
acuity—the macula and fovea. The achievement of stereoscopic vision is associated with the full forward position of
the orbits, and with the fact that the optical axes are more or
less parallel and that the visual fields of both sides are represented in each half of the visual cortex of the occipital lobe
of the brain. This is made possible by the crossing over of
about half the fibres of the optic tracts from each retina.

(c) Concomitantly with the high development of vision,
the olfactory mechanism undergoes a major degree of reduction. This is particularly evident in the loss of the prosimian
rhinarium—the naked and glandular skin stretching across
the upper lip and binding it down by a connection with a
strong fold of mucous membrane to the underlying gum.
With the loss of the rhinarium the Anthropoidea achieve a

mobile lip musculature. The grimace is an anthropoid, not merely a human, attribute.

(d) The greatly improved visual power, the elaboration of manipulative, locomotory and postural activity; the consequent need for a high degree of motor-visual co-ordination; the marked ability of the anthropoid for exploration of its environment using its mobile limbs and hands: all these are major factors responsible for the enlargement of the brain and its greatly increased internal complexity. The most noticeable changes are in the expansion of the forebrain, the increased fissuration of the cortex, the enlargement of the occipital lobe, which projects posteriorly and becomes distinct from the adjacent parietal area; the temporal lobe, like the precentral cortex, also undergoes a marked elaboration.

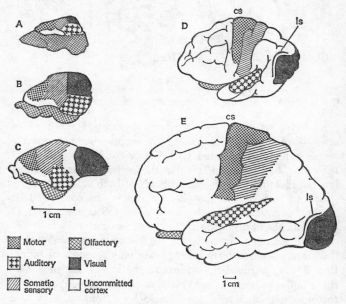

5 Development of the cerebral cortex amongst the primates.
A = ground shrew; B = tree shrew; C = tarsius; D = chimpanzee;
E = man

The olfactory neural mechanism (rhinencephalon) becomes much less conspicuous.

(*e*) The changes in the visual and olfactory system, of posture and locomotion are clearly reflected in the structure of the skull.

The pronounced tendency to the frequent assumption of the orthograde posture and the sitting habit means that the head is set at an angle to the vertebral column. This has been facilitated by the migration of the occipital condyles (and necessarily the foramen magnum) so that they are directed downwards as well as backwards. The tendency reaches a greater development in the apes and its maximum in man, in consequence of their upright posture. The morphological accommodation to the sitting and erect posture finds further expression in the flexion of the face on the braincase; a tendency which again has progressed farthest in the higher an-

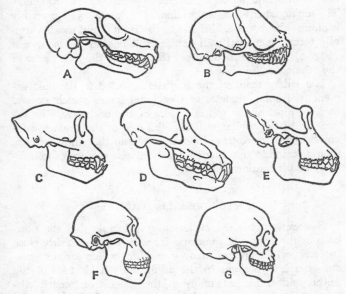

6 Primate skulls. A = galago; B = tarsius; C = rhesus; D = papio; E = gorilla; F = *Australopithecus*; G = man

thropoids. In the fully quadrupedal animal the face is a continuation of the braincase, but in all primates it tends to be
placed partly underneath the braincase with the production
of a distinct basi-cranial angle, a tendency which again has
progressed farthest in the higher anthropoids. The reduction
of the snout due to the diminished importance of olfaction,
and the greater role of the hand in food handling, has accompanied this flexion and accounts for the trend towards
reduction of face, jaws and teeth in the hominids. It is significant that amongst those primates which become mainly
quadrupedal on the ground, the baboon and related genera,
a long snout is re-evolved but the basi-cranial flexion remains.

The enlargement of the eyes and their migration on to the
front of the face is obviously reflected in the size and position
of the orbits. In the Anthropoidea the orbit is more or less
completely separated from the temporal fossa by the expansion of the zygoma and the greater width of the sphenoid.
The enlargement and migration of primate eyes probably
explains why bones additional to the frontal and maxilla usually form the medial wall of the orbit behind the lachrymal
(Fig. 9). In all primates other than lemurs the os planum of
the ethmoid is involved.

The enlargement of the brain is reflected in the enlargement of frontal, parietal and occipital bones which expand
to form most of the top and sides of the braincase. The expansion of the orbital wall and the side of the braincase involves some interesting differences within the Anthropoidea;
their taxanomic significance has been the subject of controversy and is considered below.

Developmental patterns

It is a well-established evolutionary principle that the newborn or the young of those species which share a fairly close
ancestral origin present many similarities which are not present or not so obvious in the adult. This holds true of the
Anthropoidea. Indeed, many of the species or generic distinctions as seen in the adult man, ape and monkey make
themselves manifest as differences in the development of

particular features, or more precisely in the differential rate of growth of the components of some feature. The profile of the infant monkey or ape resembles that of the infant human being quite remarkably, but the differences between the adults are very obvious (Fig. 7). Schultz has given many telling illustrations of these ontogenetic patterns of early resemblance giving way to later divergence. Some of his most striking examples concern the development of posture as reflected in the position of the skull and the configuration of the vertebral column—features of fundamental importance in the evolutionary history of the Anthropoidea.

The position of the skull on the vertebral column is a par-

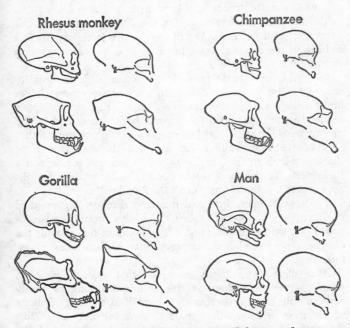

7 Shape and posture of skulls at birth and in adults. In each group the upper pair represents the infantile, the lower the adult condition; the figures on the left are profiles and to the right sagittal sections. In the latter the vertical bar represents the position of the occipital condyles (modified from Schultz)

ticularly impressive example. The occipital condyles, which
provide the fulcrum for the movement of the head, are situated relatively far forward on the skull base in the foetus of
all the anthropoidea. In all, with the notable exception of
man, during growth this joint (the atlanto-occipital joint)
shifts backwards. The poise of the head of man balanced as
it is on the vertebral column with the occipital condyles in a
central position on the skull base, contrasts sharply with the
forward hanging head position of the other anthropoidea—a
contrast which is entirely due to the differential growth process affecting the other anthropoidea.

The lumbo-sacral forward convexity of the vertebral
column is greatly pronounced in man; it is clearly a structural
modification of the backbone for the erect posture and gait
so characteristic of man. Yet this convexity is clearly present
at birth in monkey and apes, but only in man does it develop
strongly.

In limb-proportions there would seem little uniformity
amongst adult Anthropoidea; man obviously possesses lower
limbs which are greatly elongated in relation to his upper
limbs. In the great apes the reverse is the case, and in the
monkeys for the most part the proportions do not show either
of these extreme values. Yet at birth the lengthening of
the lower limb in man, or the upper in the ape, is not nearly
so evident. The ratio of the upper to the lower limb lengths
approaches a value of unity in all the foetal anthropoidea.

The foot of man, apes and monkeys displays a great deal
of divergent development when the adult structures are compared yet in the foetus (Fig. 8), as Schultz has shown, the
closeness of resemblance between man and monkey is astonishing.

It is clear from these examples that many characters
which serve to distinguish the anthropoid families really
emerge only during the course of growth as a result of either
acceleration or retardation of developmental processes. Thus
the poise of the skull in man represents a retention of the
infantile condition, whereas the formation of the promontory
at the lumbo-sacral junction remains slight in monkeys and
the infantile condition is retained; in apes and much more
in man it appears early and progresses to a greater degree.

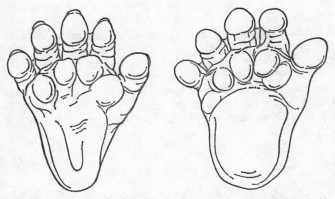

8 Feet of rhesus monkey foetus (left) and of human foetus (right)
(from Schultz)

It is appropriate here to refer to the shape of the canine
teeth, which in man are, of course, small and spatulate and
contrast with the projecting conical canines of other anthropoidea. Yet we can argue that the canine of *Homo sapiens*
is only secondarily modified from the anthropoid condition.
The newly erupted canine, particularly the deciduous tooth,
does often project and is often pointed. Moreover, the permanent canine has an unusually long root and its eruption is
relatively late—after the two premolars. The affinities with
other anthropoidea are thus by no means absent even in this
feature.

The distribution of variable characters

Claims have repeatedly been brought forward that certain
skeletal characteristics are absolutely distinctive of one or
other of the anthropoid sub-divisions. But when larger samples have been examined the alleged distinctiveness has
been found to rest simply on differences in the frequency of
occurrence. Such findings, in fact, serve to show the degree
of continuity or of overlap within the Anthropoidea.

In the skull there are a number of features which were

once claimed as entirely unique to man (by Wood Jones). Thus, in the anterior fossa of the cranium (Fig. 9) the ethmoid bone in man was said always to articulate directly with the sphenoid; the alternative configuration in which the frontal obtrudes between the ethmoid and sphenoid was said to be wholly confined to other anthropoidea. It is true that the latter formation is found in one hundred per cent of Old World monkeys, but its occurrence is very variable in other anthropoidea—seventy-six per cent in New World

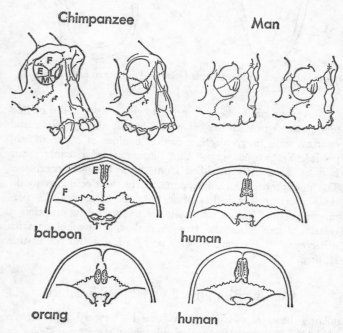

9 Above: construction of orbit. Below: construction of anterior fossa of cranium. F = frontal; S = sphenoid; E = ethmoid; M = maxillary; L = lacrimal

monkeys, fifty-two per cent in the gorilla, twenty-three per cent in chimpanzees, thirteen per cent in the orang and nine per cent in man and the gibbon.

A second example concerns the bony formation of the orbit. Wood Jones claimed that the characteristic mode of contact in man was that of the lacrimal bone with the ethmoid, the fronto-maxillary articulation being wholly absent. When sufficient numbers are examined it turns out that this contact is not entirely absent in man but is present in three per cent of human orbits; it is, in fact, absent in New World and Old World monkeys, and in the gibbon and orang. In the gorilla and chimpanzee the frequency of contact is high, about fifty per cent.

For a long time it has been said that suprasternal ossicles, quite common in man, are entirely absent from apes; they were eventually detected in gibbons, gorillas and chimpanzees, but not in monkeys or orangs.

The search for 'hallmarks' to distinguish the different anthropoidea has only served to show how difficult it is in fact to discover absolute distinctions between them.

Serological genetics

That the structure of proteins is under genetic control is now well-established. Thus similarity of protein structure (as tested by immuno-chemical and electrophoretic methods) can be used as a sensitive criterion of phylogenetic relationship of man to other primates.

The sera of these primates are compared to each other and to human serum by precipitin testing with antibodies directed against purified human plasma proteins. In the two-dimensional starch-gel electrophoretic (diffusion) method the serum proteins are separated into patterns of discrete components and these patterns can then be compared (Goodman). By such methods chimpanzee and gorilla proteins show an extensive correspondence to human proteins, orang and gibbon proteins show less, the Old and New World monkeys (ceboid) progressively less. Prosimians display by far the least correspondence.

The phylogenetic relationships adduced by serology demonstrate also that the sub-order Anthropoidea is a valid phylogenetic taxon. Ceboids are found to be more closely related to the catarrhine primates (Old World monkeys and hominoids) than to the lorisoid and lemuroid lower primates. The serological findings on the relationships within the Anthropoidea indicate, very much in line with the morphological evidence, that the Old World Anthropoidea divided into the monkey and hominoid branches not long after the Old World monkeys had separated from those of the New World (Goodman).

Monkey-like resemblances

To illustrate still further the reality, however distant, of the kinship amongst the Anthropoidea, it is possible to list features which the great apes of today share with many monkeys, and equally to identify elements in modern man which are of an ape-like or a monkey-like character. The monkey-like resemblances of modern man comprise a miscellaneous list of items in the skull, jaws, teeth and limbs.

In the shape of the tooth rows of the mandible man resembles not the apes, but the New World monkeys; particularly striking is the absence of the simian shelf (or internal buttress). This lack is indeed a primitive character. In the great apes the milk canine, like the permanent canine, erupts late, after the second milk molar, but in man, Old World monkeys and the gibbon (which, consistent with its earlier evolutionary emergence, so often resembles monkeys more than do the great apes) the milk canine erupts before the second milk molar.

The human thumb (metacarpals and phalanges) is long in comparison with the other fingers, whereas the great apes have relatively short thumbs; the platyrrhines are, in this respect, more like men, with the cercopithecoids intermediate. Schultz does not regard these differences in the adult as affording a real distinction, since thumb length in relation to trunk length is not so different in man and in the great apes. In the ridges or dermatoglyphics of the palm, man is closer to monkeys than to apes.

In postural characters it is interesting that in the quadrupedal position man (or rather the human child), like Old

World monkeys and many New World monkeys and the gibbon, places the palm with extended fingers against the ground. The three great apes have their hands slightly dorsiflexed with fingers flexed so that the body rests upon the middle phalanges. It is also remarkable that in the hand and leg musculature man shares many traits in common with monkeys (according to Straus). The midtarsal bones are not shortened as in gorilla or chimpanzee, and in this man resembles gibbon and monkey.

In the trunk we may note that the distance between thorax and pelvis is relatively wide in man, gibbons and the catarrhine monkeys; in great apes the thorax and pelvis are much closer together.

The ratio of radius to humerus and of fibula to femur—the intermembral index—in man is about seventy per cent, a value similar to that of monkeys but much smaller than that of apes, which is one hundred per cent and over. As a developmental feature Straus has found that the pattern of epiphysial union (in the region of shoulder and hip joint) shows a basic agreement of man with Old World monkeys, gibbons, but not with the great apes.

Finally, in the absence of a sexual skin in the female, man resembles the gibbon, New World monkeys and prosimians, but the great apes resemble many of the catarrhines.

The common anthropoid precursor

The general pattern of resemblance puts man, the four ape genera and the thirty or so monkey genera into one sub-order (Fig. 2). The implication of this grouping is that at some very early evolutionary stage there must have existed anthropoids which not only displayed the salient features of the sub-order as a whole, but were more closely inter-related than are those of today. Some of these would not yet have developed the specialisations peculiar to their different families. At this stage these ancestral Anthropoidea would have comprised small generalised monkey-like creatures without the peculiarities of dentition found in modern monkeys, or the upper limb elongation of modern apes, or the lower limb

elongation of hominids. We cannot, of course, expect to find
a perfect 'composite' early unspecialised anthropoid. At this
stage, evolving populations would have been undergoing differentiation, probably at a rapid rate, and these diversifying
populations would have served as the network or matrix from
which later forms emerged.

Such few fossil remains as are available from this remote
period unfortunately do not give us a clear picture of the first
anthropoids (see Fig. 1). In the oecene period, fifty or sixty
million years ago, some of the prosimian tarsioids, as Elwyn
Simons (1960) has shown, display tendencies of an anthropoid kind. In the Eocene from Burma the fossil remains of
Amphipithecus and *Pondaugia*, represented only by fragments of lower jaw and some teeth, testify to the emergence
of anthropoids from a prosimian stock. *Amphipithecus* with
three premolars is dentally still primitive yet in some dental
details it has affinities with the later ceroipithecoid-like
Oligopithecus in the Oligocene. The teeth of *Pondaugia* (according to Le Gros Clark) while suggesting affinities with the
gibbon stock do 'present primitive features which possibly
indicate a transitional phase linking a prosimian (tarsioid)
level of evolution with the initial emergence of the suborder
Anthropoidea as a whole'.

Apart from these somewhat problematical eocene remains,
there are in the next period, the Oligocene, besides the remains of early monkeys (*Apidium* and *Oligopithecus*), other
Anthropoidea which rank as the first known precursors of the
hominoid (the dryopithecine–pongid–hominid) stem. These
are represented by *Parapithecus* (Fig. 10A), *Aegyptopithecus* (Fig. 10C) and *Propliopithecus* (Fig. 10B). Scanty
though they are, thanks to the important work of the Yale
expeditions under Simons in the Fayum, some sixty miles
southwest of Cairo, they provide sufficient material to confirm the existence in this forested shore line of a diversity of
anthropoid ancestral forms some thirty-five million years ago.
Of *Propliopithecus* Simons says that it probably represents a
hominoid ancestor more generalised than has usually been
thought to be the case; it seems to have been an anthropoid
on or near the line of evolution that led to the living hominoids—to pongids and man.

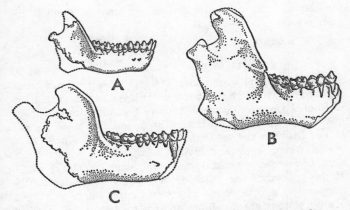

10 Mandibles of the earliest known anthropoid precursors of the hominoid (dryopithecine: pongid: hominid) stem. A = Parapithecus (after Le Gros Clark) B = Propliopithecus (after Simons) C = Aegyptopithecus (after Simons)

So already by the oligocene period the primal ancestral Anthropoidea, of which we still know very little, had long given way to a series of branching stocks. In the Old World the separation of the cercopithecoid line from the hominoid was already in evidence; the further branching of hominoids into the dryopithecine, pongid and hominid lines was not as yet under way. In the New World the anthropoids which emerged were the platyrrhine monkeys represented by a number of extinct genera (see Fig. 1) and the present day Ceboidea (marmosets, etc.). The origin of these monkeys from a pre-anthropoid stock, like their subsequent evolutionary development, seems quite independent of the Old World Anthropoidea and it is still by no means clear what their early relationship to the Old World monkeys really is. Some of the resemblances of the New World Anthropoidea to those of the Old World point to an ultimate common ancestry; but many similarities must represent the outcome of parallel evolution. That sufficient affinity is thought to exist is indicated by their inclusion in the same sub-order, but the American representatives have only the most distant bearing on the evolution of the human stock and little further reference to them is required here.

Hominoids—apes and man

The same general evolutionary picture emerges from comparisons of living forms of the great apes and modern man as from the palaeontological study of their remains and their geo-chronological background. The many points of resemblance between the modern representatives are witness to a period when, amongst the Anthropoidea as a whole, there must have been a common ancestral hominoid stock; while at the same time the existence of strong divergences superimposed on a background of resemblances points to a long history of separate development of these two major families of pongids and hominids. The fossil evidence fully confirms this general pattern of evolutionary differentiation.

What then are the features which link man and ape and exclude monkey? A number of the more obvious characters in which the anthropoid apes of today resemble man more closely than they do the monkeys are: the relative enlargement of the brain and the greater complexity of its configuration; the absence of a tail; many details of the foot structure, especially the size and musculature of the great toe; the absence of ischial callosities or 'sitting pads' (though these are present in the gibbon which in this and some other respects shows affinity with monkeys); many details in the skeleton of both man and ape, for example a broadening of the thorax in contrast to the narrow laterally compressed chest of the monkeys.

In the proportions of the limbs man seems at first sight quite different from the great apes and rather similar to the monkeys. Thus the ratio of the length of the lower to the upper limb is somewhat greater than one hundred per cent in monkeys, as in man, and less than one hundred per cent in the great apes. Yet, Schultz maintains that the simple intermembral index is misleading. If limb lengths are related not to each other but to trunk length (distance from suprasternal notch to symphysis pubis (see Fig. 58)), it turns out that man and apes both possess upper and lower limbs which are relatively elongated as compared to monkeys. Thus, taking the ratio of lower limb length to trunk length as 100 for the macaque monkey, the human value is of the order of 175, gorilla 130 and gibbon 150. Similarly for the upper limb, taking the macaque value as 100, the gibbon reaches 225, lowland gorilla and chimpanzee 170, mountain gorilla and man 150. (For detailed comparative values and ranges of variation, see Schultz.) In other words, by comparison with lower anthropoidea, both upper and lower limbs undergo elongation in the hominoids, reaching extreme values for the upper limb in brachiators and for the lower limb in the fully bipedal hominid.

Another apparently striking difference concerns the thumb. At first sight, and especially by comparison with man, it would seem that the thumb of the great apes has undergone diminution or that the human thumb has greatly lengthened, for in relation to the length of the hand the total length of the thumb (in relative values) is for man 125, macaque 100, apes 80 or so. Schultz, however, has shown that relative to length of the trunk all the hominoids have thumbs longer than the macaque taken as 100; for gorilla 150, orang 160, chimpanzee and man 170, siamang 200, gibbon 225. It is, in fact, increase in the other fingers that 'shortens' the thumb in the apes, e.g. the chimpanzee, like man, has a thumb length twenty-four per cent of trunk height, but a hand length of fifty-three per cent of trunk height as compared to only thirty-six per cent in man.

Another character in which man is near to the great apes and different from the monkeys is in the shape of the upper ribs (Schultz). This in fact separates 'brachiators' from quadrupeds amongst the Anthropoidea.

Yet another striking similarity is afforded by the musculature of the upper limb. Despite the special developments that have taken place in association with selection for manual dexterity in man (particularly the extrinsic muscles of the thumb), the relative sizes of some twenty of the muscles are amazingly similar in man and chimpanzee (Ziegler 1964). The configuration of the muscles testifies to the increased strength of attachment of the arm to the body, the greater power of supination and the more efficient mechanisms of forearm and digital flexion'. Man has without question retained a set of upper limb muscles which still carry the clear marks of the requirements for arboreal brachiating and climbing activities.

Yet another interesting link is in the reduction of the tail (caudal) vertebrae which has gone far in all the Hominoidea; most marked in the gibbon, orang and siamang (with an average number of caudal segments of 2.0), the chimpanzee and gorilla average 3.3, and men—interestingly enough affected least—average 4.2.

Finally, we should look at the molecular composition of the blood proteins as studied by immunological reactions and electrophoretic diffusion. The similarities between the Hominoidea and the gap that separates them as a group from the monkeys are clearly apparent, while the five hominoid lines (*Homo, Gorilla, Pan, Pongo* and *Hylobates*) are clearly distinguishable. 'Each hominoid line is more closely related to the others than to cercopithecoids or other primates' (Goodman 1963). Indeed, this method of serological classification brings *Gorilla, Homo* and *Pan* into a close relationship separate from *Pongo* and *Hylobates*. It leads to the important conclusion that the phyletic line which branched to give rise to *Gorilla, Pan* and *Homo* did so after it had separated from more ancient lines leading to *Hylobates* and *Pongo* (see Fig. 1).

Superimposed on the structural and developmental similarities between modern man, apes and monkeys, are of course the striking divergences which reflect the separate evolutionary history and ecological specialisations of the different families. It is quite obvious that modern man could not have arisen from any ape, let alone monkey, at all similar to those of today. When Huxley in 1863 called the anthropoid apes 'blurred copies of man' he was not, of course, making any claim of direct descent, but indicated nothing more than the facts of general similarity and indirectness of relationship.

The determining factor in the differences between hominid and pongid development arises from the contrasts of their ecological radiation, in other words, in the strikingly independent lines of development demanded by an arboreal existence in the one family and by erect bipedal locomotion in the other. In the relative growth of the limbs the Pongidae and the Hominidae have followed two opposing trends. In the Hominidae the bony elements of the foot and the ankle joint became modified in shape and proportions to permit the structural stability required for bipedal progression; in the Pongidae the mobility of these parts was enhanced for specialised prehensile functions. The grasping power of the hallux is characteristic of all the anthropoidea except man. This grasping ability depends on the abduction of the hallux combined with a convergent flexion of the toes, the arboreal specialists having greatly elongated digits. In the anthropoid apes the functional axis—the axis of grasp—shifts medially to a position between the first and second digits.

In the Hominidae the pelvic skeleton underwent quite far-reaching changes directly related to the erect posture; in the Pongidae the pelvis retained the general shape and proportions found in lower primates generally. The 'total' pattern of limbs and pelvis present one important criterion for distinguishing between the two families and for assessing the taxonomic position of early hominoids. No fossil can be allocated to the hominid line if it does not meet the criterion of bipedalism. And this is one reason why it is ridiculous to describe man as a 'naked' or any other kind of ape.

In its combination of a low iliac height and extreme breadth, and the short distance between the ischial tuberosity and the lower edge of the sacrum with the relatively broad sacro-iliac surface, the human innominate stands in strong contrast with the pongidae (Fig. 11). But this contrast is far more in evidence in comparison with monkeys or prosimians. In these the ilium is long and narrow and only slightly flattened. The ilium articulates with a relatively small number of vertebrae. This kind of pelvis is clearly adapted to the quadrupedal to and fro swinging of the leg.

In the small gibbon the proportions of the ilium are like those of monkeys. In the larger apes there is some expansion of the iliac plate. This is related to the need to support the viscera and to provide for a greater attachment of the trunk muscles as the trunk is held in the vertical position both

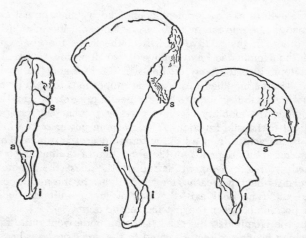

11 Medial view of right innominate (pelvic) bone of rhesus monkey, mountain gorilla and modern man. (a) = highest point of acetabulum (socket) shown on same horizontal plane; (s) = lowest point of sacral surface; (i) = ischial tuberosity

in sitting and climbing. This change is vastly accentuated in man. Here the attachment of the innominate bone to the sacrum is very strong; the ilio-sacral surfaces which carry the entire weight of the body as it is transmitted to the lower limbs is exceptionally large—much larger than it is in the brachiators. The pronounced development of the sacral promontory in the adult is another striking hominid feature.

It follows that the human pelvis could not be derived from one possessed by any existing anthropoid ape; the fact that the gorilla shows some parallel changes clearly points to the influence of the orthograde posture so often assumed by the great apes.

The ischial tuberosities in monkeys and apes are splayed out to form a flattened base for the characteristic callosities. Clearly this is related to the squatting sitting posture. The callosities are very occasionally present in gorilla, but never is man where the ischial tuberosities are padded by muscles.

The poise of the head affords a contrast between man and

the other anthropoidea (Fig. 6, E and G). In the great apes the head is not poised at the mid point of the skull vertically on the vertebral column, but is slung forward with the foramen magnum far back, and the strong neck muscles act as a counterforce to the forward and downward pull of the head and jaws. Consequently, the strongest attachment of the neck muscles is not on to the base as it is in man where the mastoid processes are enlarged to form a strong attachment for the downward pulling muscles; in the ape the greatest attachment is high up on the posterior surface of the skull so that a strong occipital ledge is necessary.

Yet the contrast is not really an absolute one. If we look at the prosimians, who are pronograde, the head is held in the same horizontal axis as the body slung from the end of the vertebral column. Consequently the foramen magnum faces almost directly backwards. In the Anthropoidea with their progressive orthograde tendencies the head is carried rather more in the vertical position and the foramen magnum becomes displaced forwards on to the back so as to lock more downwards. With this change of poise there is a bending of the face on to the cranial base.

Another important difference between pongid and hominid is provided by the dentition (Fig. 19). We may note here the widening of the incisor in the pongids and its smallness in the hominids; the parallel tooth rows as compared to the rounded arcade; the powerful overlapping tusk-like canines (with pronounced sex-dimorphism) in contrast with the reduction in size, blunting and lack of overlap (except in some individuals of Java man); the sectorial premolar (the main cusp having anteriorly a cutting edge which shears against the upper canine) as contrasted with a non-sectorial bicuspid premolar of the hominids. The large chinless jaw of the ape with its strong projecting canine and the simian shelf (or internal buttress) are all features absent in modern man.

The proportion of jaws to cranium provides an obvious contrast between man and ape (Fig. 6). In the latter, the combination is of heavy prominent jaws and a small cranium, in man the reverse. This points, of course, to a distinction of great significance—in brain size. The range in man (1000–2000 ml) compared to the outside limits of all the anthropoidea (50–500 ml) ranks as an outstanding taxonomic and evolutionary distinction.

Fossil evidence of ancestral hominoids

If the evolutionary relations between apes and man are at all in accordance with the pattern sketched above, we should certainly expect to find that a number of characters held in common by present day apes and man turn out to be inherited in common from actual fossil ancestors. Such features are not the only evidence by which to identify a fossil as a true hominoid ancestor; there may well be primitive or generalised features which we may recognise as capable of being modified later, either in parallel or even along quite divergent lines leading to the peculiar adaptations and specialisations of the groups today. Finally we should expect in some fossil hominoids a retention of cercopithecoid features just as we recognise some of these in modern hominoids.

We have already referred to the earliest anthropoids which are recognisably hominoids; for these we go back to the Oligocene. In the Miocene and after, hominoids are much more in evidence in Europe, Asia and Africa; remains are known from Spain, France, the Rhone Valley and Austria; from the Siwalik beds of India; from China and from east Africa. Scattered and fragmented as most of the material is, the morphological affinities of these oligocene and miocene fossils are fairly clear, clear enough to suggest that they represent the matrix from which both pongids and hominids manifestly emerged (see Fig. 1).

The earliest of the known hominoids, the oligocene *Aegyptopithecus* and *Propliopithecus* (Fig. 10), in their dental features, particularly the molars and the shape and proportions of the jaw, not only resemble each other, but have much in common with later miocene hominids as well as with still more recent pongids and hominids (Fig. 14).

Propliopithecus is of special interest in that, according to Simons, it was a generalised creature capable of yielding a hominid precursor; while *Aegyptopithecus* has affinities with that dryopithecine complex which by late miocene times was yielding the separate lineages leading to modern apes. By the end of the Miocene and early Pliocene the fossil hominoids make up a wide spectrum, comprising a gibbon-like line ('*Limnopithecus*' of Kenya and *Pliopithecus* of Europe, Fig. 12), the dryopithecine precursors of the orang (*Sivapithecus* of India) and of the gorilla and chimpanzee (*Proconsul* of east Africa, Fig. 13, and *Dryopithecus* of Europe), and as a further development from *Propliopithecus* there were forms quite pronouncedly on the hominid line represented by *Ramapithecus* and the affiliated '*Kenyapithecus*'.

Pliopithecus has miocene representatives in Kenya ('*Limnopithecus*') and in Europe; these geographical groups

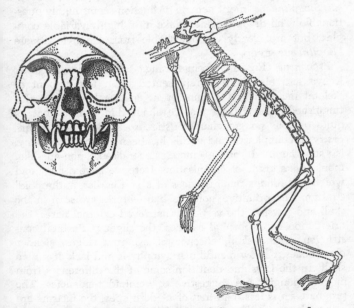

12 *Pliopithecus*: front view of skull and skeleton reconstructed (from Simons)

are distinguishable as separate species. It is likely that the European species persisted into the Pliocene, and that they were in evidence from about twenty-five to thirteen million years ago. For *Pliopithecus* (Fig. 12) most parts of the skeleton are available including the skull, jaws, teeth and limbs. The skull and particularly the teeth place the genus close to the ancestral stock of the gibbons; but the forelimb elongation so very distinctive of modern gibbons has not yet developed. This branch of the Hominoidae thus bears witness to the existence of less specialised limb structure and proportions in the Miocene—an inference we have already made. The ancestral hominoid would thus not have been a brachiator of an extreme kind. We shall find that this inference is confirmed in other branches of the Dryopithecinae.

Whether the variously named taxa—*Dryopithecus, Proconsul, Sivapithecus*—merit generic distinction seems highly questionable. The dryopithecines make up a highly variable complex, but are clearly distinguishable from the hylobatinate *Pliopithecus* group.

Proconsul (Fig. 13) from Rusinga Island, Lake Victoria, Kenya and elsewhere is represented by a fair amount of skeletal material and a number of species have been distinguished. The striking feature about this form is that its quite obvious pongid characteristics, so marked that its ancestry to chimpanzee and gorilla has been accepted by many, is superimposed on a more generalised, non-ape-like, monkey-like grade of organisation. Here we have a hominoid which still retains reminiscences of a still earlier 'anthropoid' stratum. The primitive 'non-ape'-like features are seen in the skull and jaws, in the vertically narrowed external nares, the orientation of the orbital cavities, the slight postorbital constriction of the skull, absence of eyebrow ridges, slender cheekbones, narrow mandibular symphysis and lack of simian shelf. In the jaws and dentition some of the differences from modern pongids are suggestive of hominid tendencies. The prognathism is less than that of modern apes, the incisors are rather hominid-like, the molar construction is 'primitive enough to serve as the foundation for that of almost any later accessory hominids' (Simons): but the enlarged canines and the premolars are pongid.

The forelimb and shoulder anatomy of *Proconsul,* as in *Pliopithecus,* reveal a semi-arboreal, partial brachiator, with

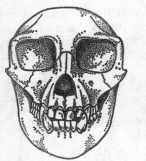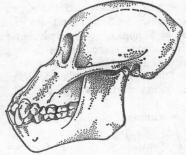

13 Proconsul: front and side views of skull

few highly developed commitments to brachiation. *Proconsul* affords a most satisfactory corroboration of the view that the earliest common hominoid ancestors would be generalised and at the same time somewhat cercopithecoid. At the same time *Proconsul* could have served as an ancestral form to the later *Dryopithecus* and indeed some workers regard it as a variant of that genus.

Dryopithecus (Fig. 14)—the 'oak ape', while present over a wide area, is very incompletely known; the cranial and limb-bone remains are fragmentary. The European specimens reveal a medium sized hominoid about as big as the chimpanzee; there is an incipient simian shelf, the canines are larger and the premolars are like those of modern apes, but the incisors are smaller and narrower than those of living forms. Amongst the Indian dryopithecines, some specimens show pongid features in the projecting and conical canines, sectorial lower first premolars, elongated and usually large molars, increasing in size from front to back, and the nearly parallel teeth rows. The jaw is deep and markedly projecting.

It was Gregory who pointed to the five-cusp pattern of the lower molars of *Dryopithecus,* with the Y-shaped pattern of valleys between the cusps, as a common possession of the hominoidea as a group, and as an important evolutionary connection between the dryopithecines and the hominids. In 1922 Gregory remarked that 'man is a late Tertiary offshoot of the *Dryopithecus–Sivapithicus* group, or at least of apes that clearly resembled these genera in the construction of jaws and dentition'. And the present situation was summed up by Simons in 1964: 'Both *Ramapithecus* and *Kenyapithecus* show strong resemblances to *Dryopithecus* and *Sivapithecus* as well as the Hominidae.'

The fossil *Ramapithecus* (Fig. 14) from the Siwalik hills in India reported in 1934 by G.E. Lewis (and thought by him

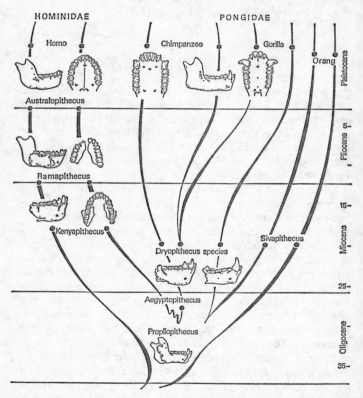

14 The evolutionary relationships (as illustrated by the upper and lower jaw) of the hominid and pongid lines from hominoid dryopithecine precursors. Note the postulated prehominids Kenyapithecus and Ramapithecus and the prepongids Dryopithecus, Sivapithecus

to be a hominid) comprises a portion of the right upper jaw containing two premolars and two molars along with the canine and incisor sockets. The smallness of the low-cusped molars, premolars, and the canines and incisors serve to distinguish it from other miocene pongids; a significant reduction of the face can be inferred. *Ramapithecus* shows a low degree of prognathism with a parabolic contour of the upper dental arcade. Another Siwalik fossil *Bramapithecus* known only from the lower jaw, which is small and with a foreshortened face, comes into this prehominid group, as does the somewhat earlier '*Kenyapithecus*' from Fort Ternan, Kenya: so much so that there is no reason to retain all three generic names. The Fort Ternan specimens consist of a pair of upper jaws, with a comparatively small upper canine and a low-crowned upper premolar. In the construction of the maxilla, the relatively small canines, the form of the upper premolar, the placement of the anterior bone of the zygomatic arch and the deep canine fossa and the facial foreshortening, *Kenyapithecus*, like *Ramapithecus*, foreshadows the hominid condition.

If we bear in mind that adaptive radiation of the hominoids of the late miocene and early pliocene periods comprised not only arboreal habitats but the adoption of partial or complete terrestrial life by a number of groups, we can understand the peculiar combination of characters exhibited by the extinct hominoid *Oreopithecus* (Fig. 15). In 1958 Hürzeler of Basel finally assembled a nearly complete skeleton of this creature. In some ways it is cercopithecoid, in others hominoid or even hominid. Its exact evolutionary position has occasioned much controversy. Very few regard it as directly on the prehominid line, though the 'hominid resemblances are admitted in the morphology of the canine, in the shortness and flatness of the face, and in the somewhat widened pelvis with a pronounced anterior inferior iliac spine, which suggests the possibility of an erect walking posture'. But far more telling is the evidence of adaptation for quadrupedal locomotion. The mid-sagittal keel on the centra of the lumbar vertebrae is associated with attachments of the diaphragm characteristically developed in quadrupedal animals.

Also cercopithecoid is the large talonid on the lower molars. The hominoid traits include the well-developed clavicle, the relatively wide pelvis, the indications of a brachiating ability in the shape of the ribs, the curved phalanges and somewhat lengthened arms, comparable to the chimpanzee rather than

15 The pliocene anthropoid *Oreopithecus* reconstructed (from Simons)

the gibbon. The steep symphysis of the chin with vertically placed incisors recalls the ape *Gigantopithecus* of a later (pleistocene) time. *Oreopithecus*, as large as a female chimpanzee and probably some four feet tall, may have been mainly quadrupedal but capable of some erect walking: the verdict today is that it was outside the line of hominid development.

With the emergence of separate gorilla, chimpanzee and hominid lineages in the Pliocene we become aware of a profound change in the ecological disposition of the Anthropoidea. Arboreal niches at every level of tree cover are fully occupied by the great multiplication of monkey genera; in Asia the brachiating gibbon and siamang and the climbing orang adapt themselves fully to a mode of life in the arboreal canopy, while the Colobinae occupy as wide a variety of niches as the Ceropithecinae of Africa. It is difficult to escape the conclusion that intense competition for arboreal space must have been going on in the Miocene and that this must have led to the exploitation of the forest floor, to a lesser or greater extent, by some of the anthropoid genera. As Washburn has pointed out, the large body size of gorillas and chimpanzees gives them an advantage over monkeys, but this in turn necessitates their spending substantial periods of time on the ground. The chimpanzee feeds in the trees, mostly on fruit, supplemented by leaves, bark and pith and occasionally insects licked off branches or tree trunks (Reynolds); it moves rapidly over the ground between feeding areas and sometimes food is carried clutched in the hand. Reynolds estimates that chimpanzees spend from fifty to seventy-five per cent of the daylight hours in trees. The gorilla is largely confined to the ground and only juveniles spend much time tree climbing (Schaller 1963). Amongst monkeys, patas monkeys and baboons have moved away from the trees.

The movement from arboreal canopy on to the forest floor, then to the forest fringe and later into the savannah and beyond, represents the whole series of ecological transitions experienced by the hominids in their miocene and pliocene evolutionary periods. After the end of the Pliocene we have in the Australopithecinae evidence of the establishment of hominids away from the forest and on the open savannah.

Washburn has insisted that the forest floor in Miocene and later times was so extensive that it is not necessary to suppose that the prehominids or even the first australopithecines were forced out from an arboreal existence immediately into the open savannah. There could have been a long period of adaptation to the forest floor and to its fringes. For the development of a bipedal and highly mobile existence in the savannah, probably the most cogent explanation remains that based on the geological evidence of climatic changes which occurred in the east African region at the beginning of the Pleistocene, in the early Villafranchian phase. This phase appears to have been one of gradual deforestation leading to the establishment of a savannah parkland terrain. Such an event would clearly eliminate those creatures not able to sustain a full terrestrial life, to find new food sources and to band together for protection in the open plains. The loss of much vegetarian sources of food would make recourse to hunting or scavenging and a change to a much more carnivorous diet vital. In such hunting activities the use and enhancement of the orthograde posture offers clear advantages. It has been suggested that throwing of missiles while running would only be possible to those creatures with a stabilized bipedal locomotion; that these would be the more successful in securing the game; that much more game could be carried back to safety by a bipedal creature than is possible to a pronograde or partially bipedal creature; that the already keen-sighted near-hominid could use his sight and hearing to special advantage in the upright posture to maintain a lookout for game and enemies above the long grass. These were some of the factors favourable to the survival of the incipient hominids who took to bipedalism.

The first hominids

In his *Descent of Man* nearly one hundred years ago, Darwin arrived at a reconstruction, admittedly schematic, of the earliest hominid. To do this he could use only the facts of comparative anatomy, since the fossil material (described in the preceding sections) was almost entirely lacking. Darwin recreated a hypothetical stage (in fact two such stages), the so-called 'missing link', which would manifestly reflect the gradual transformation of an ape-like early hominid into present day man. To do this, Darwin interpreted the facts of comparative anatomy in the light of the formative processes of evolution he had himself adumbrated: transformation proceeds by gradual steps, correlated changes take place in the body generally and the overall modifications, impelled forward by natural selection, would have demonstrable (or plausible) survival value.

Darwin asked first 'what are the features distinctive of man compared to apes and monkeys'; and he recognised these, of course, in the large brain and the erect posture as well as in a number of facial, cranial and dental features related to the expanded brain and bipedal gait. Now Darwin argued, as a deduction from the comparative data, that the adoption of the erect posture was the primary change (in the transformation of hominoid into hominid) and that the large brain was a later and resultant consequence. Indeed, in opposition to most of the taxonomists of his day, he thought that the possession of a large brain did not give man claim to any special taxonomic treatment. As he put it: 'In determining the position of man in the natural or genealogical system, the extreme development of his brain ought not to outweigh a multitude of resemblances in other less important or quite unimportant points.' The early progenitor was apelike in his small brain, but was set on the hominid course by the adoption of the erect posture; the primacy of the change to bipedalism and its consequences is elegantly argued by Darwin.

Man could not have attained his present dominant position in the world without the use of his hands . . . But the hands and arms could hardly have become perfect enough to have manufactured weapons, or to have hurled stones and spears with a true aim, as long as they were habitually used for locomotion and for supporting the whole weight of the body, or, as before remarked, so long as they were especially fitted for climbing trees . . . From these causes alone it would have been an advantage to man to become a biped; but for many actions it is indispensable that the arms and the whole upper part of the body should be free; and he must for this end stand firmly on his feet.

The next step in the argument is this:

If it be an advantage to man to stand firmly on his feet and to have his hands and arms free, of which, from his pre-eminent success in the battle of life, there can be no doubt, then I can see no reason why it should not have been advantageous to the progenitors of man to become more and more erect and bipedal. They would thus have been better able to defend themselves with stones and clubs, to attack their prey, or otherwise to obtain food. The best built individuals would in the long run have succeeded best and have survived in larger numbers.

As the progenitors of man became more and more erect, with their hands and arms more and more modified for prehension and other purposes, with their feet and legs at the same time transformed for firm support and progression, endless other changes of structure would have become necessary. The pelvis would have to be broadened, the spine peculiarly curved and the head fixed in an altered position, all of which changes have been attained by man.

The free use of the arms and hands, partly the cause and partly the result of man's erect position, appears to have led in an indirect manner to other modifications of structure. The early male forefathers of man were probably furnished with great canine teeth [*this would have been an early dryopithecine stage*]; but as they gradually acquired the habit of using stones, clubs or other weapons for fighting with their enemies or rivals, they would use their jaws and teeth less. In this case, the jaws, together with the teeth, would become reduced in size.

As the jaws and teeth in man's progenitors gradually became reduced in size, the adult skull would have to resemble more and more that of existing man.

As the various mental faculties gradually developed themselves the brain would certainly become larger.

In regard to bodily size or strength, we do not know whether man is descended from some small species like the chimpanzee, or from one as powerful as the gorilla;

and, therefore, we cannot say whether man has become larger and stronger, or smaller and weaker, than his ancestors. We should, however, bear in mind that an animal possessing great size, strength and ferocity, and which, like the gorilla, would defend itself from all enemies, would not perhaps have become social; and this would most effectually have checked the acquirement of the higher mental qualities, such as sympathy and love of his fellows. Hence it might have been an immense advantage to man to have sprung from some comparatively weak creature.

The hominid progenitor, as reconstructed by Darwin, is ape-like in its combination of small brain case and relatively large, if somewhat reduced, jaw; the teeth are nevertheless reduced in size; the pelvis is broad and man-like; the animal was small and the small brain would enlarge in the later descendants.

That the evolutionary line beyond the *Proconsul–Dryopithecus–Ramapithecus* hominoid sequence passed through a stage quite like Darwin's inferred hominid we now know to have been the case. The stage comprised the misnamed 'southern ape' or *Australopithecus* of Africa (Fig. 21). The genus is known to us from a period of about two million years ago, when the pliocene epoch gave way to the first phase, the Villafranchian phase, of the ensuing pleistocene epoch.

At the end of the Pliocene, east Africa offered climatic conditions probably hotter than those of the present time with a more wooded parkland. The forested terrain, as we have seen, had harboured the prehominid dryopithecines in some variety for millions of years. Now a fully terrestrial somewhat ape-like hominid emerged. The northern hemisphere at this time was experiencing a major cold phase and the glacial conditions persisted probably during the whole time that *Australopithecus* developed, flourished, differentiated and underwent further transformation. With the general amelioration of climate came a spread of the most advanced of the australopithecine groups over a wider area.

The hominid ancestor delineated by Darwin is, obviously, an abstraction, an idealised representation. The reality resides, of course, in the existence of a Villafranchian group of species displaying a range of variation in all characters—those that testify to a hominid status, and those that 'look back' to a more pongid past. Today, with the material from east and south Africa from half a dozen sites at our disposal, we can distinguish clearly two and probably three important phylogenetic groups, but there is no doubt of the overall similarity between the east and south African representatives. As a group, the australopithecines fulfil the major criteria so clearly predicted by Darwin. Let us first concentrate on the essential traits and then consider the important generic or sub-generic divergences within the group as a whole.

The first impression given by all the skulls (Fig. 16) from the different populations of *Australopithecus* is of a distinctly ape-like creature. This is seen in the combination of the large, heavy-jawed muzzle and protruding face with the relatively small cranial vault. Even the infant from Taung (see Fig. 21), the first australopithecine recognised by Raymond Dart, conveys this impression (and so prompted the cumbersome and now inappropriate name). The ape-like profile of *Australopithecus* is so pronounced that its outline can be superimposed on that of a female chimpanzee with a remarkable closeness of fit. In this respect, and also in the lack of chin and in the possession of strong supra-orbital ridges, *Australopithecus* stands in strong contrast to modern *Homo sapiens* but less to archaic varieties. The australopithecine skulls from Olduvai, Tanzania ('*Zinjanthropus*') and from Kromdraai, Transvaal ('*Paranthropus*') display another unmistakable ape-like or gorilla-like feature—a sagittal crest (Plate 1). But this crest differs from that of the ape in that it does not extend so far back on to the nuchal region. Close and detailed examination reveals that many other features depart significantly from the pongid condition, such as the shape of the orbit, the slope and shape of the zygomatic arches and the nasal aperture. In Fig. 16 the eyesocket can be seen to possess a convexity which looks forward and downward in quite clear contrast to the straighter and more up-

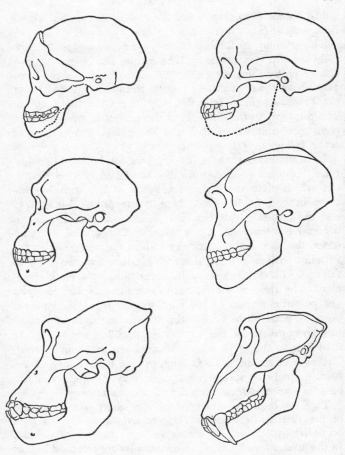

16 Skull profiles of Australopithecus (top four), gorilla (bottom left), and baboon (bottom right)

ward looking margin of the pongid orbit. The change in plane of the orbit is clearly related to the change to a more vertical carriage of the head—manifestly a hominid modification. Despite the strong jaws, the zygomatic arches are not pulled downwards as in apes, the temporal line of the zygomatic bone is shortened and the level of the arches is more horizontal as in the hominids.

The contour of forehead and vertex when studied carefully are also very revealing. The feature can be given a precise value by calculating the ratio of the height of the brain case above the supraorbital margin to the total height above the Frankfurt plane (see Fig. 58) (Le Gros Clark 1959). The ratio for *Australopithecus* is demonstrably greater (sixty-eight per cent) than that of the gorilla, chimpanzee or orang (all about forty-eight per cent).

In addition to such rather unobtrusive hominid-like features, there are a number of other cranial and dental characters which place the hominid affinities of the australopithecines beyond doubt. First there is the poise of the head and the associated attachments of the neck muscles. In his perceptive assessment of the infantile Taung skull, Dart asserted that the occipital condyles (where the skull rests on the vertebral column) were relatively further forward than in the ape. This conclusion is fully borne out by the adult specimens. The ratio of the distance from the occipital condyles (or posterior margin of the auditory aperture) to the most posterior point of the skull to the distance in front of the auditory aperture (i.e. to the front of the maxilla) is much larger than it is in the apes, where the foramen magnum is much further back on the base. In modern man these distances are nearly equal—the foramen magnum is in the middle of the base, in *Australopithecus* it is not quite so far forward.

That the head was balanced in an upright position on top of the vertebral column is also clearly shown by the area occupied by the muscle attachments on the occipital base. In the apes, as we know, the neck muscles are attached higher up on the nuchal region; in *Australopithecus*, as in primitive or modern man, the attachment is much lower down. The much greater height of the nuchal crest above the Frankfurt plane in the ape is obvious. The mastoid process, which gives strong attachment to neck musculature, even in the young Taung specimen is strongly formed and pyramidal, resembling that of modern man.

The far reaching conclusion to be drawn from these findings is that *Australopithecus* was, in fact, an erect hominid, habitually bipedal, with hands completely free.

To say that these features are mere parallelisms developing in a still arboreal, but highly orthograde, ape is to ignore the existence of many other features of the total morphological pattern, which point sharply in the hominid direction. And, in fact, direct proof of the deduction that *Australopithecus* was hominid in his posture and locomotion is forthcoming in the structure of the pelvis (Fig. 17) and of the fragments of the leg and foot bones.

The pelves of hominids and pongids, as we know (Fig. 11), provide a strong morphological contrast based on the divergent modes of locomotion. The form of the innominate bones and sacrum thus offers a test case of the true status of *Australopithecus*. But just as the poise of the skull is not fully hominid, nor are the pelvis or the limb bones: some prehominid features persist.

Robinson has assembled the whole pelvic girdle (and the lower vertebral column) (Fig. 17) and as is obvious, it contrasts radically with that of any pongid. Instead of the elongated narrow iliac blade with a shallow sciatic notch, the australopithecine ilium is short and broad and the sciatic notch is deep. As in man, the broad ilium provides the attachment for the strong muscles of the back for maintaining the trunk erect, and also for the gluteal musculature behind and the long exterior muscles in front of the hip joint to secure the erect trunk on the lower limbs during standing and moving. In particular, the way the gluteal musculature is attached is in conformity with its role as an extensor in *Australopithecus*, as in man, an attachment making it possible for the creature to walk erect (Washburn). Moreover, the acetabulum (or thigh socket) occupies a position making for stability; there is a well-marked anterior inferior iliac spine for the ilio-femoral ligament (which reinforces the capsule of the hip joint) and for the rectus femoris muscle which keeps the knee extended in the upright posture.

Just as the small skull presents a superficial pongid aspect, yet is demonstrably hominid, the small pelvis looks remarkably like that of a Bushman but nevertheless still carries some

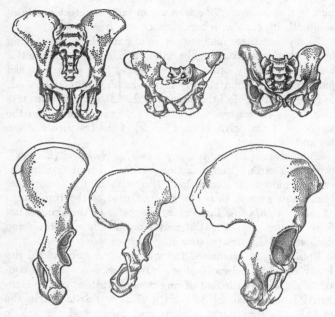

17 Top row: (From Robinson) pelves from in front: gorilla, Australopithecus, modern man. Lower row: (From Harrison *et al*) innominate bones from side: chimpanzee, Australopithecus, modern man

pongid features. Thus the ape's ilium has a characteristically forward expansion which is also evident in the Australopithecinae. The ischial tuberosity is not so close to the acetabulum as it is in *Homo* and the sacro-iliac area is relatively not so extensive (Fig. 17B). The fragment of the lower limb skeleton also reveals some pongid resemblances.

Darwin pointed out that the earliest bipedal hominid would necessarily have his hands free and he argued that manipulative proficiency would remove the need for strong canines and large teeth generally. This prediction is exactly fulfilled. Amongst all the australopithecines the hominid nature of the dentition is outstanding. The contour of both upper and lower jaws exhibits (Fig. 18) a clear departure from the parallel

U-shaped ancestral hominoid and pongid condition to the more rounded hominid curvature. Nor is there in the parabolic arcade any break between the four front teeth and the parallel tooth rows behind, as there is in the pongid. The total lack of a diastema in both upper and lower dentition is an advanced character.

The dentition has been the subject of extremely detailed examination and intensive controversy. Here only the salient features of both the permanent and milk dentition can be mentioned. The australopithecine canine is small, spatulate and bluntly pointed instead of large, conical and sharp as in the ape. Instead of the well-marked internal ridge or cingulum prolonged into a distinct talonid, the cingulum is reduced and there is no projecting talonid (Fig. 18). The teeth wear down in man-like fashion—they wear down flat from

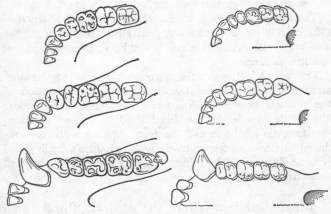

18 Teeth of Australopithecus (middle) compared to those of gorilla (below) and modern man (above). Left column: lower jaw; right column: upper jaw

the tips and any projection beyond the occlusal level is soon lost.

The first premolar is another tell-tale tooth. Again the strong contrast between pongid and hominid puts the aus-

tralopithecines with the latter, since in them the premolar is
of bicuspid (non-sectorial) type. The molar teeth are again
man-like in the even flat wear in the earliest stages of at-
trition; this happens only late in the lifespan of the ape. The
canines erupt early, before the second molar.

The deciduous dentition may be summarily described:
lower canines are spatulate, relatively short and bluntly
pointed and with no projecting talonid. In the pongid, the
lower canines are conical and sharply pointed, projecting
well beyond the level of the molar, with an approximately
straight internal cingulum extending back to form a talonid.

The first lower milk molars of *Australopithecus* are multi-
cuspid with four or five cusps disposed at approximately the
same level and with a well-marked anterior fovea. The first
lower molars of pongids are of sectorial type with the
crown composed mainly of large pointed protoconid and a
depressed talonid and no well-marked anterior fovea.

The mandible in its lack of a simian shelf and absence of
chin carries on the primitive generalised condition of the
hominoids, the dental foramen is single, as in man, and not
multiple as in apes.

The salient features of the Australopithecinae may be summarised by paraphrasing Darwin's prophetic description of
the 'progenitors of man'—'becoming more erect and bipedal',
'the pelvis broadened, the head fixed in altered position',
'the free use of the arms', 'the jaws together with teeth reduced in size', 'a comparatively weak creature'; finally 'man
became divested of hair from having aboriginally inhabited
some tropical land'.

Micro-evolution within the Australopithecines

As a recognisable group the australopithecines endured for a
very long time, perhaps a million years or so, spanning the
period between the earliest specimens of Olduvai in east
Africa to the last known survivors at Kromdraai in the Transvaal. Naturally, over this great space of time and territory,
evolutionary changes occurred within the genus; we should
expect to find clear evidence of various phylogenetic trends—

radiative trends towards the formation of distinct varieties or even species, or 'phylal' trends showing divergence in some characters along specialised lines; in the long run, we look for trends indicative of the emergence from the australopithecine nexus of still more advanced hominids. In Julian Huxley's terminology the australopithecines represent a grade of development through which the hominid line demonstrably has passed. We have already identified numerous hominid elements within this grade of evolution; these will provide the matrix which lead on to *Homo erectus* (*Pithecanthropus*) as the next 'grade'. Can we identify an advanced stage or phyletic segment within the australopithecine grade itself?

On purely morphological grounds, two taxonomically distinguishable but related australopithecine taxons have generally been recognised (Fig. 16), usually designated as *Australopithecus robustus* (e.g. Swartkrans) and *Australopithecus africanus* (e.g. Sterkfontein) and, as always, we must appreciate that each displays a range of variation from one local population to another. Both in south Africa and east Africa it has been claimed that a third entity, outside the range of *Australopithecus robustus* and *Australopithecus africanus*, is discernible and that this represents the advanced extension into the next grade of hominid organisation. In south Africa the claim rests on the fragments called 'Telanthropus', in east Africa on the remains labelled *Homo habilis*. The controversy which still surrounds these claims has less to do with the inherent probability of the existence of an advanced australopithecine than with the statistical credibility of the evidence as presented.

Australopithecus robustus and *Australopithecus africanus* have some interesting points of difference. Of these the sagittal crest of *Australopithecus robustus* is particularly arresting. It is prominent (Plate 1) in so-called 'Zinjanthropus' of east Africa and in 'Paranthropus' of Swartkrans. As already remarked, this crest despite its general appearance, is not really like that of the gorilla. It is not continued back into a high nuchal crest. Indeed the crest is variable in its extent and in some specimens does not travel as far back as the occipital bone. As in later hominids, the nuchal ridge in both species of *Australopithecus* is relatively low and the nuchal area reduced. The braincase of *Australopithecus robustus* is more spheroidal than that of *Australopithecus africanus*.

Another striking contrast is that in *Australopithecus robustus* the front teeth—canines and incisors—are much smaller in size relative to the premolar or molar series (Fig. 18). In *robustus* the anterior teeth are appreciably smaller and the post-canine teeth larger than those of *africanus*. Robinson has argued that this indicates a distinct ecological difference —*robustus* subsisting on a vegetarian and *africanus* on a carnivorous diet.

In south Africa the two forms *Australopithecus africanus* and *Australopithecus robustus* seem to be well separated in time; the former is the earlier and ascribed to the Upper Villafranchian or Lower Pleistocene and the latter to the 'Basal Middle Pleistocene'. The *Telanthropus* fragments are contemporary with *Australopithecus robustus*.

In east Africa *Australopithecus robustus* (*Zinjanthropus*) is Upper Villafranchian in time, and as it has been dated back to 1.7 million years ago it has been suggested that the south African form 'arrived' in the south long after its appearance further north. In east Africa, however, the remains of *Australopithecus robustus* (*Zinjanthropus*) are geologically very close in time to the material claimed to represent a separate form, the so-called *Homo habilis*.

It is now necessary to consider whether in the fragments of either *Telanthropus* or of *Homo habilis*, or both, we have representatives of creatures morphologically different from or even more advanced beyond the range of specimens making up *Australopithecus robustus* and *Australopithecus erectus*. Unfortunately, the remains from both east and south Africa are meagre, and the fact that they come from the same sites as their local representatives of *Australopithecus robustus* makes the onus of proving that the finds are distinctive all the greater. *Telanthropus* is represented by two mandibles, one incomplete, and by the front piece of an upper jaw (Plate 2). The molar teeth are admittedly smaller than those of the *Australopithecus robustus* specimens found

at the site, and they are comparable to those of some specimens of *Homo erectus*. Nevertheless all these teeth can be
matched by specimens within the limits of variation of the
australopithecine range taken as a whole. Nor are the small-
ish mandibles distinguishable in size from certain of the australopithecine jaws (those from Makapan).

Now the largest cranial capacity or brain volume for an
australopithecine specimen is 620 cc. Taking the group as a
whole the upper limit on statistical grounds could have been
as high as 800 cc. Thus Tobias' estimate of 680 cc. for *Homo
habilis* does not really extend materially beyond the probable
australopithecine range (and even this estimate must be
treated with reserve, based as it is on the two imperfect
parietal bones). Nor is the *habilis* figure outside the largest
values reported for ape crania—the gorilla values go up to
750 cc.

On the basis of the present material and the analysis so
far made, it seems unlikely that *Homo habilis* represents a
separate species poised between *Australopithecus* and *Homo
erectus*, or the earliest of *Homo erectus*. It may yet turn out,
with more material and by adequate statistical treatment, to
represent an advanced form of *Australopithecus africanus*.

Genesis of hominid behaviour

The change from an arboreal to a terrestrial life, evidenced in
the transformation of the ancestral hominoid (dryopithecine)
stage to the first hominid (Australopithecine) stage, ranks as
the crucial event in anthropogenesis.

Once on the ground, survival would have depended on the
fullest exploitation of characters already incipiently present
in the arboreal phase. Of such pre-adaptations, we have already noted that the orthograde posture with the occasional
bipedal gait, the freeing of the fore-limbs, the prehensibility
and mobility of the hands, are specially characteristic of the
higher primates; indeed they represent the culmination of
long developing progressive trends in the primates as a group.

The structural changes in posture and locomotion, the exploitation of manipulative ability and visual acuity, are only

part of a complex of behavioural adjustments. Survival depended greatly upon the further development of the social cohesiveness and inter-communication so characteristic of higher primates in general. These qualities are no less the product of evolutionary processes than are morphological and functional attributes. As Darwin, true to his conviction of the adaptive outcome of the struggle for survival, concluded . . . 'the social qualities, the paramount importance of which to the lower animals is disputed by no-one, were no doubt acquired by the progenitors of man in a similar manner, namely through natural selection aided by inherited habit'. Of 'mental faculties', on which social qualities rest, Darwin was convinced 'that there is no fundamental difference between man and the higher mammals'. As an inescapable corollary to the morphological affinities between man and other living Anthropoidea, and particularly between man and the great apes and because of the parallelism in the ecological experience of their early forebears, there should be discernible clear links of a mental and behavioural kind amongst the Anthropoidea. The information available to us shows that this conclusion of Darwin's is completely justified. We possess a good deal of comparative data on the biological basis of mental activity, that is to say, on the configuration and organisation of the nervous system and special senses, and on the hormonal system which plays a role in both development and behaviour. We possess, moreover, information on social behaviour itself, on social interaction, communication and emotional attitudes, and learning capacity. Important in these respects as are the resemblances between man and other primates, it need hardly be stressed that hominid evolution has entailed a development of neurological organisation and of social behaviour and mental capacity, as evidenced particularly in conceptual thinking and communication through speech, far beyond that of any ape, past or present.

(i) *Manipulative ability*

For both pongids and hominids the free use of the hands is of cardinal importance to survival. The handling of objects in an exact and purposeful way is widespread amongst mon-

keys and apes. In captivity, an astonishing capacity for ac-
quiring manipulative skill is revealed. The capuchin monkey
can quickly and expertly make use of a variety of differently
shaped sticks as well as wire, rope, cardboard and other objects for obtaining food out of reach. A capuchin in the London Zoo used to place a nut on the floor of the cage and
grasping a heavy marrow bone in both hands would bring it
down sharply on the nut to crack it (Plate 3). This kind of
behaviour is evinced quite naturally during their ordinary
feeding conditions in the wild. Hard fruit or nuts or beetles
may be carried off to be beaten against neighbouring trees.

It is true that by comparison with the hand of man the
typical monkey hand is long and narrow, the metacarpals are
short relative to the phalanges, the finger-tips are slender and
narrow (Fig. 19). Yet true opposability is a property of the
living Old World monkeys. The carpo-metacarpal joint has
a saddle shape quite comparable to the corresponding human
joint. The thumb can turn about its longitudinal axis and move
across the palm to bring the pulp of the thumb directly
against the pulp surfaces of one, or more than one, of the
other digits. There is also, as in man, a fair range of movement at the metacarpophalangeal joint.

In apes the hands do not have the same degree of freedom.
Yet the young chimpanzee or orang-utan can make efficient
opposition of thumb to first finger and also grip by flexion
of the fingers or by interaction of the fingers and thumb
(Plate 4), even though, as Napier has shown, these two basic
actions differ very much from the human power grip and
the human precision grip. The limitations and restrictions
that the ape suffers in executing these movements are of
course the outcome of the specialisation for the kind of holding movement of particular consequence for its arboreal mode
of life.

Anatomical capability is one thing; performance is another.
When we come to look at actual manipulative achievement
we find that the ape can transcend to a pronounced degree
the limitations of his hand structure—his 'urge', so to speak,
to use his hands 'forces' him to find ways of carrying out hand
actions which the Old World monkey, with his apparently
better ordered structure, does not or cannot develop.

In captivity, the great apes often construct rough shelters, handle a variety of objects as rudimentary tools; chimpanzees especially can imitate or adopt human equipment with surprising facility (Plate 4). Of the many accounts of the complicated manipulations which the chimpanzee can perform, that by Dr and Mrs Hayes is especially impressive.

In the wild, situations which demand from apes and monkeys the handling of objects as tools or weapons have often been documented. Kortland has given a summary of the available information: '. . . the use of dislodged branches as raking tools for reaching fruit or other objects was reported once for gorillas and once for an orang. Two observers saw chimpanzees use sticks to collect honey from bees' nests. One observer reported that he watched baboons, mangabeys and colobus use pieces of wood as digging, boring or chiselling implements to widen the entrance of ants' and termites' nests and baboons have been seen using sticks to stir up insects that were hidden under stones. One observer reported that he saw a squirrel monkey use a stick, in a sweeping movement, to move fruit along the ground, dislodging the ants on it. Two observers report the use of leaves as "medicated pads" by a chimpanzee and colobus. Finally, the use of small sticks and fruit as "toilet" aids was observed in howlers and capuchins and once in a chimpanzee.'

Kortland draws attention to the fairly accurate throwing of objects (food, stones, sticks, etc.) evinced by apes in captivity, by chimpanzees and gorillas more than by orang-utans. Gorillas in the rain forest, and chimpanzees in the bamboo and rain forests, throw in an indiscriminate way; the highest proficiency has been observed amongst savanna-inhabiting chimpanzees. Throwing activity is clearly aggressive or defensive in nature, often accompanied by an intimidation display.

The mother chimpanzee (Goodall) and mother gorilla (Schaller) both use one hand to help their infants on to their backs.

In the light of the evidence of manipulative ability possessed by apes and monkeys and from the anatomical structure of the hand of living anthropoids, it is a simple inference that ancestral hominoids at the dryopithecine or even earlier levels should have possessed hands of a sufficiently generalised kind, well adapted for handling activities.

The possession of manipulative skill, for food getting and for using objects for defence or offence, must have been an important factor favouring the survival of dryopithecine pre-hominids of the *Ramapithecus* lineage, since as we have seen (Fig. 14) the reduction in jaw and tooth structure is already evident.

Proconsul turns out to be in this, as in other respects, more specialised than we would expect of a truly generalised hominoid ancestor. Even so, according to Napier, it does not show the hand specialities of living apes. The hand was prehensile, the hand of a tree-climbing anthropoid, but the thumb was opposable, though imperfectly so.

At one of the Olduvai sites, sufficient of the hand bones of at least two individuals of a date little different from that of *Zinjanthropus* were discovered and these turn out to be, in some but not all respects, unlike those of modern *Homo sapiens* (Fig. 19). This hand must have been that of the maker and user of the closely associated stone tools (Fig. 20).

Although it was a smaller hand, the relative lengths of the metacarpals and phalanges indicate that the proportion of digit to palm was much the same as it is in man. In addition, the tips of the terminal bones of all the Olduvai fingers are quite wide and the finger-tips therefore broad. This is another similarity to the human. In the marked curvature of the phalanges and metacarpals there is a resemblance to the gorilla (Napier).

The evidence suggests that the Olduvai thumb, like the thumb of the gorilla, was set at a narrow angle and was somewhat shorter than the thumb of modern man, reaching only a little beyond the metacarpal-phalange joint of the index finger. The Olduvai wrist bone that articulates with the thumb is also gorilloid in some respects. The thumb was opposable, and permitted the hand to exert a strong power grip, but probably not to perform actions as precise as those of modern man. The power grip alone, as Napier demonstrated, would have sufficed for the construction by a stone-on-stone technique for pebble tool or simple hand-axe construction (Plate 5).

As far as the meagre evidence goes, the hand bones of the south African australopithecines were similar to those found at Olduvai Gorge. A metacarpal bone of the thumb

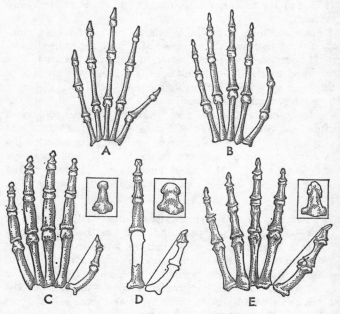

19 Hand skeleton of primates (from Napier): (a) = tarsier, (b) = capuchin, (c) = gorilla, (d) = Australopithecine, (e) = modern man. Insets show terminal phalanx of thumb

from Swartkrans is robust and strongly curved and comparable to the Olduvai finger bones; it carries on its articular surface gorilloid characters similar to those of the Olduvai wrist bone already mentioned. Of three wrist bones from Sterkfontein, the capitate resembles that of man, but carries certain ape-like features; and in these respects it is very like a capitate bone from Olduvai. The fact that the south African hand bones are so much in accord with those from Olduvai argues strongly (as Le Gros Clark has emphasised) against any real phyletic separation of so-called *Homo habilis* from *Australopithecus*.

The skeletal make-up of the australopithecine arm and hand with its opposable thumb gives evidence unmistakably of their grasping and holding abilities and is consonant with the use of ready to hand objects as tools, and even with the capacity to manufacture crude stone or bone implements.

When we recall not merely the tool-using capabilities of chimpanzees in captivity or in the wild, but take into account the evidence of deliberate though rudimentary tool making, we can have little doubt that *Australopithecus*, by structure as from necessity, was well capable of both tool using and tool manufacture.

Before any early Pleistocene pebble tools, already long known from east and south Africa (Fig. 20), were found in direct association with *Australopithecus*, Dart had brought forward some fairly strong indirect evidence of tool-using. In the south African caves a number of the fossil baboon skulls appear to have been deliberately fractured by the use of some form of club. This view has received support in that on the Olduvai living floors, for in association with pebble tools, broken animal bones in great abundance are to be

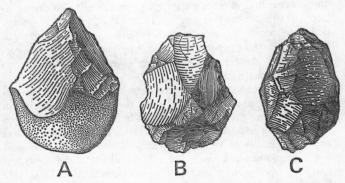

20 Tools of the Oldowan culture (pebble tools): (A) from Olduvai, (B) from Sterkfontein, (C) from Swartkrans

found. There seems little doubt that these represent the food debris of animals that could well have been hunted; their bones were split for the marrow.

It is above all the presence of the Oldowan industry that finally establishes the tool-making capacity of the australopithecines. The industry consists of pebbles of lava and quartz flaked by percussion to form crude chopping and cutting tools, varying in size from about the dimensions of a ping-pong ball to that of a croquet ball (Leakey). Oldowan tools have been found over a wide area of Africa (Fig. 20).

We have now in our possession much evidence—skeletal, archaeological and behavioural, as well as indirect information from living primates, establishing firmly the dependence of the first hominids on their tool- and weapon-making and using abilities.

The 'feed back' between bipedalism and tool making has been well recognised from Darwin onwards; clearly the orthograde posture and bipedal tendencies of the arboreal phase when transferred to the terrestrial in an animal so small and physically so defenceless as the first near-hominid placed a high premium on the survival advantage of the dexterity of the hands and on tool-making, and on their continued enhancement through selection.

The high development of manipulative skill among the hominids is reflected in a corresponding elaboration of the motor areas and effector pathways of the brain. The organisation of the pre-central cortex (Fig. 21) (sigmoid gyrus) which subserves the execution of muscular movements is such that in man the proportion devoted to hand and limb movements is far greater than in monkeys, with that of chimpanzees intermediate in size.

In the Anthropoidea the precentral motor cortex has assumed nearly absolute control over the skeletal musculature and when the precentral cortex (Fig. 5) is removed from both cerebral hemispheres total paralysis follows—the affected animal is unable to sit, stand, walk, climb or grasp food and the only movements made are reflex and certain stereotyped grasping and pulling responses. By contrast, dogs and cats from which the entire cerebral cortex has been removed still stand and walk almost as well as normal animals.

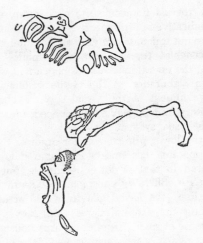

21 Representations of the 'body image' on the motor area of the cerebral cortex of monkey (above) and man (below) (After Woolsey *et al* and Penfield and Rasmussen)

The adoption of the erect posture seems to have brought with it a great increase in motor control as a whole. Thus, the cerebellum which controls general postural balance as well as the muscle tone for fine grading of movement is also much more enlarged. Once again, this enlargement is a primate and anthropoid evolutionary trend, particularly marked in the hominids.

The interaction between bipedalism and tool making must have faded in intensity once the upright posture and locomotion were fully effective. The later improvements in tool making, including the techniques of hunting and shelter making, could not have arisen from further changes in locomotion.

(ii) *Perceptual ability*

The accurate handling of objects or (in the widest sense) the manipulation of the environment, demands highly developed powers of sensory perception. These are certainly possessed by the Anthropoidea. The comparative study of the living anthropoids reveals unmistakably, once more, an evolutionary trend indicative of a progressive modification of the structures subserving touch, vision and smell, culminating in man. We can recognise three inter-woven trends—a progressive reduction in the neural mechanisms concerned with the sense of smell, an elaboration of the tactile system and an even greater development of the visual system. The elaboration of the auditory system, while pronounced, is not so striking as that of the visual system.

Even in the lower primates, as for example the lemur, the olfactory apparatus has undergone some degree of reduction compared to that of lower mammals, but the various components are still fairly conspicuous. The muzzle with its moist rhinarium (the naked glandular skin across the upper lip connecting the external nares) still serves for a well-developed sense of smell. From the conspicuously coiled nasal turbinals the olfactory nervous pathway (the olfactory bulbs and the olfactory tracts) run into those parts of the brain which make up the still elaborate rhinenpallium (the area of cortex concerned with small perception). Within it, the pyriform lobe, an important receiving area for the olfactory tracts, still takes up most of the cerebrum (as seen in lateral view (Fig. 5)) and another part of the rhinenpallium—the dentate gyrus and the hippocampus—from the corpus callosum to the base of the brain—is prominently exposed on the medial surface (Fig. 22). The ventral commissure (which links the olfactory bulbs) also remains large.

In the Anthropoidea, however, and specially in man, all these elements, the receptor surfaces, sensory tracts, relay centres and cortical areas exhibit a most remarkable attenuation. The nasal region is greatly modified with a loss of the rhinarium, reduction of turbinals, flattening of olfactory bulbs, diminution of the central commissure and the pyriform lobe becomes so restricted that the pyriform cortex is almost entirely displaced on to the basal and median surface. The dentate gyrus in the Anthropoidea is no more than a crinkled band and the hippocampus only exposed at its lowest extremity.

The decisive elimination of smelling as a primary mode of

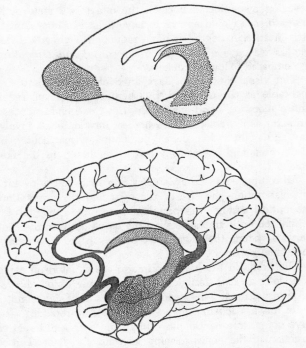

22 Rhinencephalon (olfactory tracts and areas) in Galago (above) and man (below)

obtaining information is associated in man with the almost complete disappearance of skin apocrine glands. Amongst prosimians, the apocrine secretion plays a socialising role—the material is left on branches to serve as a 'trail'. But apocrine glands (and the hairs to which they are embryonically related) whilst still numerous in the skin of monkeys, are less so in apes; in man they are confined to a few small areas, to the axilla (perhaps because this provides a particularly effective olfactory site) the pubic region and around the lips, and the glands become functional only at puberty.

If we place significance on the size of the nasal aperture and cavity and on the general conformation of the brain, as revealed by endocranial casts, the olfactory system of *Australopithecus* would appear to have been less important than it is in apes. A degree of nasal reduction is already discernible, as we have noted even in *Proconsul* and *Dryopithecus* as compared to lower primates.

The visual system displays an evolutionary trend as remarkable as the olfactory, but here of course enlargement and elaboration stand out. Again, this trend characterises the primates as a whole, but the highest developments involving day and night vision, colour perception, visual acuity, wide visual area and stereoscopy are to be found in the Hominoidea.

All components of the visual system share in the evolutionary elaboration—the size of the eyes and the orientation of the optical system, the peripheral receptor elements of the retina, the optic tracts carrying the nerve fibres to the central nervous system, the visual relay centres in the mid-brain and the visual cortex.

The orbits in the higher primates are situated on a plane and along an axis designed for stereoscopic vision and for a wide visual area. The incomplete orbits of the Prosimii, not quite forward looking, give way in the Anthropoidea, as we have noted, to a continuous orbital ring with a different construction of the bones forming its walls and floor. The configuration of man's eye-socket, like his hand skeleton, is an ancient hominoid heritage and owes to the anthropogenetic process only a minor elaboration.

The orbital cavity is anatomically similar in *Proconsul*, *Dryopithecus* and man. The external contour of the orbital margin, to be sure, assumes a recognisably hominid appearance in *Australopithecus* and this is connected no doubt with the erect posture and the hominid carriage of the head. But the optical system and retinal structure are in detail similar in man, apes and the majority of the monkeys. In man and the Anthropoidea generally, the optic nerve fibres from each eye do not undergo the almost total crossing over to the opposite cortex which is the case in lower animals and even in *Tarsius*. In man and the higher primates as much as forty per cent of the fibres travel on uncrossed. Thus each eye has a representation of its visual field on the calcarine or visual cortex on both sides of the brain. The organisation of rods and cones, the provision of a macula lutea within the foveal area, provide the basis for the night and day vision, colour perception as well as the visual acuity which the higher Anthropoidea all possess in common to a highly developed degree. The arrangement so essential for stereoscopic vision is again a heritage in man from the prehominid stage. But when we examine the nerve pathways and connections within the central nervous system, substantial changes associated with full hominid status become manifest.

The optic fibres (Fig. 23A) after the decussation travel up in the optic tracts to the lower visual centres in the thalamus (the lateral geniculate nucleus) for sorting out the retinal impulses into discrete image patterns (Hubel) and these are then transmitted along the optic radiation to the visual cortex where they are combined and interpreted. The lateral geniculate body becomes progressively more elaborate (Fig. 23B) and enlarged amongst the higher primates; in the Anthropoidea the laminated arrangement of the receiving (lenticulate) cells undergoes a conspicuous folding forming a concavity downwards, and the optic tract enters into this concavity. In man and ape the lamination is composed of six layers of which the second, third and fifth receive uncrossed fibres, and the first, fourth and sixth receive crossed fibres. This laminated arrangement is most probably associated functionally with colour vision.

The fibres of the optic radiation emerge from the lateral geniculate nucleus to run backwards to the occipital lobe ending on the cells of the visual (calcarine) cortex. This is particularly an area of the brain which develops and enlarges with the emergence of hominid status.

On the lateral surface of the occipital lobe we note the 'sulcus lunatus' which marks the forward boundary of the visual cortex (Fig. 5). This sulcus (the 'simian' sulcus) makes its appearance characteristically in the highly convoluted anthropoid brain. In man other areas of the brain expand so greatly that the visual area gets pushed back to such an extent that on the lateral surface it is confined to the occipital

pole and the simian sulcus becomes rather small and incon-
spicuous. It seems safe to state that in *Australopithecus,* judging from the endocasts, the lunate sulcus is placed well back,
as in modern hominids, and not as far forward as in the
chimpanzee or gorilla. The final 'improvement' in the visual
system affecting in particular the calcarine cortex would thus
have been under way in the anthropogenetic phase. The extensive elaboration in the visual cortex is indicated by the
development on the medial surface of the occipital lobe of
a deep calcarine sulcus which provides the extensive axial
folding necessary to accommodate the whole extent of the
visual receptor layers as these develop with the overall in-

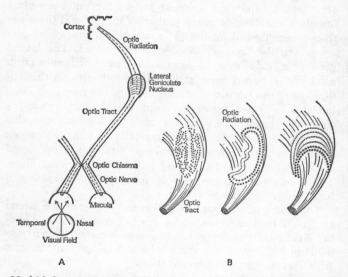

23 (A) Optic tract from eye to visual cortex relaying in lateral
geniculate nucleus; (B) Visual relay in lateral geniculate nucleus
of lemur, tarsier and man (Le Gros Clark)

crease in brain size and complexity. The number of nerve
cells greatly increases in man while the fibre connections to
the cells increases even more. As compared to the chimpanzee

the ratio of grey matter to cells is greater in man by some fifty per cent.

The perception of light signals, to indicate with great exactitude spatial relations, or of colours, seems quite as rich and detailed in the apes as in man if we may judge from the optical connections from retina to cortex. But the cortical organisation for interpretation, for associating and collating visual with tactile or auditory information, interpreting and utilising these complex images for action through speech or movement, or for storage as memory, is clearly far more advanced in man. The neurological basis for this, as far as visual improvement is concerned, is to be found in the differentiation of the secondary visual areas, the visual association areas and the augmented connections from these to other sensory and associated areas as well as to motor, and speech areas of the brain.

The hearing system has a roughly similar developmental history to that of vision amongst the primates in that the great and decisive changes are not in the peripheral mechanisms, the auditory nerve pathways or the subcortical areas. Indeed the modifications to the external ear suggest some reduction of directional hearing acuity in man as compared to lower primates. There is a complete loss of mobility of the ear, but the retention of the intrinsic and extrinsic muscles, vestigial as they are, point to the derivation of the modern human ear from a form with a freely mobile ear. In general shape the ears of man and ape are rather similar, whereas in macaques and baboons the upper free margin of the helix is drawn out into a point; this point region gets inverted in man, but is still recognisable as a small prominence (Darwin's tubercle) on the inner edge of the helix. Man and apes are similar too in the construction of the inner and middle ear. The small ossicles of the latter, which serve to conduct the vibrations from ear drum to the cochlear receptors, show some differences from the monkeys.

It is at the cortical auditory level (Fig. 5) that man diverges decisively from the Anthropoidea generally. An outward indication is the much larger size of the human temporal lobe. It is true that the external configuration of this lobe is basically alike in all the Anthropoidea, and that in man and the apes, the disposition of the sulci and of the sylvian sulcus (the upper boundary of the lobe) are very similar. There is, however, in man a greater development of separate sulci and this is an outward reflection of the much greater differentiation of the internal cycto-architecture of the receptor and related association areas. That all this is associated with the perfection of sound discrimination and the auditory memory required for vocal communication seems clear enough.

Precise information transmitted through the sense of touch is of course essential for an arboreal, balancing, handgripping and object-holding animal such as an anthropoid primate. Man's peripheral receptor equipment for obtaining tactile information is in essentials similar to that of the ape. Men and apes have also in common the complete loss of the tactile vibrissae on the face and wrists, characteristic of the prosimians, and still present, though reduced, in monkeys. A vestige of this appears during foetal life as a small cutaneous papilla in the carpal region—a short-lived reminiscence of an affinity with more primitive primates.

These tactile hairs are no doubt useful to nocturnal animals, but they are supplanted by the much more sensitive tactile pads which develop on the terminal phalanges of the digits in association with true nails instead of claws (Fig. 4). Only some New World monkeys—the marmosets—among the Anthropoidea retain the primitive sharp claws. In apes the terminal digital pads with their flat nails and the epidermal ridge system with its dense complement of touch and pressure receptors are as well developed as they are in man.

Whether there is any real difference between man and ape in the density and discriminatory power of receptors over the general body surface for recording heat, cold, touch, pressure, vibratory and pain stimuli cannot be stated. The nerve pathways from the skin surface to the spinal cord and thence to the brain via relay centres are laid down very similarly in all the Anthropoidea. But for the representation of the 'body image' on the receptor and interpretative areas of the brain, the human neopallial cortex of the parietal region (Fig. 5) possesses a highly elaborate structure. The general convolutional pattern of the parietal lobe of man resembles that of ape or monkey, but the convolutions are more developed and the whole area greatly expanded. This expansion can definitely be seen in the endocast of *Australopithecus* in terms of the distance between the forward and posterior boundaries of the lateral parietal area (that is between the central sulcus and the lunate sulcus) relative to the brain length as a whole.

We may perhaps sum up with the statement that the establishment of the hominid way of life rested ultimately on a large scale elaboration and development of the brain, or in Elliot-Smith's words on 'the simultaneous cultivation of the visual, auditory, tactile and motor areas of the cerebral cortex'.

(iii) *Communication*

In the anthropoid world communication by language is the outstanding and peculiar attribute of man alone. Yet on closer examination some phylogenetic links can be traced in the development of the neurological and allied mechanisms concerned with articulate speech and of the patterns and repertoire of sound-making and gesture that enter into social communication.

Speech requires the activity of several areas of the brain (Fig. 24) so that co-ordination can be effected between incoming and stored information and the motor control of the muscular activities of speaking. The motor association area for speech (Broca's area) is situated in the lower portion of the third frontal convolution. This area is 'an old constituent of the frontal lobe' (Bonin) with intracortical connections linking it with vision and hearing. The 'anlage' of the motor speech area is patently identifiable in the analogous position of the frontal cortex throughout the Anthropoidea. On the receptor side, speech areas are present in the auditory areas of the temporal lobe (areas 41 and 21); areas for processing and interpretation of information obtained from writing and reading, as well as from hearing, are present in the parietal lobe. How these receptor and association areas with their

complex intra-cerebral connections function is far from clearly
understood. What can be said is that in size and structure
the areas involved display a progressive elaboration in apes
compared to monkeys, and in men compared to apes.

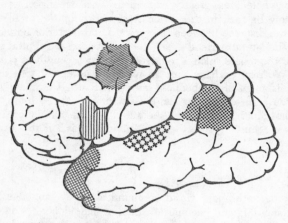

24 Areas of the brain concerned with speech

The evidence on the evolution of articulate speech offered
by the fossil skeletal material is meagre in the extreme. The
bony spines (the superior genial tubercles) on the posterior
surface of the symphysis of the human mandible, give attachment to muscles essential to speech; in the apes these
tubercles are absent. It was long believed that the presence
and size of these tubercles in fossil hominids reflected the
functional development of these muscles and therefore of
speech. In fact, these tubercles display a marked variability
not only in fossil forms but in living groups as well. In Europeans they are absent in three to five per cent of mandibles;
in some populations in Indonesia and among Bushmen they
are said to be absent in as many as twenty-five per cent of
specimens; there may be a flat surface or a fossa (as in apes).
Obviously the absence or presence of these tubercles has no
relation to the development of speech.

It is equally unreliable to use the markings or convolutions on endocranial casts as indicators of the extent of the brain areas involved in speech. The casts do not reflect faithfully the cerebral surface and many features fail to register on the casts. In any case, the external morphology of the brain is no guide to the complex organisation and the structure of the areas within the frontal and other lobes concerned with speech (Fig. 24).

Thus we really do not know at what hominid stage, whether as early as *Australopithecus* or as late as the first (archaic) *sapiens* populations, communication by language was established. It seems difficult to believe that co-operative hunting could be performed or skilled tool-making taught without language. The neurological evidence links the acquisition of language with the overall increase in size and complexity of the brain. It is brain development that is crucial since the anatomical structures of the larynx, the vocal cords and associated muscles and controlling nerves, are in many respects similar in all the Anthropoidea. Indeed the repertoire of mouth movements for vocalisation is much more extensive among the non-human Anthropoidea than is usually realised.

While man's superior capacity for articulate speech rests essentially on neurological organisation, there are also some important differences in the anatomical positioning of the laryngeal 'sound-box'. As one of the many consequences of the upright posture and the bending of the cranio-facial axis, the laryngeal 'voice-box' in man has moved away from contact with the soft palate. The oral chamber so formed makes possible the vocal performance characteristic of man (Keleman). In non-human primates the 'voice-box' is close to the soft palate and base of the tongue. This is why chimpanzees cannot make long resonant sounds. Vocalisation by apes and monkeys certainly plays an important role in their communication system, but not to the same extent as does signalling by bodily and facial movements and gestures.

In many of the main components of facial expression and vocalisation 'the Old World monkeys and apes . . . differ little from ourselves' states Andrew; a few of his many interesting examples will suffice for illustration.

The application of the lips to a fellow in greeting—the

kiss—is a form of facial display practised by apes as well as man. It derives, no doubt, from the tongue and lip movements used in suckling by the infant, and from the important primate social bonding activity of mutual grooming. The snarl, in which the upper lip is raised to reveal the canines as a threat to bite, is a gesture used by baboons, apes, as well as man (Darwin). Frowning, in which the brows are knit and lowered, is a facial movement common in the Anthropoidea and primates in general, and used by apes and man as a threat gesture; it is probably an exaggeration of the fixed aggressive stare of primates.

Facial expression for conveying information about future behaviour is essential for the development of stable social groups among the primates and particularly the Anthropoidea. Amongst monkeys selection for such a mode of communication has been intense, leading to the evolution of complex facial and bodily gesture.

Selection has also favoured vocalisation for the purposes of social communication (Andrew). Baboon society is very close knit, the members remaining always close together since the troop provides the main security against surprise attack. One mode of communication in such a society is provided by the so called 'humanoid grunts' which are used in a wide variety of special encounters. In these sounds, a wide range of resonances are made audible and therefore can carry many shades of meaning. Reynolds records that chimpanzee groups in the Budongo forest call from time to time throughout the day and also during the night. Crescendos of calling were produced in a variety of social occasions—meetings of groups, new arrivals, splitting of groups, in groups on the move, in answer to calls, etc. Their outbursts provide information on the location of food and act as a summons to those following behind during large-scale movements. This noisy vocalisation and drumming is seen by Reynolds as correlated with their loosely organised society, itself an adaptation to the needs of fruit eaters in a forest environment. The possible evolutionary relationship of chimpanzee vocalisation to human speech is not clear since the tonal structure of their calls in the wild remains to be elucidated. The 'humanoid' grunt of baboons may well be a parallelism, in that it evolved under the same selective pressures as affected the hominids, since there was a similar need to keep large social units close together in open savannah conditions (Andrew).

In human language, communication involves the use of vocal signals combined in an elaborate symbolic system. The neural basis of human speech and communication, though far from understood, is clearly one that requires a considerable expansion, not only of the motor speech centre and of 'input' or 'feed back' sensory centres and connections to make possible the range and expressiveness of articulation, but also of the co-ordination and association areas whereby vocal or visual symbols are comprehended as such.

This complex neurological structure (Fig. 24) makes possible what Hebb has termed the 'syntactic' mental activity of communication—the capacity to entertain a combination of symbolic acts (words, gestures, writing); it is therefore one highly important aspect of conceptual activity as it implies an ability to associate together diverse concepts.

While true language is unique to man, the evidence suggests that the chimpanzee is close to the 'liminal [neurological threshold] level that would make language possible' (Hayes and Hayes). The infant chimpanzee can be taught to utter a few sounds or very simple words (two or three) conveying a specific meaning, e.g. 'cup', 'papa', 'mama'. The conceptualising ability of the chimpanzee is well displayed within the human domestic environment, where the animal can learn to convey and receive a fair number of messages by the use of non-vocal symbols and signals by gesture. Hayes and Hayes give many examples.

(iv) *Learning capacity*

The evolution of learning amongst the primates must be considered in terms of behaviour and also as a function of the complexity of the nervous system. Monkeys and apes possess (though to a much lesser extent than man), the peculiar ability to master the general kind of problem that is used to measure human conceptual abilities. Such tests reveal no intellectual gulf at any point; there is a demonstrable gradation from man down the primate scale. Harlow has used learning tasks that serve as tests of discrimination or judgement. In a simple discrimination problem the animal must learn to assess the significance of a particular symbol in a particular position as the necessary condition for a reward. The number of different symbols, their colours and positions, are progressively increased in these tests. At the three-factor level of complexity no sub-primate can solve the problem, but some apes and rhesus monkeys can do so even when some men cannot! Chimpanzees have solved tasks in which five different factors have to be taken into account. Moreover, very significantly, the monkey has the ability, which is so marked in man, to transfer the learning of one problem to the solution of another.

The young monkey learns very readily. The infant macaque, with its much shorter dependency period—probably two or three years—becomes an effective learning machine more rapidly than does the human child. The macaque can solve simple black-white discriminations by fifteen days of age, and learn to cope with sets of such problems by the end of the first year. The learning capacity of the chimpanzee is without doubt in between that of monkey and man.

The learning ability of monkeys and chimpanzees can thus be shown to involve a capacity for appreciating abstract concepts or configurations to a degree far superior to that of any other sub-human mammal. This is another illustration of the 'syntactic' or conceptualising ability which also underlies communication, tool-making and purposeful co-operation—all modes of behaviour present to a discernible degree in the chimpanzee.

Amongst the prime biological determinants of the learning ability of the higher primates are the relatively long dependent growing period and the production of single young. Schultz has shown that the lengthened growing period is a common evolutionary trend of the higher primates (Fig. 25), present to the greatest extent in man. The postnatal growth period increases from two to three years in lemurs, to seven years in monkeys, eleven years in the great apes, and to twenty years in modern man. The prolongation of immaturity is a prenatal phenomenon; in the tree shrew gestation lasts no

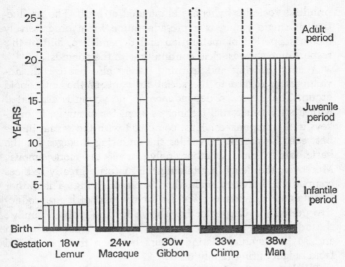

25 Developmental periods of primates (after Schultz) showing gestation period (in weeks), infantile period, juvenile period

more than six weeks, in the lemur eighteen weeks, in macaques and other Old World monkeys twenty-four weeks, reaching thirty-three to thirty-nine weeks in great apes and man. The prolongation of the growing period could not have happened unless man and the great apes had not developed as 'monotocous' forms, that is, creatures in which the offspring are usually only single at birth. In polytocous creatures intra-uterine selection would put a premium on the quicker-growing embryo, since space and nutrition are limited. Only few of the prosimians produce single young. Twins are common in *Callithrix* (which on many counts is the most primitive of the New World monkeys) but in the rest of the Anthropoidea single birth is the rule. The supersession (by selection) of the multiple condition in man is evidenced by the fact that it still occurs, but in very low frequency (about one in ninety). Selection against multiple births proceeds both naturally and artificially. The vigour and life expectancy of twins is somewhat below that of single infants, and in many primitive societies twins are eliminated at birth. The production of single young is a pre-adaptation for a progressively increased period of maturation and dependence, and in this respect man shows a clear continuity with the pongids.

A long growing and learning period also has certain advantages in regard to the social structure of the anthropoid group. The increased dependence of the young is associated with a strong maternal instinct as seen, for example, in monkeys and chimpanzees. This, combined with the sexual bonds between the parents, provides the enduring linkages for the basic family unit, whether 'polygamous' or 'monogamous'. Moreover, the delay in attaining full maturity greatly reduces competition between males and their offspring. The father maintains his dominance for the greater part of his reproductive period. As Carpenter has shown for the gibbon 'family', the adolescents are in due course excluded from the group and so 'exogamous' mating occurs between those displaced from neighbouring family units.

The long maturation period may justifiably be regarded as another primate pre-adaptation which in the hominids makes possible the long process of cultural and technological training and the emotional discipline necessary for the stability of the human social group. Once flexibility of learned behaviour and the capacity for acquisition of learning reached a high level, further active advance in technology and accumulation of effective knowledge becomes a matter for social action and transmission.

Co-operative existence has finally liberated mankind from the need to rely on the slow processes of genetic selection for improved mental efficiency. Like the making of tools, or the use of language, or the ability to learn, successful social co-operation requires the operation of these mental processes we designate as conceptual thinking. In conceptual activity there is the ability to perceive an existing situation in one way while thinking of an appropriate response to another, to plan a series of actions of which only the first is immediately feasible, to size up the relationship between things or events. Chimpanzees' behaviour, so far from constituting merely 'immediate' responses to specific stimuli, displays a good deal of purposeful co-operative activity. Captive chimpanzees (in Crawford's experiments) will co-operate in solving a learning problem in which monkeys were quite unsuccessful. Many examples of co-operation by chimpanzees in captivity and in the wild are known. The 'empathy' described by Köhler illustrates how one animal watching another facing some problem is able to put himself in the place of the other—a situation, as Hebb points out, clearly requiring the existence of several sequences of thought side by side in the brain.

For behaviour of this kind, in fact for the expression of a whole variety of social attitudes, including attitudes of friendship and mate preference, the chimpanzee displays in some degree a freedom from responses purely reflexive, hormonally dominated or stereotyped in nature. This implies that controlling and interpretative areas in the brain are already present in the chimpanzee, even if in rudimentary form. Modern ethological studies, particularly in the wild, of sub-human primates have in fact revealed an unexpected complexity of group inter-relationships and of purposive group behaviour. There can therefore be no surprise in the attribution to the australopithecines of a recognisably 'human' level of group activity and co-operation (Bartholomew and Birdsell), an inference which gains support from behavioural studies of present day higher primates.

(v) Brain size and complexity

The brain sizes of the Anthropoidea make up a 'progressive series of which man forms the climax' (Keith). This is accompanied, as already described, by enlargement of the specialised sensory and motor areas of the cortex and elaboration of the internal structure. There is a striking multiplication of the interconnected projection systems which is reflected in an increase in the total number of neurones and neuronal connections. The brain volume is closely related to both the cortical volume and the total number of cortical neurones (Fig. 26). This relationship is expressed by the equation $N = KE^{\frac{2}{3}}$ where N is the number of cortical neurones and E is the brain weight (or volume) and K is a constant. The

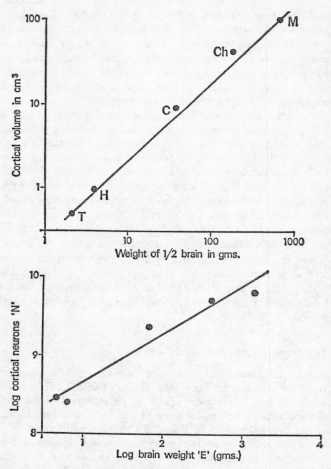

26 Relation of brain weight to cortical volume (top) and total number of cortical neurones (bottom) (from Shariff)

linear relation between the logarithm of N and the logarithm of E is shown in Fig. 26.

While the number of neurones increases with brain size, cortical volume increases even more. Bonin (1937) uses the 'gray cell coefficient' (ratio of cortical volume to cell volume) to illustrate that, in layer 4 of the cortex, the density of neuronal elements becomes less in bigger brains. (Macaque brain weight 86 gms, coefficient 870; chimpanzee brain weight 112 gms, coefficient 400; human brain weight 1400 gms, coefficient 233.) The explanation is that though there are more cell bodies in the bigger brains, the number of connections and pathways is multiplied to an even greater extent and indeed, according to Bonin, to accommodate the greater number of synapses, the Betz cells have increased in size (man 6.3 mμ^3, chimpanzee 5.1, *Cebus* 3.7). The larger size of the cells and their lower density permits the multiplication of neurone connections and of combinations between them and therefore a corresponding enhancement in the brain's capacity to handle a vastly greater number and complexity of messages. In neuronal terms this permits the production of pattern of synchronised activity and the employment of reverberating, 'feed back' and storage systems of the variety and intricacy which make human mental functioning possible.

For an evaluation of the brain development of past species we have, of course, to rely on the endocranial cast. From this we may get useful if limited information on the relative sizes of the different parts and lobes of the brain, but more important is the estimate of total brain size that can be obtained from it. In Table 1 the brain sizes of present day and extinct

Table 1. Means and ranges of cranial capacities of hominoids (from Tobias)

	No.	Range ml.	Mean ml.
Gibbon	86	87– 130	89
Siamang	40	100– 152	125
Chimpanzee	144	320– 480	394
Orang-utan	260	295– 475	411
Gorilla	533	340– 752	498
Australopithecines	7	435– 600	508
Homo erectus	8	755–1225	974
Modern *sapiens*	–	c. 1000–2000	1300

Anthropoidea are given. Crucial in this series is the brain capacity of the australopithecines as the earliest known hominids displaying the properties, structural and behavioural, appropriate to the ancestor of *Homo*. As already noted, the endocast shows in a general way that the visual, motor, association and probably, the auditory areas of the brain of *Australopithecus* have advanced in the human direction. But in gross size the brain volume is not different in range from that of the gorilla. Tobias reports that for some 650 known gorilla specimens, the mean, 498 ml., is practically the same as the value of 508 for seven australopithecine specimens. This similarly gains support from the fact that the foramen for the internal carotid artery, the main artery to the brain, is no larger in *Australopithecus* than in the gorilla (Washburn). But, as has often been pointed out, it does not follow that because gorilla and chimpanzee brains are of the same order of size this betokens a similarity of mental or intellectual capacity. Note should be taken of the fact that in relation to body size the australopithecine brain is a good deal larger than that of the gorilla. A case can be made for the belief that the small australopithecine brain, in keeping with the more complex behaviour demanded of it, was in fact in advance of the brain of the gorilla.

Brain size (E gms) has long been known to be related to body weight (P gms) which may be expressed as $E = kP^{\frac{2}{3}}$ where k is the so-called index of cephalisation. The value of k is 0.12 for modern mammals as a whole, excluding the primates, for which the value is 0.24. This implies a doubling of the typical primate brain as compared to the typical mammalian brain for any given body size. Amongst the primates, the hominids including the Australopithecinae, stand out as possessing still bigger values for k (Fig. 27). Jerison proposes an ingenious evolutionary interpretation of this finding. He postulates that brain size or total number of neurones is composed of two components, one closely dependent on body size by a relationship which applies to all mammals, and a second component of excess neurones, independent of body size, reflecting the particular level of 'adaptive capacity' attained by the animal group. Calculations based on these two assump-

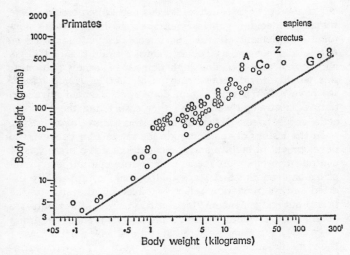

27 Brain weight as a function of body weight in primates (from Jerison). The line is the equation $E = 0.129P^{\frac{2}{3}}$; C = points for chimpanzee, G = points for gorilla, A = *Australopithecus africanus*, Z = '*Zinjanthropus*' (from Jerison)

tions reveal a phylogenetic progression throughout the primates. When the australopithecines and *Homo erectus* are included (using of course brain size values from endocranial casts and reasonable guesses for body weight) they are seen to be (Table 2) 'clearly, if only slightly, in advance of the level of brain evolution achieved by the anthropoid apes of

Table 2. Estimates of 'extra neurones' (after Tobias and Jerison)

	Brain size (ml.)	Estimate: Total Neurones ×10⁹	Estimate: Extra Neurones ×10⁹
Rhesus	100	1·7	1·2
Baboon	200	2·7	2·1
Chimpanzee	400	4·3	3·4
Gorilla	600	5·7	3·6
Australopithecines	435– 600	4·6– 5·7	3·9–4·9
Homo habilis	680	6·2	5·4
Homo erectus	775–1225	6·7– 9·3	5·8–8·4
Homo sapiens	1280–1450	9·4–10·3	8·4–9·2

our time'. Between *Australopithecus* and *Homo erectus* there remains a decided gap in brain size and in the excess neuronal complement. If the specimens designated as 'Homo habilis' did possess, as Tobias claims, a brain size of 680 cc. and thus a corresponding high number of 'excess neurones', this would provide convincing proof that in 'Homo habilis' we have either a true intermediate species or an advanced form of australopithecine, in either case filling the phylogenetic gap between the australopithecines and *Homo erectus*.

In the history of the hominids the interaction between the development of culture and the evolution of the brain was of central importance. At the so-called proto-cultural level, tool-using or even the first steps in tool-making, apparently exerted only a moderate selective effect on the size of the brain, but judgement on this must remain cautious until we obtain reliable values for the *Ramapithecus* prehominid group (Fig. 14). We know that the australopithecine brain was of the same order of size as that of the gorilla. The demonstrable advance in brain capacity, up to australopithecine times, was brought about by factors quite different from those operative after the advent of *Australopithecus*. After *Australopithecus* the brain case nearly doubled in size in *Homo erectus*, increasing thereafter by another fifty per cent by the early *Homo sapiens* stage. In the struggle for survival through technology, selection for bigger and more efficient brains would seem to have been at work. For tools to be greatly improved and diversified, the appropriate brain capacity had to evolve.

A selectionist explanation, not merely for the emergence of the first viable hominid group, but for its subsequent physical and mental development, should recognise the great driving force provided by a whole complex of mutually enhancing agencies arising from ecological circumstances. On the one hand, there is the complex of genetically controlled attributes, in particular bipedalism, carnivorous habits, developmental slowing down, cortical control, brain structure and size, and on the other the basic social and cultural components, tool using and making, symbolic communication, socially sanctioned rules regulating inter- and intra-group conduct.

The two complexes must have evolved together, mutually

reinforcing each other; changes in each of the genetic characters would have favoured changes in each of the components of culture, and conversely progress in the latter would have stimulated further development in each of the former. These are 'feed back' mechanisms which themselves underwent evolution.

With the advent of the first *sapiens* variants there is a slackening of the 'feed back' of tool-making as a selective force for brain size. The ability to fashion even better tools and contrivances grows continually, despite the fact that the limitation of brain size to a value of about 1300 to 1500 ml. had been reached. Selection for brains of greater mental capacity (but not size) remained in operation. In this phase improvement in speech may have been the cerebral character selected, as it would play the central role in the increasingly complicated requirements of the more complex social groupings, their increasing dependence on co-operative activity and particularly on learning and the transmission of complex skills.

The selection we have considered so far, selection for efficient bipedalism, for greater brain size and for the superior conceptual ability underlying tool making and speech, all depend on the struggle for survival of individuals pitting themselves against the stresses of the environment. The more successful the individual, the greater the life span available for reproduction, at a time when life expectation was perhaps no longer than about twenty years. To be cleverer, more inventive, more dextrous, quicker in action and in learning, meant, in the palaeolithic hunting society, the possession of qualities making for superior Darwinian fitness. These were the qualities, over and above the properties of biological adaptability, which ensured survival for the more resilient and resourceful of the small hunting and gathering bands living in harsh environments or moving into unknown terrain. Indeed, the transmission of higher intelligence must have been favoured in that the chief, the most able man, often had the greatest number of offspring, and the survival of a superior group must often have been brought about in this way.

The 'feed back' involved in the drive for improved mental capacity, through improved technological achievement, was itself destined to slacken off. There is no reason to believe that learning capacity, conceptual power, memory or other mental functions, are at all different now from that of the *sapiens* men of 30,000 years ago. The potent factor reducing the selection for *individual* brain-capacity was the appearance of larger co-operative bands. Individuals of very varying mental ability could now survive by means of social mechanisms permitting them to contribute different kinds of skill to the common good. In the building up of larger social units, no doubt selection for the ability to behave in a co-operative manner came into play, favouring those individuals with the appropriate mental and emotional make-up. Some relaxation of selection for this character finally comes about when society becomes heterogeneous enough to tolerate a wide spectrum of personality.

(vi) *Behavioural evolution*

Long ago, Darwin, as already mentioned, insisted on the role of natural selection in bringing about modes of social behaviour and social organisation adapted to particular ecological requirements. The recent field work by primate ethologists has demonstrated in detail that while social cohesiveness is a fundamental property of all anthropoid primates, its manifestation ranges from the single-male small family party of the gibbon, the multi-male band of the gorilla, chimpanzee, howler monkey, macaque and common baboon, to the one-male harem group of hamadryas baboon, gelada and patas monkey. It is now clear, also from these studies, that the size, structure and functioning of these sub-human primate groupings are closely influenced by particular features of the habitat. At the same time, it must be appreciated that much of the ecologically determined variation between different primate social systems represents modifications of basically similar behaviour patterns. Recognition of the co-existence of evolutionary continuity with differentiation makes it possible to frame hypotheses to explain the derivation of the hominid hunting band and family organisation from pre-hominid forms of social system. Inferences of this kind are inevitably speculative; their plausibility depends on the support afforded by the evidence both from the fossil record and from contemporary primate groups.

As we have seen, this evidence points to a succession of ecological stages in the evolutionary history of prehominids and hominids on the *Ramapithecus–Australopithecus* lineage. Following Napier, these can be considered as a progression of at least five stages—tropical forest, forest floor, forest fringe, woodland savannah and grassland or arid savannahs—before the final emergence of *Homo sapiens* into a 'world wide' ecology. Modern anthropoids are found in all these five zones. The exploitation of these different habitats for food, water, sleeping places and defence imposes definite limits on the kinds of social system and behaviour compatible with successful survival. How far is it possible to regard human social attributes as the outcome of exposure to and transition through these zones? Are such human 'end products' as permanent pair-bonds for mating, all-year breeding, lack of strong sex dimorphism, close co-operation in food getting, in food sharing and for defence against predators, and above all the monogamous nuclear family institution, to be understood as the modifications of successive social systems which prevailed in the ecological sequence from prehominid to *Australopithecus*?

A social bond basic to all anthropoid society, yet showing variations with environmental circumstance, appears in the mother-infant relationship. The closeness and continuity of this strong social linkage has been documented in detail for various sub-human primate groups, for gorillas (Schaller), chimpanzees (Reynolds, Goodall), baboons and monkeys (Crook, de Vore); the presence of infants serves as a focus of friendly and protective behaviour on the part of other females in the group and rather less frequently from males. In times of danger the troop, group or band makes determined efforts towards preservation of the female and the young. In detail the behavioural patterns of mother to offspring, of non-parental animals to young, of the males in their defensive role, are regulated, as are all social activities, by the social and status differentiation characteristic of the particular group.

The important feature of the infant's social role is for it to acquire the learned behaviour necessary for its survival. It has to become socialised. In the higher primates this period of dependence, as we have noted, becomes progressively longer. The gorilla infant remains with its mother about three years, during which time she does not become pregnant (Schaller). The young chimpanzee is to be found from the age of about six months to the age of four or five years feeding in the same tree within a few yards of its mother (Reynolds).

A second biological bond which has long been regarded as a major agent for maintaining the structural inter-relationship within primate societies is that of sexual attraction and sexual activity. Zuckerman's classical work established the central role of the reproductive physiology of the female in determining the pattern of sexual interactions amongst the Anthropoidea.

Those Anthropoidea which exhibit a sexual skin change are also (like lower animals at the true oestrus 'heat' period) maximally receptive about midway in the menstrual cycle and mating may take place within a restricted period of a few days at this time. This phase of receptivity by the female restricts the sexual attachment of the male to a period which varies to some extent individually, and with different species of monkey, but which can occupy from one-eighth to one-half of the total cycle.

Where male sexual interest does not fluctuate it follows that more than one female attachment is possible and indeed is the case. In this way there develops the 'harem' system consisting of an overlord and several consorts. It has been calculated by Chance and Mead that with two females in the group, the males will be in competition for more than half the time when the female is in oestrus for one-quarter of the cycle, and for eighty per cent of the time if female receptivity occupies one-half of the cycle. It is this competitive situation which brings about the system of dominance hierarchy, the overlord male exacting submission from his consorts, who are loyal to him only. The harem system is relatively stable, comprising several females in various reproductive stages, together with their young, and often, but not

invariably, with bachelor males also present. It appears that
strong ties also exist between the adult males, which appears
amongst them as a definite rank order.

Subordinate monkeys of the breeding hierarchy are always aware of the place occupied by, and the movements
of, the monkeys higher in rank than themselves, keeping often
at about the same distance from them, so that the potential
threat implied in the presence of a more dominant male is
constantly felt by those subordinate in rank. This threat has
presumably acquired an ambivalent element by arousing
some attraction as well as being a repellent influence
(Chance).

These social relationships are reflected in monkey, baboon
and chimpanzee colonies by patterns of social grouping.
Family parties of baboons move and feed as separate groups
unless they become involved in fights. The overlord asserts
his authority either actively by enforcing various acts of submission or at a distance by threatening gestures. The consorts are conscious of this and acknowledge their status by
acceptance postures. The overlord's social power is thus an
outcome of his sexual monopoly and this, in turn, is the result
of his dominance. In animals organised on the 'harem' system sexual dimorphism is very marked, as the maintenance
of the overlord's dominance demands greater strength, size
and aggressiveness.

Recently objections have been raised to the theory that it
is the persistent sexual interest of males and females in each
other, which to a major degree holds the primate group together. Some monkeys (Japanese and Gibraltar macaques)
have sharply defined breeding systems, yet the social structure is maintained throughout the year. Such exceptions may
be more apparent than real. The weight of evidence points
to the strong conditioning role on the developing juvenile of
the constraints imposed by sexual competition and antago-
nism within the hierarchical system; once incorporated into
the animals' learned behaviour in this way, status relationships are reinforced by other events of the animals' day to day
existence. The relationship to dominant and other animals,
the permitted use of 'social space', are continually reaffirmed
by the access allowed to food sources and to sleeping areas,

and in the disposition of the group when moving from one place to another or when danger threatens.

In recent years emphasis has been placed on ecological factors in influencing the structure and cohesiveness of the group, as reflected in such features as its size, dispersion, sex ratio and social differentiation. Crook and Gartlan have allocated primate species to a series of 'grades' representing levels of adaptation to forest, woodland savannah, grasslands and arid environments. The small size of the gibbon social unit—single mating pair and offspring—and the dispersion of such units are conditioned by the limited food supply of the tropical rain forest, and the need for individual food seeking. Their non-seasonal breeding is thought to be linked with a low copulating frequency and a low population replacement necessitated by irregularity of food supply. The gorilla, who remains a leaf and fruit eater, maintains a loose organisation in response to individual foraging.

Forest fringe and savannah woodland species enjoy favourable open country conditions of predation and food sources. This makes for increase in group size and *Papio* baboons and *Rhesus* monkeys congregate in strong social groups: this also decreases the danger from predators which scattered individuals would face. The aggressiveness of the males in these troops is related to their role, externally for group defence, and internally in the competition for females. The increased body size and other characteristics, such as the hairy mane, are no doubt an outcome of selection through these agencies. For troop defence the males take their place round the periphery of the moving troop with females and young grouped inside. The aggressiveness of the male baboons and of male rhesus monkeys imposes restricted access to females, so that the dominant male exercises exclusive right to mating with oestrus females at the time of greatest receptivity. Many features of the harem system (for example, occupation of 'social space' and grooming partnerships) can be traced to this pattern of sexual behaviour.

On the grassland savannah with its abundant food supply and in the interests of mutual defence, the baboon social group becomes much larger. The multi-male troop consists of a number of big-bodied dominant males with a large number of smaller females, bachelors, juveniles and infants.

Where the savannah is arid (Crook and Gartlan) or where the dry seasons are very severe, sparseness of food sources does not favour the large multi-male troop; these are the conditions where the one-male group characteristic of, for example, *Papio hamadryas* is found. In these conditions it is an advantage for the groups to be small and scattered; it allows the smaller-sized but more numerous females sufficient access to the available food.

If, as seems the case, selection by environmental factors has played a role in bringing about the different types of grouping appropriate to tree-life, forest floor or savannah, there is no reason why the selection may not have acted by favouring particular patterns of sexual linkage compatible with the social behaviour necessary for survival. Ecological factors would impose the controlling and limiting conditions, sexual relations would act as the main regulatory mechanisms.

Crook and Gartlan have suggested that early hominids 'had initially a social organisation not unlike that of the chimpanzee' (presumably derived from a similar forest floor phase). In the all-male groups of *Pan* they see a 'source for the loyalty and co-operation necessary in the development of group hunting expeditions'. Later, confronted with the need for a hunting existence and dangers from predators, early hominids formed either 'groups guarded by weapon-bearing males or moving in one-male family units—the males playing a part of guardians and watchdog'. Fox suggests that these developments meant that in new habitats the social structure was 'tightened up' from the looser chimpanzee system towards baboon-like types of organisation. 'A multi-male dominant hierarchy and its appendages would have characterised the declining numbers of hominids that remained in the shrinking woodlands, and a one-male group type of structure that took to the open grasslands'. Such groups would have retained the ability to congregate in suitable conditions and form hunting bands (Crook and Gartlan).

A difficulty inescapable from attempts to derive hominid behaviour directly from gorilla-like, chimpanzee-like or baboon-like social structures, is the high degree of specialisation characteristic of their sexual and social interactions, reflected in dominance behaviour patterns, their peculiar sex-ratios and their strong sexual dimorphism.

We may accept that changing ecological conditions must have progressively influenced the social structure of the evolving prehominid-hominid line. Let us assume also that to some extent clues as to the nature of such modifications are to be found in the behavioural adaptations of present day monkeys and apes. This does not mean that hominid social evolution actually went through phases of chimpanzee-like or baboon-like social systems as we know them in their specialised form today. A much simpler hypothesis would start with the postulate that the dryopithecine prehominid group in its arboreal state showed a marked analogy with gibbons. Taking into account the particular arboreal conditions influencing food supply, shelter and movement, the pre-hominid family group could likewise have been based on the simple one-male pair formation, with its concomitants of a moderate degree of sex dimorphism and year-round breeding, and little intra-group aggression. In their dexterity and potential for weapon-use, the physically less well-equipped pre-hominids were well in advance of other Hominoidea such as the forest gorillas and chimpanzees. With their greater mental capacity it would be possible for the early hominids during their jungle floor, jungle fringe or tree savannah phases, while retaining their primary family units, to combine in aggregates for defence comparable to the loose multi-male gorilla bands. In open savannah these family aggregates would become more co-ordinated and more aggressive for both hunting and defence by analogy with the behaviour of chimpanzees in the open (Kortland) or Hamadryas baboons or patas monkeys. The adoption of a carnivorous mixed diet would be enforced by the shortage of vegetable food. These first hominids could thus intensify the co-operative intra-group behaviour while retaining the small basic family unit; their survival would thus depend on their bipedal mobility, powers of observation, their developed communication system and above all their hunting and tool-making technology. This would have been a path of development quite different from that characterised by an aggressive male dominant hierarchy with its 'threat' system, its intra-group competition and marked sexual dimorphism.

CHAPTER 3

THE ESTABLISHMENT OF THE GENUS HOMO

The replacement of the australopithecine populations by more advanced forms of hominid, those belonging to the genus *Homo,* occurred over the time span, roughly, of 800,-000 to 500,000 years ago. The first species, *erectus,* of the new genus, survived for the next 200,000 years, that is, until approximately 300,000 years BP. The outstanding feature of this transformation to *Homo* was the breakaway from the small brain size of *Australopithecus,* which was still in the pongid range, barely exceeding 600 ml., to values of 800 ml. and over. Indeed, it is particularly significant of this evolutionary phase that the brain size undergoes continuous enlargement, paving the way for the more advanced still larger brained *sapiens* species of *Homo.*

From *Australopithecus* to *Homo*

Evidence of the actual transition from the one genus to the other is far from conclusive and we have to rely on rather fragmentary fossil specimens, such as the *Meganthropus* mandible from Kedung Bubus, Java, the *Telanthropus* mandibles from Swartkrans, Transvaal and the *habilis* material from Olduvai, east Africa (Plate 2). Despite the controversies about their exact taxonomic status, they do provide some demonstration of the change from the Australopithecine to the new hominid level.

The affinities of *Meganthropus* to *Australopithecus* were urged by Robinson. He pointed to a very close similarity in the cusp patterns of the molar teeth and to a number of resemblances in the contour of the jaws. More recently, von Koenigswald and Tobias have remarked on resemblances of *Meganthropus* to *habilis.*

Table 3. Regional varieties of *Homo erectus* and possible predecessors (older and present nomenclature given)

Approx. time Years BP	East Africa	South Africa	North Africa	Java	China	Europe
Possible transition group						
900–550,000	Olduvai (Bed I) (*habilis*)	Swartkrans (*Telanthropus*) (*habilis*)		Kedung Brubus (*Meganthropus*) (*?erectus*)		
Established groups						
550–350,000	Olduvai (Bed II) (Chellean) *Homo erectus leakeyi*		Ternifine (*Atlan-thropus*) *Homo erectus mauritanicus*	Modjokerto and Trinil (*Pithecan-thropus*) *Homo erectus erectus*	Choukoutien (*Sinan-thropus*) *Homo erectus pekinensis*	Heidelberg (Mauer) *Homo erectus heidelbergensis*

Le Gros Clark has, however, stated a strong case for maintaining *Meganthropus* within *Homo erectus*. Although the teeth and mandibular body of the fossils referred to as *Meganthropus* are very large when compared with the *Pithecanthropus B* mandible, 'they do not indicate a range of variation exceeding that found, for example, in the single species *Homo sapiens*'. Further, the total morphological pattern of the two pre-molars and the first molar of the specimen is very similar to the dentition in the 1936 mandibular fragment of *Homo erectus* from Sangiran.

Telanthropus has also been regarded by Le Gros Clark as falling within the range of the South African Australopithecines whereas Robinson has argued for its status as an early *Homo erectus* form. Finally, the exact relationship of *habilis* both to the Australopithecine and *erectus* assemblages remains to be clarified. If Tobias' claim of a brain capacity near 700 ml. can be confirmed, the shift of *habilis* towards *erectus* would be undeniable. The fact is that the comparative study of all these remains is badly in need of multivariate statistical treatment to reveal their degrees of affinity in quantitative terms, particularly as there seem to be grounds for the existence of a smooth continuum stretching from *Australopithecus* to *Homo erectus*.

Distribution and character of *Homo erectus*

Remains attributable to *Homo erectus* have been recognised in middle pleistocene sites from a wide geographical area (Fig. 28). This widespread dispersion is important evidence of the greater biological adaptability of this species, by comparison with that of its Australopithecine forerunner. It follows that material (Plate 6) coming from so wide an area—east and north Africa, central Europe, Java and China—would be expected to exhibit a substantial degree of regional differentiation. For the two best known series, those from Java and Choukoutien, Weidenreich's classical study clearly reveals the development of a significant degree of regional subspeciation. He made a direct character by character comparison using some seventy-four features. In fifty-seven of

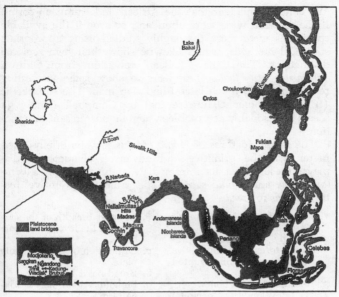

28 Asia: sites of fossil man

these agreement was close and in only four were there very striking differences. A generic distinction was therefore not justified; the contrasts warrant recognition only at the sub-specific or 'racial' level.

	Java man	*Pekin man*
Cranial capacity	900 cc.	1,075 cc.
Maximum cranial length	190 mm.	194 mm.
Cranial height	105 mm.	115 mm.
Frontal bones	Very receding	Not so receding
Frontal sinus	Moderately developed	Poorly developed
Supra-orbital torus	Not separated from curvature of frontals	Separated by a furrow from curvature of frontals
Palate	Smooth	Rough
Body of mandible	Massive	Not so massive
Mental eminence	Absent	Incipiently developed
Molar teeth	Large	Not so large

We can be confident that the African and European forms, if the material were more abundant, or even if the available specimens were more thoroughly studied using appropriate statistical methods, would likewise show their own regional distinctions. Thus, the 'Chellean' calvarium from Olduvai (*Homo erectus leakeyi*) appears to show some interesting resemblances to much later Rhodesian man. The subspecific (trinomial) nomenclature set out by Campbell (Table 3) seems a reasonably acceptable system on our present information.

The salient features of *Homo erectus* may be briefly listed in terms of the 'primitive' and 'advanced' characters it displays; these reflect its intermediate status between *Australopithecus* and *Homo sapiens*. The principal 'primitive' features are as follows:

1. Bones of the cranial vault very thick.
2. Strongly developed supra-orbital torus extending above the orbits as an uninterrupted bar of bone.
3. Receding frontal bones.
4. Well-developed occipital ridge which extends into the supra-mastoid region and produces an angular contour to the occipital bone.
5. Small mastoid processes.
6. Greatest breadth of the cranium at the level of the ear-holes.
7. Disposition of the tympanic plate.
8. Broad nasal bones.
9. Pronounced sub-nasal prognathism.
10. Massive body of the mandible.
11. Absence of a projecting chin.
12. Frequent occurrence of multiple mental foramina.
13. Large upper incisors.

The advanced features comprise:

1. Cranial capacity overlaps the lower range found in *Homo sapiens* and the cranial vault is 'inflated'.
2. Compared with *Australopithecus*, increased flexion of the face on the braincase so that the anterior cranial fossa extends well over the orbits.
3. Relative size of the face reduced more than in *Australopithecus*.
4. Foramen magnum is positioned more anteriorly than in *Australopithecus*.
5. Conformation of the temporomandibular joint as in *Homo sapiens*.
6. Dental arcade parabolic in shape.
7. Dental morphology more like *Homo sapiens* than is that of *Australopithecus*.
8. Incipient development of a chin in Pekin man.
9. Limb bones in size and proportions indistinguishable from those of *Homo sapiens*.

Some idea of the range of variation displayed by *erectus* can be obtained from the skull and mandible dimensions given in Table 4. The overlap of the cranial capacity with that of later *sapiens* man (Steinheim and Saccopastore for illustration) is noteworthy. The range and variability of *Homo erectus* was clearly such as would provide the matrix for the development of the next stages, namely the archaic (Neanderthal, Rhodesian, Solo) and the modern varieties of *Homo sapiens*.

Ecology of the middle pleistocene populations

Let us now consider the way of life and the living conditions of the widely dispersed populations of *Homo* during the long period from roughly 600,000 to 300,000 years BP. As we have seen, the sites in Africa, Europe and Asia containing skeletal material are, not surprisingly, very few, but fortunately many more localities yielding evidence of human occupancy are known.

In Africa the non-*sapiens* populations during this period were able to exploit the open savannah country over an enormous area. They could travel and hunt effectively in conditions which were mostly hot, sunny and dry with high intensities of ultra-violet light.

Growing out of the older indigenous African Oldowan culture (Fig. 20), the Acheulian—'the great hand-axe culture' —provided the basis for a way of life which sustained simple hunting bands not only in the African expanse but far beyond, across Morocco into Europe and eastwards to the Punjab (Fig. 30). Nevertheless, the Acheulian culture, it must be understood, afforded only a bare minimum of protection against the stresses of the natural environment. In the never-ending struggle for survival, the search for food, the intensive exploration of the terrain, withstanding extremes of climate, in devising improved hunting implements and methods, selection in favour of the more able, the more adaptable, the more ingenious, the bigger-brained, went on, changing the human populations biologically as well as culturally.

The making of some of the early Acheulian tools (Fig. 30)

Table 4. *Homo erectus:* Skull and mandible dimensions, compared to *Australopithecus* and *Homo sapiens*

Skull

	Australo-pithecus (Av.)	Java *Homo erectus erectus*			Pekin *Homo erectus pekinensis*					Olduvai *Homo erectus leakeyi*	*Homo sapiens fossilis* Stein-heim	Sacco pastore	*Homo sapiens sapiens* (Australians) M	F
Skull capacity ml.	482	775	900	935	915	1015	1030	1030	1225		1170	1200	1347	1180
Cranial length mm.	147	177	199	183	188	192	194	186	199	209	185	182	183	175
Cranial breadth mm.	99	135	158	130	137	140	141	143		150	133	142	132	127
Cranial height mm.		105	102	105 (?)	115						111	109	131	125

Mandible

Mandible	Pekin *Homo erectus pekinensis*		Ternifine *Homo erectus mauritanicus*			Heidelberg *Homo erectus heidelbergensis*
Length mm	103	94	110	110	129	123
Bicondylar mm.	146	102	–	158		132
Symp. Ht. mm.	40	32	39	35	39	36
Thickness mm.	16·4	15·4	19	16	20	21

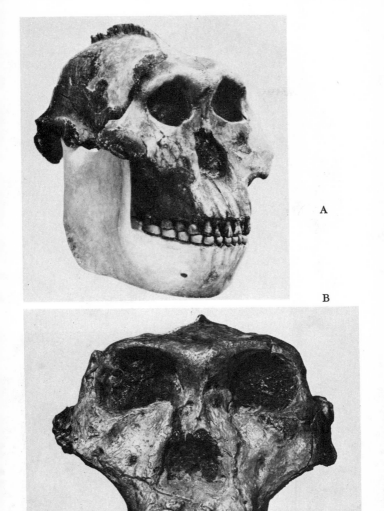

A

B

1 The skulls of *Zinanjthropus* (A) and *Paranthropus* (B) to show the sagittal crest

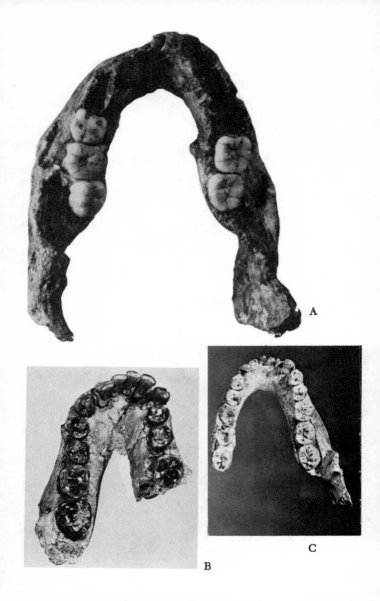

2 Mandibles of the advanced Australopithecines: (A) *Telanthropus* from Swartkrans (Robinson); (B) *Homo habilis* from Bed I, Olduvai; (C) *Homo habilis* from Bed II, Olduvai

3 Capuchin monkey cracking nuts

4 Young chimpanzee (A) holding a cigarette with good precision grip (Hayes & Hayes); (B) gripping a club and charging (photo courtesy of Dr. A. Kortland)

5 Top, stone on stone technique of hand-axe construction using a power grip only; bottom left, 'Oldowan' pebble-tool; right, 'Chellean' hand-axe using the above technique

6 Remains of *Homo erectus:*
(A) Pekin; (B) Java; (C) East
Africa; (D) Heidelberg;
(E) North Africa

A

B

C

D   E

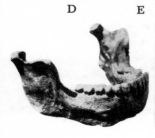

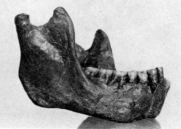

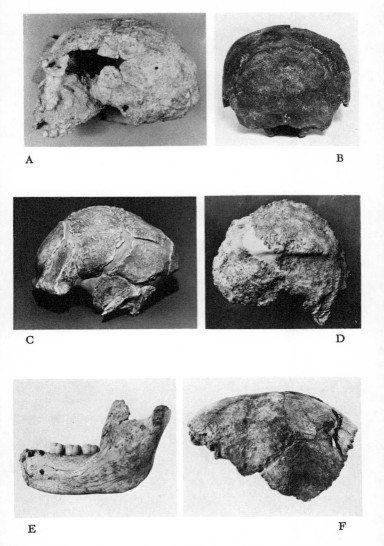

7 Representatives of the earliest varieties of *Homo sapiens:* (A) Steinheim; (B) Swanscombe, (C) Ehringsdorf; (D) Vertosszollös; (E) Montmaurin; (F) Fontéchevade

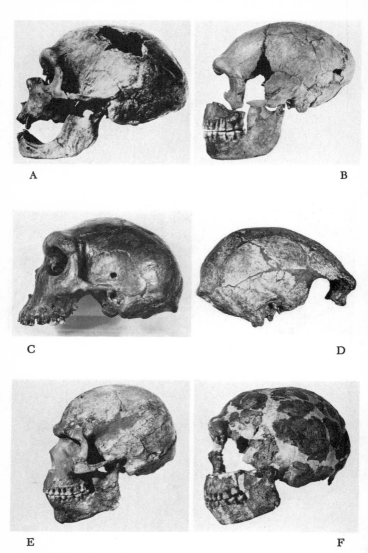

8 Photos of Rhodesian, Solo and neanderthal intermediaries: (A,B) neanderthalers: La Chapelle-aux-saints and La Quina; (C) Broken Hill (Rhodesian); (D) Solo man; (E) Skuhl V; (F) Tabun I

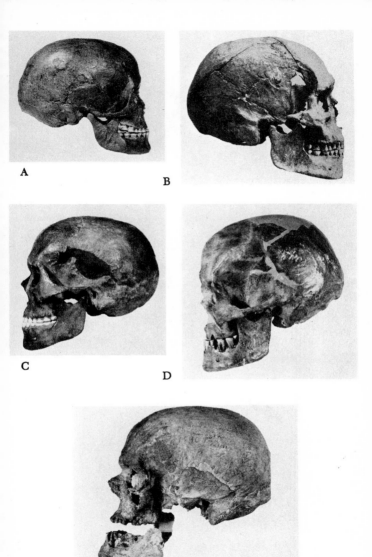

9 Peoples of the Upper Palaeolithic (Europe): (A) Vestonice; (B) Combe Capelle; (C) Oberkassel; (D) Chancelade; (E) Les Eyzies

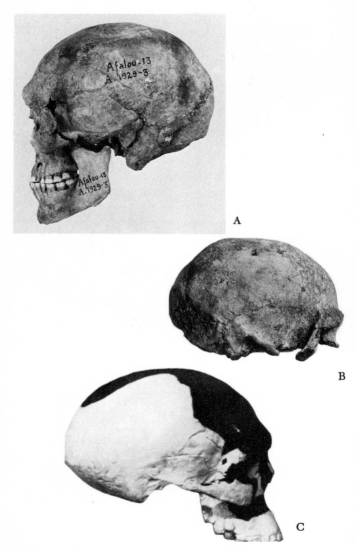

10 Peoples at the end of the Upper Palaeolithic: Africa: (A) Afalou, Algeria; (B) Singa; (C) Florisbad; Asia: (D) Niah (Borneo); (E) China: the 'Old Male', 'Eskimo' woman, and 'Melanesian' woman from Choukoutien

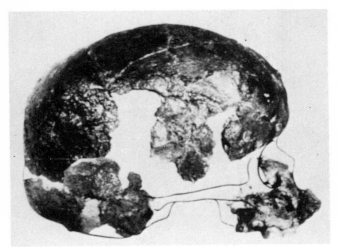

D

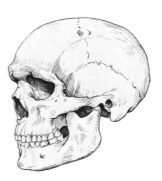

E

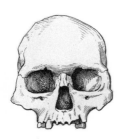

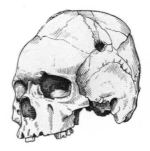

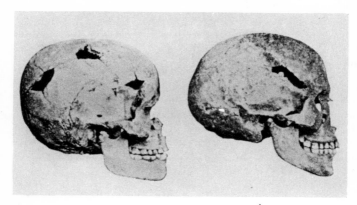

A

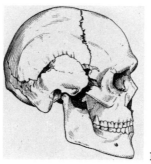

B

11 Representatives of mesolithic peoples in Europe: (A) Offnet, Bavaria; (B) Teviec, Brittany

required only a rudimentary technique. The stone was rested on a slab of rock and the flaking was done by direct blows from a hammerstone. But later in the Acheulian the knapping was performed in more refined and sophisticated ways to get the right shape and trimming. It seems, however, that the relatively large-brained Pekin man did not make tools as skilfully as the people at Olorgersaile in east Africa, where fine flaking by a wood technique was practised.

The technical achievements of the later middle pleistocene peoples are impressive. They travelled considerable distances to obtain suitable raw materials, and they acquired such good mastery over stone that the form of the biface is indistinguishable whether it be made in lava, dolerite, ironstone or quartzite. Even the fineness of craftsmanship was scarcely affected by the type of rock (Oakley).

The hand-axe is a very distinctive and easily noticed implement; but it formed only part of a larger kit, which would have contained some pebble and flake tools, also cleavers, corescrapers and picks, as well as hammerstones. The 'hand-axe' implement almost certainly served a variety of purposes, in the food quest for digging game traps or digging up roots, or, like the cleaver, for skinning game and chopping up meat. The variety and size of the animals hunted, emphasises a considerable skill, not only in flint working, but in the making of traps and blinds, throwing of sling stones and bolas. Simple wooden pointed spears, with points hardened in fire, are known from interglacial deposits at Clacton, Essex and Lobringen, Lower Saxony.

Africa was the 'heart-land', as Oakley has termed it, of the Acheulian culture (Fig. 30), and the hominids responsible for it included Homo erectus of Olduvai (Upper Bed II). Industries are known also from many sites in Kenya and Rhodesia, and in South Africa (where it was once called the 'Stellenbosch' culture) from the Karoo and the River Vaal.

The Olorgesaile people of Kenya living in the open at a lakeside have left abundant remains of their game food. The main animal hunted was, at different times, a great baboon, an extinct horse, or a giant pig. Of fire there is no evidence.

The utility of the Acheulian technology was such that it

Years B.P.	ERA	EUROPE CLIMATIC STAGE	EUROPE Archaeological Stage	EUROPE MAIN CULTURES	AFRICA South of Sahara CLIMATIC STAGE	AFRICA Archaeological Stage	AFRICA MAIN CULTURES	Northern MAIN CULTURES	ERA	Years B.P.
	HOLOCENE	Modern Climates	Age of metals Neolithic	Advanced farming Farming Societies	Wet Phase (Nakuru) Drier Oscillation Wet Phase (Makalian)	Neolithic Later Stone Age	Late Wilton Kenya Capsian Late Magosian	Neolithic Capsian	HOLOCENE	
10,000		Retreat of Ice	Mesolithic	Maglemosian Ertebollian Tardenoisian Azilian	Dry Phase		Final Lumpemban	Oranian		10,000
40,000	UPPER PLEISTOCENE	4th Glaciation Würm (Wisconsin)	Upper Palaeolithic	Magdalenian Solutrean Gravettian Aurignacian Chatel-Perronian	Main Gamblian	Middle Stone Age	Stillbay/ Pietersburg Sangoan/ Fauresmith	Aterian Levalloiso-Mousterian	UPPER PLEISTOCENE	40,000
60,000 70,000			Middle Palaeolithic	Mousterian	Drier Oscillation Early Gamblian		Final Acheulian	Late Acheulian		60,000
160,000 200,000	MIDDLE PLEISTOCENE	Third Interglacial 3rd Glaciation Riss (Illinoian)		Levalloisian technique Acheulian		Earlier Stone Age			MIDDLE PLEISTOCENE	160,000 200,000
250,000		Second Interglacial	Lower Palaeolithic				Early Acheulian			250,000
450,000	LOWER PLEISTOCENE OR VILLAFRANCHIAN	2nd Glaciation Mindel		(Choukoutien in Asia) Abbevillian	(Lower Palaeolithic)			Early Acheulian (Morocco) (Abbevillian)	LOWER PLEISTOCENE OR VILLAFRANCHIAN	450,000
600,000		First Interglacial 1st Glaciation Günz					Oldowan	Pebble culture (Oldowan) (Morocco)		600,000
2,000,000		Preglacial								2,000,000

29 Climate, archaeological and cultural stages, Europe and Africa

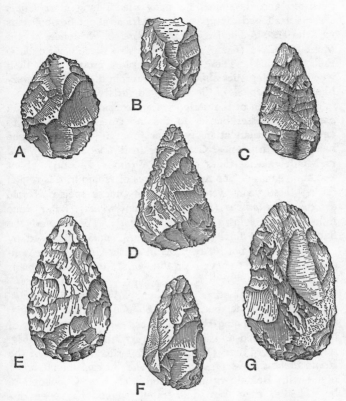

30 Acheulian tools: (A) Hand-axe, Chelles-sur-Marne (after
Oakley, *Man the Toolmaker*, Fig. 17(c)); (B) Madrasian cleaver,
Madras (after Oakley, *Frameworks*, Fig. 74); (C) Acheulian
hand-axe, Olorgesailie, Kenya (after Oakley, *Man the Toolmaker*,
Fig. 18 (a)); (D) Acheulian hand-axe, Swanscombe, Kent
(after Oakley, *Man the Toolmaker*, Fig. 32); (E) Fauresmith
hand-axe, Brakfontein, OFS (after Oakley, *Frameworks*, Fig. 55);
(F) Upper Acheulian hand-axe, Combe-Grenal, Dordogne (after
Bordes, Fig. 17(1)); (G) Late Acheulian, from India (after Terra
and Patterson)

persisted and developed in many places long after *Homo erectus* itself had disappeared. In Africa, about 60,000 years BP, the last Acheulian peoples were in evidence at the Montague Cave (Cape) and the lakeside sites near Kolambo Falls (Zambia). These were fire-using groups and their wooden digging sticks have also been found. They were very likely *Homo sapiens* of the rhodesioid variety.

During much of the period we are considering, the Sahara presented a lesser barrier to the movement of populations and cultures than at many other times in its history. The hand-axe industry near Casablanca in Morocco can be dated to Mindel glacial times of north Europe (Fig. 29), about 400,000 years BP. The representatives of *Homo* in this region during these years were of the non-*sapiens* species, *Homo erectus mauritanicus* (Plate 6) (*Atlanthropus*). Later stone industries are known also from Algeria, Tunisia and the Sahara. But the final phases of the Acheulian practised by cave dwellers in north Africa, as in south Africa, can reasonably be supposed to have been the work of men of the *sapiens* species.

In Europe populations based on early Acheulian industries are found as far north as the Somme Valley and Britain, their occupancy being confined to the warm interstadials of the Mindel period and the Mindel-Riss interglacial (see Fig. 29). Heidelberg man (Plate 6) of this time is a man of the *Homo erectus* pre-*sapiens* variety. The broken animal bones found with Heidelberg man resemble those at Choukoutien, but whether they were deliberately shaped has been disputed. Further refinement of the Acheulian (the Levalloisan technique) was achieved by some groups who lived through the cold Riss phase. In Europe, as in south and north Africa, the peoples of the middle and latest Acheulian were the more advanced *sapiens* men of neanderthal and 'intermediate' stock represented by the men of Swanscombe and Steinheim (about 250–200,000 years BP) and later by the men of Montmaurin and Fontéchevade (about 150,000 years BP) (see Fig. 29 and Plate 7).

In Asia the Acheulian spread into India over a wide area. Here it met, and in some places fused with, the contemporaneous and distinctive chopping tool/chopper industry (Fig. 31) characteristic of the whole Far East, and an indigenous product springing from a preceding simpler Oldowan-like technology. (The chopper is a 'large unifacial tool, made on a pebble or angular chunk, with one curved or straight cutting edge'; the chopping tool is usually bifacial, in that the cutting edge has been flaked from both faces.) No fossil remains of the makers of either of the two industries in India have so far been recovered. In the Far East the Chinese representatives of *Homo erectus* ('*Sinanthropus*') conducted their hunting cave-dwelling life on the chopping tool/chopper complex, about 300,000 years ago. The culture associated with the older Javanese *Homo erectus* is now known, though on other grounds it seems likely that it must have belonged to the same tradition as that at Choukoutien. The Choukoutien deposits also contain many pieces of broken and shaped bones used as tools.

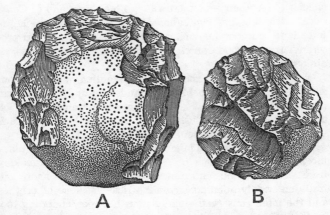

31 (A) Chopper: locality 1, Choukoutien (after Bordes, Fig. 27(4)); (B) Chopper-tool: Patjitanian, Java (after Oakley, *Man the Toolmaker*, Fig. 20d)

Unlike Java man, Heidelberg man and the African 'Chellean' man, Pekin man was exposed to a cool climate (Fig. 29) and his survival clearly owed much to his use or perhaps invention of domestic fire-making. Evidence of fires in the form of charred bones and antler, charred seeds, fragments of charcoal and baked clay floors are known at many places in the occupation deposits of Pekin man. The caves and clefts at Choukoutien had formerly been the haunts of carnivores but they came into permanent human possession presumably as soon as Pekin man had discovered how fires could be renewed and maintained.

Pekin man, it can be inferred, had available and ate (judging from broken and burnt bones) now extinct species of bison, horse, rhinoceros, flat-antlered deer, brown bear, big horned sheep, mammoth, camel, ostrich, antelope, water buffalo, wild boar, hyena and others. Most of these are known with certainty to have been successfully hunted by other hunting communities, both extinct and recent. The charred fragments at Choukoutien include as well remains of foxes, large cats, macaques and baboons. The ashes of the firewood reveal the existence at that time of *Celtis sinensis*—a dwarf species of hackberry—now growing 30 feet high, and of *Celtis occidentalis* bearing fruit about ¾ inch long of which the juice is sweet, containing sucrose and other hexoses, and providing a very good source of vitamin C. *Homo pekinensis* ate a pea-sized variety.

The raw material of the early Choukoutien industries consisted mostly of local pebbles of sandstone and quartz from nearby hills, with a few artifacts made in transparent rock crystal. Comparable industries, but showing local peculiarities, are known from numerous localities in North China.

It seems that over the inhabited world during middle pleistocene times, the epoch of *Homo erectus,* two tool-making traditions prevailed and developed—the bifacial hand axe tradition widely adopted beyond Africa—its place of origin—and the more conservative indigenous chopper/chopping tool tradition in the Far East.

In this epoch there is already displayed in a particularly clear pattern, the major characteristic of all human cultural development—the co-existence of cultural innovation and cultural diffusion. Innovation may take the form of a large scale separate development as in these two middle pleistocene traditions, or it may appear merely as small local modifications within each tradition. Diffusion and exchange may proceed over an enormous area as in the case of the Acheulian hand-axe culture, or over the smaller, but still vast area of the Eastern tradition, or again it may remain quite regional and circumscribed. Already at this period we may regard every cultural response as compounded, in different proportions, of borrowing with modification in a way adapted to meet the needs of different localities and biotopes. Despite the distinctiveness between the two middle pleistocene technologies we should remember that both emerged from similar tool-making origins; the prototypes of chopper and chopping tools can be recognised in assemblages of Oldowan pebble-tools and also as elements in early hand-axe industries such as in the Clactonian. Our belief is that a single species, *Homo erectus*, was responsible for these developments, so that even where, as in the northern Punjab, the two cultures were in close contact, there seems no reason to suppose, as Oakley has pointed out, that the tools were made by different kinds of men. Finally, the two traditions not only showed a capacity for steady development, but in later stages underwent a marked convergence by the adoption of similar techniques, particularly the Levalloisian core-shaping technique.

Brain development of *Homo erectus*

With *Homo erectus* one major component of hominid evolution is fully accomplished. The upright stance and bipedal locomotion have reached their final development. The femur of Java man and the limb bones of Pekin man differ in essentials not at all from those of modern man. The interaction (or 'feed back') between the acquisition of an effective tool-handling culture and the improvement in the bipedal mode of locomotion, so vital in the Australopithecine phase, has ceased to operate. The hand, too, was now fully 'human' in structure and manipulative ability. But the brain and skull continued to change, rapidly throughout the *Homo erectus* stage, more slowly as *Homo erectus* gave way to *Homo sapiens*.

Because the Acheulian culture complex afforded only a

minimum of protection against the biological stresses of the environment, positive selection in favour of still larger brain capacity and with it, for a better technological equipment, went on. Improvement in tools and elaboration of the brain acted as mutually reinforcing processes, making possible the fuller development of speech, the organisation of co-operative activity, the acquisition and transmission of technical skill, all the faculties needed for survival. Over the time interval between the tool-making Australopithecines and the pre-*sapiens* phase of *Homo erectus* (as represented by Pekin man) brain size expanded from about 500 to nearly 1300 ml., a nearly threefold enlargement, and continued to expand to the 1500 or 1600 capacity of neanderthal and the first modern varieties. This powerful evolutionary interaction between the need for advance in toolmaking and communication and the development of brains capable of meeting these demands, had far-reaching consequences. It was apparently so intensive and cumulative a process that in the course of successfully coping with the demands of middle pleistocene conditions, the brain achieved a surplus capacity and a mental potentiality only partially used at that time. The final expansion of the brain and remodelling of the skull with the emergence of *Homo sapiens* presumably represents the last stages of this particular selective process. This surplus mental capacity in which there lay the potentiality for all the future cultural advance by *Homo sapiens* is the most dramatic example of the pre-adaptation phenomenon, and ranks with the pre-adaptedness of the orthograde posture evolved by the prehominid as one of the outstanding and crucial events in the evolution of man.

As *Homo erectus* merges into *Homo sapiens* the brain size expands more slowly to reach its maximal value. The selective pressures for larger brains of earlier times cease to operate. Yet in the late Pleistocene (and onwards) technological innovation is greatly accelerated. The inherent mental power of the brain combined with co-operative planning and co-operative thinking and memorising, presumably made its further enlargement unnecessary.

Climatic factors in the differentiation of *Homo erectus*

The men of the *Homo erectus* species in Africa, east, south and north, like those of *Australopithecus africanus* and *robustus* before them, lived the active life of hunters and collectors in a hot climate. So too did *Homo erectus* of Java. *Homo erectus heidelbergensis* is firmly placed by Oakley in the first interglacial period, and by Kurten in an interstadial within the second glaciation. On either dating the European variety of *erectus* was a warm climate dweller. The presence of early Acheulian in India and southeast Asia also testifies to the restriction there of (probable) *Homo erectus* populations to warmer habitats.

Until the appearance of *Homo erectus* at Choukoutien, the hominids had passed their long period of evolutionary development, perhaps a million years, in warm, sunny regions. From now on, the fossil and archaeological evidence indicates that some populations of *Homo* had moved into cooler climates. The growing ecological mastery by man in this *pre-sapiens* phase is well attested by the establishment of *Homo erectus pekinensis* as a cave dweller and fire maker at Choukoutien about 400,000 years BP (Fig. 29) at a time equivalent to the second glaciation (Mindel II). Early *sapiens* (neanderthal) men peopled parts of Europe in the first phase of the fourth glaciation (Würm I); later *sapiens* (for example, Magdalenian) men survived the final cold phases of the Pleistocene more successfully than those earlier inhabitants of cold regions. Yet even those groups of modern *sapiens* with a long history of life in circumpolar regions, like modern men in cool temperate climates, and modern man as a whole, have remained essentially 'tropical' animals. This fact, which is based on morphological and physiological evidence, discussed below, is one of the many strong arguments against the view, propounded by Coon and others before him, that the subspeciation of *Homo erectus* provided a multiple, polyphyletic ancestry for the emergence along separate pathways of the modern major racial groupings. If an evolutionary lineage

was established from Pekin man to the Mongoloids, and a
other from Heidelberg man to modern 'Caucasoids', bo
lines persisting throughout the great succession of climati
change in the northern hemisphere, it seems most unlikel
that their end products would possess in common the properties of tropical hominids. And it is equally unlikely that their
physiological characteristics would also be extremely simila
to those of present day racial groups, supposedly derived fron
separate African and Javanese lineages.

   That *Homo erectus* provided the immediate ancestral stocl
for the emergence of *Homo sapiens* we have no reason to
doubt. Physiological, behavioural, genetic and other char
acters of modern man point decisively to a much more r
stricted and unified ancestral stock, and the fossil evidenc
as we shall see, shows this as emerging from that of the early
sapiens 'spectrum' which followed *Homo erectus*. But it is
also a tenable hypothesis that the regional varieties of *Homo
erectus* may have made a relatively greater genetic contribution to the emergent *Homo sapiens* populations of those localities. In other words the branching development (cladogenesis) of *Homo erectus* as far as it went may have helped
to bring about the somewhat wide range of early or archaic
Homo sapiens. This differentiation is nevertheless not a 'polyphyletic' one; indeed the morphological overlapping both in
time and space is such that the whole development from
erectus to early *sapiens* is to be regarded as making up a
phyletic continuum. Because of this, and despite any local
differentiation, it is reasonable to regard *Homo erectus* as
contributing to the whole genetic pool of the emergent
Homo sapiens. Over this period of 200,000 years both biological and cultural continuity was maintained. The evidence
suggests that *Homo erectus* remained a warm-climate species; whatever minor specialisations its limited cladogenesis
gave rise to, it is certain that modern *sapiens* varieties originated from a lineage which goes back to the original tropical
species.

The transition from *Homo erectus* to *Homo sapiens*

The continuous expansion of the brain (Table 1) and the appearance of some 'advanced' characters in the skull, as in Pekin man and *Homo erectus leakeyi*, give evidence of a series of directional processes bringing about the transformation of *Homo erectus* into the variegated emergent *Homo sapiens*. Indeed, the continuity of the lineage shows itself in a number of particular resemblances to later varieties of *sapiens* men, as between *Homo erectus* at Olduvai to the much later Rhodesian man, or between *Homo erectus pekinensis* and Solo man, also far separated in time. In the immediate transitional period from *erectus* to *sapiens*, the dearth of fossil material is profound and no detailed documentation of this crucial phase of hominid evolution can as yet be made. We are faced with an enormous chronological and morphological gap. Between 300,000 and 150,000 years BP there are in the fossil record no more than six or seven specimens (Plate 7) available—none of them complete and much even now not properly described or compared. These six specimens are:

   (i)   Swanscombe man, from the lower Thames valley, consisting of three skull bones, the occipital and the two parietals; dated on geological and faunal grounds as from the second interglacial period. The material has been studied in morphological and statistical detail (Weiner and Campbell).

   (ii)   Vertesszöllos man (Hungary) from an occupation site of pebble/chopper culture, and dated to the interstadial of Mindel I. The fossil remains are of a seven-year-old child, represented by milk dentition only, and of an adult represented by the occipital squama. The material has been carefully studied (Thoma).

   (iii)   Steinheim man, near Stuttgart, comprising a single calvarium, badly broken around the foramen magnum and in the premaxillary region; the upper second premolar and all the molars are preserved. The specimen is dated as second interglacial. A detailed account has yet to be produced.

(iv)   Montmaurin man, from Haute-Garonne, France, consisting only of the mandible with all the molar teeth. The jaw (but not the four teeth) has been described by Vallois.

(v)   Fontéchevade man from Charente, France, consisting of both parietals and part of the frontal bone, and a small piece of the frontal of a second individual; dated faunistically as Riss-Würm; detailed description by Vallois; affinities studied by Weiner and Campbell.

Onwards during the next 100,000 years, that is, till near the end of the Upper Pleistocene, the number of known occupied sites increases greatly and there are some twenty-five major finds of fossil material (Table 5). The 100 or so individuals represented are still a sadly small number to represent the widely dispersed populations of the middle and upper palaeolithic hunters of Europe, Africa and Asia.

Few as they are, the five or six specimens representing the first *sapiens* populations do provide a bridge between the preceding *Homo erectus* and the heterogeneous groups of *Homo sapiens* of the late third interglacial period and of early fourth glacial times. They serve to show that *Homo erectus* had clear links with the 'spectrum' of *Homo sapiens* varieties at both early and late stages of its emergence.

The Steinheim calvarium has dimensions (Table 4) and a capacity comparable to Pekin man; the basi-bregmatic height is low; it shows only a moderate platycephaly and possesses well developed supra-orbital ridges. The nasal opening is wide; the nasal root depressed, but in other features it is well advanced in the modern *sapiens* direction and its main affinity is with the contemporaneous Swanscombe man. Steinheim with Swanscombe and Vertesszöllos represent one segment of the range of variable populations which made up the developing *Homo sapiens* of the Middle Pleistocene.

The Montmaurin jaw on the other hand is regarded by Vallois to some extent as intermediate between *Homo erectus*

heidelbergensis and the later Neanderthalers. In fact, as already mentioned, *Homo erectus* displays obvious links not
only with classical Neanderthals of Europe but with other
segments of early *sapiens* represented by forms now extinct,
namely Rhodesian man in Africa and Solo man in the Far
East. No comprehensive analysis of these links has been
made, but in descriptive terms a strong case can be made
for their existence. The probable affinities between and
within the polytypic *Homo erectus* and the emergent developing *Homo sapiens* species are shown in the diagram
(Fig. 32).

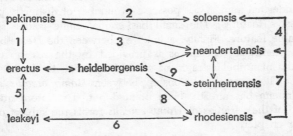

32 Affinities between *Homo erectus* and archaic varieties of *Homo
sapiens*

The linkage 1, has been described already. Weidenreich
made a strong case for it and was also a proponent of the
relationship denoted by linkage 2; he saw Solo man 'not as a
true neanderthal type but distinctly more primitive and very
close to *Pithecanthropus* and *Sinanthropus*'.

Pekin man himself shows a number of decided advances
over Java man away from *erectus* in the *sapiens* direction,
e.g. in the increase in cranial capacity, the appearance however rudimentary of the chin eminence, the loss of simian
features in the dentition. The morphological continuity between *Homo erectus pekinensis* and neanderthal man (linkage 3) was forcibly urged by Zuckerman. The logical outcome of the preceding propositions is an affinity between
Solo man and classical neanderthal man, and this (4) has
been emphasised by both von Koenigswald and by Vallois.

Preliminary assessment of the Olduvai *Homo erectus leakeyi* has aligned it (5) with the Javanese *erectus;* Leakey and others believe that the calvarium shows some distinct resemblances (6) to the Rhodesian skulls from Broken Hill and Saldanha Bay, as well as with Steinheim man (9); as an outcome of all the relationships it is to be expected that Rhodesian and Neanderthal (7) would have much in common. Morant demonstrated, in fact, that Rhodesian man was more closely related to Neanderthal than either was to modern *sapiens.* An interesting fact about Rhodesian man is that despite its enormous eyebrow ridges and orbits set in a massive face, and its platycephaly, all closely reminiscent of neanderthal man, it yet possesses a number of distinctly progressive features. The small basi-cranial angle is one such notable feature. Finally, a link (8) between the Heidelberg and Rhodesian specimens is provided by the resemblance of the mandibular fragment of Saldanha man to the Mauer jaw. The general relationship between *Homo erectus* and Steinheim has already been pointed out. The interrelationship of the varieties of *Homo sapiens* forms the subject of a later chapter.

It is on the evidence of all these linkages that we base our belief that the *Homo erectus* polytypic species engendered the broad 'spectrum' of morphological varieties of the emergent *Homo sapiens.*

Homo sapiens

The latest stages of man's evolution, from the supersession of *Homo erectus* to the establishment of the present day polytypic species (*Homo sapiens*) present a complex pattern. This complex differentiation arises very largely from the widespread distribution and partial isolation of the developing populations and their exposure to a multitude of habitats. Sites yielding the most important fossil material are listed in chronological sequence in Table 5. The material is scarce for the earlier stages, but the number of fossil and tool-yielding sites increases substantially over the later pe-

Table 5. *Homo sapiens* from *c.* 250,000 years BP till *c.* 15,000 years BP

(1) Specimens of the 'intermediate' *sapiens* group
(a) before *c.* **100,000 BP**

Steinheim	Swanscombe
Taubach	Fontéchevade
Ehringsdorf	Vertesszöllos

(b) between 70,000 and 40,000 BP

Genovce 66,000	Saccopastore 60,000
Tabun (Fig. 38) 40,900	Skuhl (Fig. 38) 39,700
Krapina	

(2) Specimens of the 'classical neanderthal' group

Europe		Middle East	
La Chapelle (Fig. 38)	35–45,000	Shanidar	50–60,000
Charente	35,000	Galilee	70,000
La Ferrassie	35,000	Jebel Gafza	70,000
La Quina (Fig. 38)	35–55,000		
Gibraltar I	35–70,000	North Africa	
Gibraltar II	50,000	Haua Fteah	40,700
Circeo	35–70,000		
Neanderthal	35–70,000		
Le Moustier	35–70,000		

(3) Specimens of the 'Rhodesian' *sapiens* group

Hopefield	40,000
Broken Hill (Fig. 38)	30,000

(4) Specimens of the 'Solo' *sapiens* group
Ngandong

(5) Specimens of the 'modern' *sapiens* group

Europe		Outside Europe	
Combe Capelle	34,000	Niah (Borneo)	38,000
Vestonice	26,000	Florisbad (South Africa)	35,000
Piedmont	26,000	Afalou (Algeria)	11,000
Cromagnon	20–30,000	Matjes R. (South Africa)	11,000
Oberkassel	12–17,000	Natchez (America)	11,000
La Madeleine	12–17,000	Upper Choukoutien	?10,000
and other French		Wadjak (Java)	?10,000
Magdalenians		Singa (Sudan)	*c.* 23,000

riods. It is only by treating all this material together that we can get a fairly reliable idea of the range of dental, cranial, facial and post-cranial features of *Homo sapiens* in the course of their development. But if we are to identify and categorise with some assurance distinctive population groups we should base our judgements strictly on some form of statistical assessment of divergence. Even for the relatively abundant material available for this last period this has not as yet been done in any thorough-going fashion. We must rely on the limited quantitative analysis of metrical characters so far carried out, combined with a consensus of opinion derived from descriptive comparisons or from simple statistical studies. We are here postulating that there are different population categories distinguishable in their 'total morphological pattern'.

Taking the whole array of material from Swanscombe man onwards, from about 250,000 years BP to the very end of the pleistocene period, about 15,000 years BP, we may distinguish five major groupings labelled (1) 'intermediates', (2) classical Neanderthalers, (3) Rhodesian, (4) Solo (or Ngandong), (5) modern. The specimens allocated to these groupings are shown in Table 6 and Plate 8.

Table 6. Comparison of skull characters of modern *sapiens* and Neanderthal

	Modern *sapiens*	Classical Neanderthal
1. Cranial capacity	Large (1300–1500 cc.)	Large (1300–1600 ml.) (wider range than modern)
2. Eyebrow ridges (supra-orbital torus)	No torus	Massive, uninterrupted shelf overhanging orbits; complete fusion of the ciliary and orbital elements
3. Forehead	Vertical frontal	'Sloping' forehead
4. Contour of cranial vault	Convexity	Marked flattening — 'platycephaly'
5. External occipital protuberance and occipital contour	Relatively low rounded occiput	Position relatively high; angular contour of occiput
6. Occipital torus	Separate and arched	Strong; horizontal
7. Naso-maxillary region	No inflation; canine fossa	Massive development, with inflation of maxillary wall; no canine fossa
8. Mandible	Variable chin eminence	Heavy mandible; lacks a chin eminence
9. Sphenoidal angle of the cranial base	More acute angle	Wide angle (about 130°)
10. Auditory aperture	? Always rounded	Rounded or transversely elliptical shape
11. Mastoid process	Relatively large	Relatively small: prominent and elongated masto-occipital ridge
12. Foramen magnum	Central position	Slightly backward position
13. Teeth	Taurodontism infrequent and slight	Molar teeth frequently taurodontic

To explain and justify this grouping of the evolving *sapiens* species, and particularly to clarify the crucial nature of the 'intermediate' groups, it is useful to start with the two best-known 'terminal' groupings—classical neanderthal and modern

man. Table 6 and Fig. 33 bring out clearly the strong morphological contrasts between these two groups.

The morphological contrast between neanderthal and modern man is strongly supported by statistical analysis of metrical traits; as Morant concluded from measurements alone,
it is clear that the (classical) neanderthal group is 'remarkably homogeneous and between it and all modern racial
types there is a distinct hiatus . . .' This last point can be
supported from a consideration of the contours and size of
the occipital and parietal bones alone. By combining all the
measurements into a single value (using the D^2 measure of
affinity or distance), it can be shown (Weiner and Campbell) that such representatives of Neanderthal as La Chapelle
(as well as the Gibraltar specimen) are completely beyond

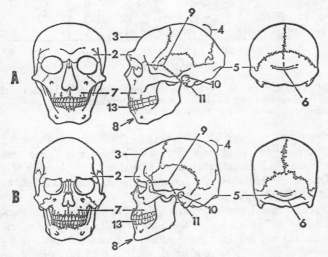

33 Comparison of skull features of (A) classic neanderthal, (B)
modern man

the whole range of individuals of modern populations (Fig.
34), as represented by Bronze Age, Medieval or present
day series.

The 'intermediate' group, it will be noted, contains material (Swanscombe, Vertesszöllos, Steinheim, Fontéchevade, Ehringsdorf, Genovce and Saccopastore) that is older than all of the known classical Neanderthalers (with the important possible exception of the Montmaurin jaw) and also ante-

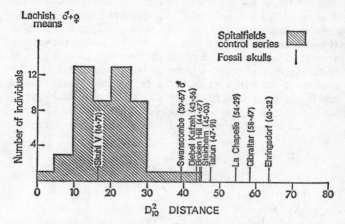

34 Histogram of D^2_{10} values of medieval (Spitalfields) series and of fossil *sapiens* with Lachish (Bronze Age) means as zero reference (from Weiner and Campbell)

dates modern man. The closeness in time between the latest 'intermediate' populations of Skuhl, Krapina and Tabun and the classical neanderthalers of Gibraltar, La Chapelle, La Quina, Le Moustier, Circeo with the earliest 'moderns', as at Combe Capelle, should be noted.

The general conclusion from the morphological data summarised in Table 6 is that these ten or so 'intermediate' specimens do not fall into the contrasting classes of 'modern *sapiens*' or 'classical Neanderthal' and that all of them show to some degree the co-existence of features characteristic of each of these two groups. Some of these 'intermediate' specimens would appear to be more 'neanderthaloid' than 'modern'; amongst such are probably Tabun, Ganovce and Saccopastore. Others (Skuhl, Krapina, Fontéchevade and Swanscombe) show a bias towards the modern group.

This leads to a picture of evolving *sapiens* man utterly different from that of the multiple or polyphyletic lineage, a view which still prevails in some quarters. The 'candelabra' family tree depicts a number of quite separate lines of development leading to the continental varieties of Neanderthal man (Europe and Middle East), Rhodesian man (Africa) and Ngandong or Solo man (southeast Asia). These now extinct terminal products are said to have been superseded by separate modern *sapiens* stock developing along yet another line—the Swanscombe–Fontéchevade lineage (Vallois). Coon's view is an extreme expression of this standpoint since the lineages are not only regarded as quite separate and distinct, but are supposed by him to have originated much further back from separate ancestral foci of *Homo erectus;* more than this, the separateness of origins and development is supposed to have given rise to five distinctive major modern races. Coon's lineages can be nothing less than separate species and to avoid confusion one should discount his idiosyncrasy of calling them 'subspecies'.

The facts controvert these polyphyletic systems. On the information available we can see that the micro-evolutionary picture of the events over the last 250,000 years or so is both more coherent and more complex. There is, as already described, a morphological continuum—the pattern which the present author has called (1958) the 'spectrum' theory of *sapiens* evolution. According to this 'spectrum' theory (Fig. 35) there existed at any one time, in different areas, from the Steinheim–Swanscombe stage onwards, aggregates or groups of the genus *Homo*, some exhibiting tendencies towards the 'archaic' varieties—Neanderthals, Rhodesian or Solo, others with strong tendencies towards modern, present-day *sapiens* and others again the 'intermediates', showing a mosaic of modern and 'archaic' features. In the early stages these groups were relatively small-brained on the average, with a relatively undeveloped technology, large-brained in the later stages and possessing a markedly improved technology. While intermediates of various combinations continued to exist in the last stages of the Pleistocene, there emerged the 'classical' Neanderthal and other 'archaic' forms along with the 'modern' varieties of *Homo*, with only the latter surviving,

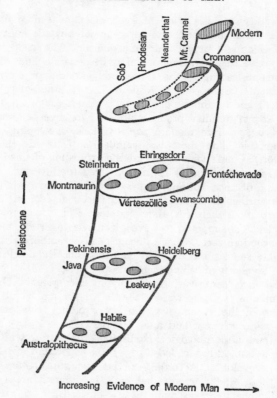

35 'Spectrum' or 'continuum' in the evolutionary development of
the hominids

spreading widely and differentiating. From the Steinheim–
Swanscombe stage onwards one can therefore discern tempo-
rally as well as spatially a spectral succession of the various
groupings that constitute the polytypic palaeospecies *Homo
sapiens*.

Why the classical Neanderthal and the African and Asian
'archaic' forms did not persist as recognisable geographical
racial groupings which, by ordinary taxonomic standards,
they undoubtedly were, cannot be explained with any final-

ity. The oft-quoted cases of the elimination of the Tasmanians, of the true indigenes of Taiwan or Japan, or of the near extinction of Bushmen and Australian and Negritoid aborigines—all at the hand of their fellow modern *sapiens*—show clearly enough that culturally and physically distinctive looking groups can be and have been marked off for deliberate obliteration. Equally possible, in some areas, was the complete genetic absorption of some 'archaic' groups by much larger stocks of incoming 'modern' populations. There is no reason to doubt that fertile hybridisation was possible throughout the polytypic *sapiens* species, then as now. The difficulty, as we have learnt, of separating 'modern' from 'archaic' features in late pleistocene groups may be taken as presumptive evidence of crossing between them. But to detect any of the specific 'archaic' contributions in the modern gene complex is in the nature of the case impossible. Nevertheless, some degree of morphological continuity between the archaic varieties and groups directly ancestral to present-day populations has been accepted by many careful workers. For example, neanderthal features in attenuated form have been claimed to be present in Cromagnon man, and some australoid skulls are reminiscent in skull features of both Solo and Neanderthal: the heavy browed Florisbad man in Africa may plausibly claim partial descent from Rhodesian man. Nevertheless, the disappearance or submergence of archaic varieties of *sapiens* remains something of a mystery and a neglected field of study.

The early *sapiens* phase

From about 100,000 years BP onwards diversification and improvement of tool assemblies are everywhere in evidence, but continuity of tradition is not interrupted; and interchange between the scattered groups leads to wide diffusion of new ideas.

In Africa the technology represents the final flowering of the Acheulian tradition. Its adaptation to the requirements of particular regions becomes pronounced. Some implements bear witness to an intensified exploitation of close wooded

country, but the occupation of the savannah continues unbroken. The Fauresmith culture extended over dry, open
country, on the grasslands and high plateaux of southern
and eastern Africa (Fig. 36). Fossil remains of its practitioners come from the Cave of Hearths (Makapansgat, Trans-

36 Africa: fossil and archaeological sites

vaal), and these are very fragmentary, and from the open
site of Saldanha Bay (Cape) both about 40,000 years BP.
As we have noted, the latter clearly belongs to the Rhodesian
variety of *sapiens* populations. Contemporaneous with the
Fauresmith was the Sangoan—a culture of more forested regions. Very widespread in Central Africa, it arose 'out of the

need of the Chelles–Acheul people to adapt their equipment to life in a wooded country'. The tools included heavy picks, scrapers and planes for cutting and working wood. Rhodesian man at Broken Hill, about 30,000 years BP, was associated with the last manifestation of the Sangoan as it developed in Gamblian pluvial times (see Table 5), into the Stillbay—a culture of open woodlands widely ranging from the Cape to the Horn. In Rhodesia and Zambia the Stillbay hunters made use of quartz as a raw material, in other places fine-grained silcrete. The people of the parallel culture, the Pietersburg, lived mainly in bushveld country and they too worked their implements in a wide variety of materials. Florisbad man of the Orange Free State, a *sapiens* man, probably of an 'intermediate' variety since he shows some affinity to Rhodesian man, produced a local variant of the Pietersburg–Stillbay complex. Far away in Ethiopia (Fig. 36), at the Dire-Dawa cave, other makers of Stillbay tools have left some skeletal remains. These have been identified as neanderthaloid in character and dating back to about 40,000 years BP.

It is important to note that these Middle Stone Age industries (Stillbay, Pietersburg and other variants) are characterised by the adoption of the Levalloisoid technique, that is, the triangular points are struck from cores with prepared faces and faceted striking platforms. This Levalloisoid working imparts an affinity to industries otherwise developmentally distinct, over the whole area of habitation of the early *sapiens* populations, roughly from 80,000 to 20,000 years BP.

In north Africa, the Near East and Middle East, and throughout Europe the neanderthal-*sapiens* populations developed an industrial complex—the Mousterian—which was flexible enough to serve for survival in many different niches during the cold phase of the late Riss (Third Glaciation), the succeeding warmer Riss–Würm interglacial and again in the next colder first phase of the Würm or Last Glaciation. Many authorities see the Mousterian as a derivation from the Acheulian. Eventually, as had occurred in Africa south of the Sahara, the long standing Acheulian tradition was replaced by a more advanced and complex industry at the hands of men belonging to a different population.

In Europe sites with many hand-axes were mainly confined to maritime lowland; a different culture, without hand-axes, was developed for life in the hilly and mountainous districts of the interior where cold conditions were more severe (Movius).

Amongst the earliest Mousterian Neanderthalers or related peoples were those at Ganovce in Czechoslovakia at least 70,000 years BP, at Ehringsdorf, in Germany, in the Shanidar Cave (Iran) at least 60,000 years BP and in the Tabun (Israel) caves. The earliest cultures of about this date show derivation from the Acheulian, and this link is apparent in the Mousterian at the name site of Le Moustier. Over the period from about 70,000 to 30,000 BP Mousterian occupation sites were established at very many localities in Europe —in Yugoslavia, Czechoslovakia, Hungary, Greece, Rumania and Spain and in France, Belgium, Germany and Britain. Some of these sites contain remains of the makers of this industry.

Amongst well-known sites (see Fig. 38) yielding fossil remains are Engis, Spy, La Chapelle, Le Moustier, La Ferrassie, La Quina and as far afield as Kiik-Kuba and Teshik Tash in the Crimea, where the industry is typically Mousterian. And the Levalloiso-Mousterian (Fig. 37) crops up frequently and from an early date—notably at Djebal Kafzeh (c. 70,000 BP) at Shanidar, Tabun, Skuhl and Jersey between 50,000 and 35,000 BP. A regional variant of the Mousterian associated with neanderthal men developed in Italy, at Saccopastore and Monte Circeo.

In Asia again we find development from the older tradition, that is, from the chopping tool industries. There is a great proliferation of occupation sites but fossil remains are exceedingly scanty. The makers appear to have been varieties of *sapiens* men. For the culture of Kwangtung of the late Middle Pleistocene (about 80,000 BP) it is claimed that a Neanderthal or similar variety of *Homo sapiens* was responsible (Ma-pa man). With the onset of colder conditions of the last glaciation the industry, while still retaining elements of the chopper-chopping tool tradition, also contains points and scrapers of the Levalloiso–Mousterian type and

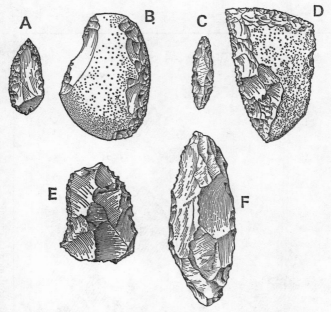

37 Mousterian tools: (A) Mousterian point, Combe-Grenal,
Dordogne (after Bordes, Fig. 33(3)); (B) La Quina-type
Mousterian convex side-scraper, Combe-Grenal (after Bordes,
Fig. 34(1)); (C) Mousterian, Shanidar, double-ended point
(from Solecki); (D) Jabrudian flake-scraper, layer Ea Tabun
Cave (after Oakley, *Frameworks*, Fig. 29); (E) Lavalloisian
flake-tool, Singa, Sudan (after Oakley, *Man the Toolmaker*,
Fig. 33(c)); (F) Sangoan pick, Sango, Uganda (after Bordes,
Fig. 44(1))

true blade tools. This industry—the Ordosian—became widespread in Mongolia and has links with the late palaeolithic
industries of eastern Siberia and Transbaikalia.

The advent of the *sapiens* variety in Java, namely solo man,
was marked by substantial technological progress. Solo man
produced in the Sangiran flake culture an assemblage derived from the earlier Patjitanian industry. This, as we have
noted, is in the tradition of the chopping tool-chopper complex.

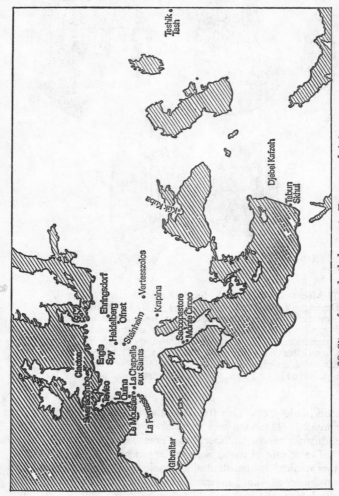

38 Sites of neanderthal man in Europe and Asia

The fact that the early *sapiens* peoples of Africa, Europe, the Middle East, the Far East and southeast Asia made marked improvements in their hunting and food gathering equipment and weapons as compared to their predecessors, is only to be expected. They were now experiencing a greater variety of habitats than ever before; in the northern hemispheres they had to endure the much colder conditions of the glacial stages of the Late Pleistocene. Fire-making was now well developed, while the occupation of cave shelters went on. Game was hunted in great variety, as the food debris from the many occupied cave shelters testifies. And in the floors of their caves neanderthal men deliberately buried their dead, sometimes along with stone tools. There were Mousterian burials at La Chapelle-aux-Saints (Corrèze) about 40,000 years ago, at Regourdou near Lascaux (Dordogne), in the Teshik-Tash cave (Czbikislal) and the Skūhl caves of Mt Carmel.

The late palaeolithic *sapiens* phase

The technological advance from *Homo erectus* times, as represented by the Acheulian sequence or the chopper-chopping tool complex in Asia, to the industries developed by early *Homo sapiens* is clear enough; at the same time continuity of tradition and diffusion of technique from stage to stage are often discernible. As compared with the technological progress made from the middle pleistocene (Mousterian) times onwards, that of the later palaeolithic *sapiens* hunting peoples, from about 25,000 BP, is still more striking in its rapidity and elaborateness. This is clearly shown in the workmanship of the stone artefacts, blades and other fine, small flints. It is even more strikingly in evidence in the skilled fashioning of antler, ivory and bone, in cave painting and in sculpture.

This advance is everywhere present, but it is uneven and earlier traditions may persist. For example, Mousterian elements survive amongst the fully *sapiens* people at Vetercina, Croatia (30,000 years BP) and at Solutré (23,000 BP) or in an Alpine cave at Salzofen, Austria (32,000 years BP).

Chopper-chopping tool traditions persist among the Niah cave people of Borneo of 40,000 years BP. Some industries of the Stillbay-Pietersburg culture practised about 35,000 years ago by the Rhodesian and Florisbad men recur at Singa in the Sudan at about 23,000 years BP and at Cape Flats, Capetown, where they are attributed to a 'Boskop' population.

Western Asia is an important area containing perhaps the earliest sites where the Mousterian gives way to the new blade and burin industries. For the remainder of the Pleistocene over a widening area of the world these industries form the basis of the technology of modern *Homo sapiens*, which now becomes firmly established as the only variety of *Homo*. Accompanying this wide diffusion these industries naturally undergo considerable regional variation. But they contain a certain number of characteristics in common.

The characteristic stone tools (mainly flint) were made on narrow parallel-sided blades struck from cores by a new technique, apparently involving the use of hammer and punch. The tools usually included specialised implements known as burins (Fig. 39) or gravers which were used for working bone, antler, ivory and occasionally soft stone, and no doubt wood. A typical burin is a flint blade with margins sliced obliquely at one end so that they meet and form a narrow chisel edge. However, this is only one form, and over twenty-five specialised types of burin were devised by the upper palaeolithic peoples, who were much more inventive than their predecessors, making a wide range of tools and weapons involving several new techniques. They mastered the working of bone, antler and ivory of which they made extensive use. They also made considerable use of red ochre, evidently for ceremonial purposes (Oakley).

The main European complex of the industry traditionally called the Aurignacian comprises a number of major temporal and geographical components. As early as 30,000 years BP the Combe Capelle people (Plate 9) practised one major version, the Châtelperronian, and indeed this may have co-existed with the last remains of the Mousterian. (This is

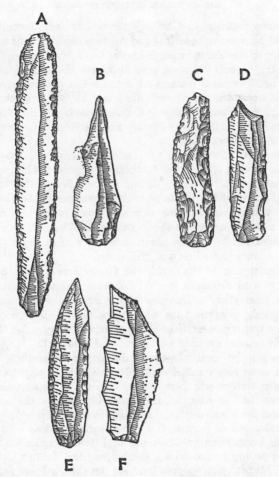

39 Blades and burins: (A) Protomagdalenian retouched blade,
Laugerie Haute, Les Eyzies, Dordogne (after Bordes, Fig. 55(11));
(B) Upper Perigordian dihedral burin, Corbiac, Dordogne (after
Bordes, Fig. 54(14)); (C) Retouched blade. Upper Palaeolithic,
Ust' Kanskaya Cave, Siberia (Bordes, Fig. 70(3)); (D) Burin.
Upper Palaeolithic, Ust' Kanskaya Cave, Siberia (Bordes, Fig.
70(1)); (E) Capsian backed blade (Bordes, Fig. 71(12)); (F)
Capsian burin (Bordes, Fig. 71(8)).

the time depicted in Golding's novel *The Inheritors* of the 'clash' between neanderthal and modern man.) A still earlier version of the Aurignacian is known from Afghanistan (Kara Kamar), 34,000 years BP, spreading over the Near East and Europe. The fossil remains of Aurignacian peoples in western Europe are widespread; they are known from sites in Britain (Paviland), France, Czechoslovakia, Stettin on the Baltic, Barme Grande in Italy, and in Rumania, over the period 30–20,000 years BP.

The local developments of the Aurignacian are complex; in the Levant strongly autochthonous cultures with affinities to the Aurignacian emerged; and in south Russia the further modification of the Châtelperronian gave rise to the Gravettian, which later became dominant over much of Europe in the period 25,000 to about 15,000 BP. This is the culture distinguished by the manufacture of carved female statuettes such as the famous Venus of Willendorf.

Overlapping in time with the Gravettians came the distinctive and elegantly worked Solutrean culture which may have originated in Hungary about 20,000 BP and moved westwards, persisting for some 5,000 years till 15,000 BP. Of the few representatives of the Solutrean people, the Chancelade remains are the best documented (Plate 9).

During the final phases of the upper palaeolithic age, there were very marked regional developments of culture in western Europe—the best known because of its outstanding achievements in cave art, carving in bone and antler and so on, was the Magdalenian. The Magdalenians (Plate 9) made extensive use of burins. The culture originated as a branch of the Perigordian or Gravettian and its time span ran from about 20,000 to 10,000 BP, overlapping the Eastern Gravettian. Magdalenian populations are represented by skeletal remains of 'Cromagnon' type at Bruniquel, Laugerie-Bas, Gourdan, La Madeleine, Oberkassel and Vestonice and by 'Chancelade' individuals at Chancelade, Le Roc and Veyrier.

The success attained by many of these upper palaeolithic peoples in their hunting life is attested by their intensive and continuous occupation of many sites. The valley of the Vezère in the Dordogne is one example. The food animals number a great number of species, including reindeer and bison, steppe horse, wolf, arctic fox and lemming.

As hunters they possessed a range of efficient weapons—spears, darts, clubs, slings. Their tools enabled them to exploit the game, not only for their food supply but also for clothing, as testified by the findings of scrapers for preparing the skins, and bone needles. Clothing was essential for survival in the cool conditions of those times and fire-making was completely mastered; numerous hearths are found in the open and in rock shelters. Their ecological success, measured in terms of effective protection against climate and efficient hunting techniques, is clearly reflected in the leisure available for artistic pursuits. Their practice of using the extremely difficult recesses of their caves for their rock paintings and sculptures was time consuming and hazardous.

The men of the Upper Palaeolithic (Plate 9) of Europe and the Middle East, the practitioners of the Aurignacian, Solutrean, Magdalenian and allied cultures, make up an assemblage of populations which conform to the range of physical variation existing today. In material such as that from Combe Capelle we have precursors of modern Mediterraneans; in the Cromagnon types, those of central and northern Europe. As already remarked, it may be that a number of these carry some marks of other early affinities with neanderthaloids and 'intermediates'. Certainly, at the time horizon of about 40–30,000 years BP there were full-fledged *sapiens* men living side by side with these more archaic and now extinct communities.

At many sites along the coast of the western half of North Africa and as far east as Cyrenaica, the Mousterian and Aterian industries were succeeded by a true blade culture which goes back to 30,000 BP and has clear connections with forerunners in the Near East. In due course it developed into a culture with a great abundance of backed blades, the Oranian. Users of the Oranian industry, the Mechta people, are represented by skeletal remains from a number of caves in Morocco and Algeria, several individuals being recovered from true burials (Plate 10). The Mechta people and the Oranian culture persisted from about 12,000 years BP until the Holocene proper, 8,000 or 9,000 BP.

Blade industries developed earlier in east Africa than further south, indeed as early as the last phase of the Gamblian pluvial. The lower Kenya Capsian 'has generally been regarded as a far-flung offshoot of the blade and burin tradition which spread from Eurasia into north Africa during the later phases of the Würm glaciation' (Oakley). It is not clear who the peoples of the lower Kenya Capsian really were. The later development of this culture—the upper Kenya Capsian—is probably post-pleistocene. The skeletons (Plate 10) associated with it, from Gamble's Cave, Naivasha and Olduvai Gorge, are similar to those of many of the present-day inhabitants of the region, the dark-skinned peoples of 'Mediterranean' build.

The blade and burin culture in east Africa existed contemporaneously with the development of Later Stone Age industries which grew out of, and were modified from, the earlier technologies of the Middle Stone Age (Stillbay and Pietersburg). Some implements were of advanced design: composite tools and weapons were made by hafting small pieces of worked stone on to wood or bone; the bone or wood was grooved, by the use of angle burins, for the reception of carefully flaked and thinned points.

Magosian assemblages and other variants of about 8,000 BP contained tools adapted for use in dry conditions (as at Magosi in Uganda) as well as in forested areas (as in the Congo). The makers of these terminal pleistocene and early post-pleistocene cultures almost certainly corresponded to local peoples of the present time.

In southern Africa long before this there were early or proto-Hottentots or Bushmen. It is probable that in the so-called Boskop remains we have evidence of pre-Hottentot stock scattered over an area much wider than that of their distribution when they were first encountered by Bantu and Europeans. Further north, the late pleistocene people represented precursors of the Bantu-negroids of today.

To establish the exact affinities of the large assemblage of skeletal material ascribed to the African Late Middle Stone Age of about 13,000–15,000 years BP, such as that from Matjes River, Fish Hoek and Cape Flats (Cape), Ingwavuma (Natal), Boskop and Springbok Flats in the Transvaal, demands a more rigorous statistical treatment than has so far been employed. Of course, these are all true modern *Homo sapiens* but the co-existence of modern with non-modern *sapiens* populations, as witnessed in Europe and the Middle East during the first half of the Upper Pleistocene (say over the period 60,000 to 30,000 years BP), is reproduced remarkably in Africa. At about the 40,000 BP date line the archaic *sapiens* Rhodesian forms (Broken Hill and Hopefield (Plate 8)) are contemporary with Florisbad man—a modern variety (Plate 10).

In the Far East the archaic solo man has the Bornean Niah man (about 38,000 years BP) as an early modern contemporary or immediate successor. The populations that emerged in the Late Pleistocene are all men of the modern stamp. It seems quite certain that the material from Kwangsi and Choukoutien (Plate 10) represents the forerunners of the present day 'Mongoloid' population. In the contemporary industries elements akin to the European Aurignacian and Gravettian can also be recognised in the Far East. Amongst artefacts of indigenous and archaic facies in the late palaeolithic industries of north China, a certain proportion of blade tools occurs.

We have thus in Europe, in the Middle East, in south and east Africa and in the Far East, very definite evidence at about 30,000 years BP of the ascendancy of peoples closely akin to modern varieties. Everywhere we see the supersession of the earlier archaic varieties by modern *sapiens* hunters. This process represents the final evolutionary transformation of the 'spectral network' (Fig. 35) which constitutes the *sapiens* species.

Some anthropologists still continue to postulate that the first modern Europeans (for example the peoples labelled Combe Capelle or Cromagnon) originated in some areas as 'pure' racial groups, which then moved in to supplant the older archaic neanderthal populations.

The same consideration would apply to modern man in the Far East (for example the Niah people), or Florisbad in South Africa, since all these rapidly supplant their 'archaic' contemporaries, solo man and rhodesian man. The sites of origin and the migratory routes remain always conjectural, and this is not surprising. The search for areas of origin is as illusory as the search for pure races themselves. It rests on a complete misunderstanding of the nature of both evolutionary change and the actual evidence. The fact is that modern *sapiens* populations developed, expanded and differentiated within a network of overlapping populations. For a long time the developing stocks were of a range which differentiated to produce a wide spectrum of diverse populations, but with time the network changed its character so that the modern form of *sapiens* predominated while itself undergoing regional modification.

CHAPTER 4

ADAPTATION AND VARIATION: THE ECOLOGY OF THE HUNTER-GATHERER LIFE

Almost the whole evolutionary history of modern man, indeed of the hominids, was encompassed within the hunting and gathering of wild food. Man's biological constitution and capacities are therefore to be understood in very large part as moulded by the stresses inseparable from this precarious way of life—an existence pursued by the hominids for over a million years, by the genus *Homo* for about half a million years and by *Homo sapiens* himself for all his quarter of a million years, except for the recent 8,000 years when at last he became a settled being.

A major evolutionary fact to be kept in mind is that the hominid period falls into two unequal parts. We must distinguish between a first period of relatively gross morphological and skeletal change when, as we have seen, the major transformation of *Australopithecus* to *Homo erectus* took place; and a second during which the latter is transformed into *Homo sapiens*. The first period is the longer, about 750,000 years at least; the second is not much more than about 250,000 years. In the first period the working of evolutionary forces is, as we have seen, prominently displayed in the fossil remains and particularly in the brain, face, dentition, hands and locomotor skeleton generally. In the second period the palaeontological record still reveals evolutionary change, but while this becomes much less obtrusive in the skeleton, there is plenty of direct and detailed evidence of the results of long continuing genetic differentiation to be *in present day populations. Throughout this period of change we are witnessing a continuous process of of the genetic basis of hominid anatomy, physiology and behaviour, as well as in the regulation of population numbers and the utilisation of resources. The basic biological equipment of the emergent *sapiens* species was fashioned in the first long period of hominid existence, in the African equatorial savannah-bush environment where *Australopithecus* gave rise to the first forms of *Homo*. It was this biological endowment that opened the way to the era of *Homo*, when the range of biotopes widens so greatly to encompass eventually nearly the whole world.

The nature of this endowment is quite clear. It consists of an array of characteristics conferring on the species as a whole a high degree of adaptive flexibility. Specifically, this affects, as we shall see, the bodily systems making for survival—nutritional and metabolic flexibility, the capacity for sustained physical work, body temperature regulation, protection against ultra-violet radiation and immunological responses to infectious disease. The adaptability displayed in the functioning of these systems remains the common property of the *sapiens* species as a whole, continuing to provide the essential biological basis for adjustment to the many changes and stresses of environment and activity to which modern man subjects himself. Since these properties are held in common by *sapiens* populations of today, and since they clearly reveal their origin in the hunting way of life in hot, sunny climates—and must have required a long period for their successful development—we may confidently regard them as the product of the environmentally restricted but very protracted period of the early hunting hominids in Africa—the Australopithecines and first varieties of *Homo erectus*.

The biological achievement of this phase (and it involves, of course, a major development of brain capacity) made possible later on the occupancy and exploitation of ever more varied ecological niches by early and modern kinds of *Homo sapiens*, culminating in their spectacular irruption, while stiⁱ in the hunting phase, into the variegated environments ot the circumpolar regions of the New World and into Australasia.

As the *sapiens* hunting populations dispersed, ⁱ came subject to the action of novel micro forces; migration and seasonal movements

from this way of life and bands are continually forming and
moving away to make contacts with new groups. The evidence from prehistory, as well as the practices of contemporary hunters, make clear that while shifting networks of
hunting bands must have been subject to virtual isolation
over long periods of time, isolation of individual breeding
within the 'network' was never complete and there was a
renewal of contact from time to time. Nevertheless, in the
geographical dispersion of *Homo sapiens* genetic differentiation was inescapable in the face of such facts as migration, environmental stress, small population size, and chance
break-up of isolates combined with intermittent hybridisation and interaction with other groups.

As part of this process of local differentiation, those features conferring general species adaptability have undergone
only a small degree of modification; it is more pronounced
in some characters but the basic adaptive property persists.

Nutrition

A fundamental biological endowment of man, the inescapable
consequence of the gathering-hunting mode of life in the
Australopithecine stage, as we have noted, is the dependence on an omnivorous, largely carnivorous diet. This departure from the general anthropoid diet was not an absolute one, but one of degree. The use of vegetable nutrients,
of fruits, nuts, berries and roots continued but the dependence on meat, rudimentary among the Anthropoidea, became greatly intensified. The hominid diet was such that
it could now be varied within very wide limits and combinations to provide calories and proteins in adequate amount for
growth, reproduction and activity. To the adaptability of
climatic response was added flexibility of diet.

While the typical hunter's diet is naturally high in animal
protein, fairly high in fat and low in carbohydrate, to ensure
an adequate energy intake, quite large amounts of food must
be eaten. A hunter's daily diet might be composed of protein
400 g, fat 150 g, carbohydrate 60 g, giving 1,600, 1,350
and 240 kCals of energy respectively to make a total of 3,190

kCals. The successful hunter utilising the resources of his environment very fully can secure this nutritional intake. The intensity of exploitation of the game may be judged from the diversity of food eaten by the hominids at Olduvai, *Homo erectus* at Pekin, *Homo sapiens neanderthalensis* and Aurignacian man, as already described.

The fluctuation in the food supply led to the consumption of very large amounts when food was available. This irregular pattern of food consumption (so different from the continuous foraging of the arboreal primates) is characteristic of hunting people of the present day such as the Eskimo, Bushmen and Australian aborigines. It has been suggested that the hunter's 'appetite' has persisted into the modern westernised world where it is now entirely inappropriate; people are apt to overeat in a kind of instinctive anticipation of long periods of dearth, which do not in fact occur. This 'overeating' is, of course, the major factor responsible for the obesity, overweight and 'endomorphic' physiques common in modern western societies but virtually absent in hunting groups.

In its ability to accept strange foods and novel combinations of nutrients, the human organism shows great adaptive capacity. There is also the ability to regulate input to supply. Faced with a sudden reduction or surfeit in the supply of a particular nutrient, the normal level in the body is kept from undue fluctuation by a compensatory decrease or increase in the excretion or degradation of the nutrient concerned; where the intake is very greatly reduced or the output greatly increased there may be some utilisation of whatever stores the body possesses until the balance can be restored. The balance between intake and output of nitrogen, sodium, iron, chloride and calcium, as well as most vitamins, is handled in this way, though not below certain limits of deficiency.

An individual losing a good deal of sodium as salt in the sweat will, during one day, hold back salt from being excreted by the kidney; the urine content of salt will become diluted and over the next few days the sweat will similarly undergo reduction of its salt content. The retention of salt under the stimulation of a negative salt balance is brought about by the action of a hormone (aldosterone) from the adrenal gland. This response is highly appropriate to conditions of desert or tropical activity, since salt loss by sweating would be disastrously high if these regulatory responses could not be made. Thus it turns out that the intake of salt is adjusted at quite different levels for different communities and even in the tropics, a balance can be maintained on an intake of say ten gms a day, no higher than the amount of salt consumed in cool climates.

There is also a large individual variation in the levels at which salt balance can be maintained, even when conditions are standardised, so that genetic differences may well be involved. It might be supposed that genetic selection for efficient salt conservation has favoured some desert peoples, but little study on this point has so far been made.

The rate of growth and the adult body size are influenced by the availability of calories, protein and calcium. Adjustments to shortages are made by reducing the losses of nitrogen and calcium and, in the growing period, by a smaller utilisation leading to a smaller body size.

An individual on a very low calcium intake will be found to have a correspondingly low calcium output; if the individual is a growing child the compensation may not be sufficient to make available enough calcium for bone growth and stunting will be the result. This risk is not run by hunting peoples but it is by many single-crop agriculturalists.

As compared with neolithic agriculturalists and men of temperate and cooler climates, the body size of tropical dwellers now and in the past tends to be relatively small. That hot climates place a limitation on body size seems likely in that, as we shall see, body heat and water regulation may be favoured in lighter rather than heavier individuals.

The possibility that food shortage also might have exerted a strong selective action on body size in some populations cannot be ruled out. In conditions of chronic malnutrition natural selection might have operated in favour of the smaller individuals requiring less food for growth and activity. In this way genotypically smaller women would produce genetically smaller offspring with much less difficulty than women stunted phenotypically by shortage of food during their growing period. The latter would experience difficulty during labour because of skeletal deformity, particularly as a result of pelvic distortion and disproportion. It seems to be the case that ill-nourished women of poor socio-economic class do suffer more difficult and prolonged labour, with greater perinatal mortality, more prenatal and greater maternal mortality, than better-off, better built and taller women; whereas women of comparably small size in communities of genetically lower average bodily stature, produce healthy small babies with little trouble.

Although genetically determined variations in body size in the polymorphic *sapiens* species may well have an explanation in terms of both nutritional and climatic selection, there is little definite evidence of the emergence in particular localities of new genotypes conferring special metabolic or nutritional capabilities or protection against particular vitamin or mineral deficiencies. Two possibilities of this kind should be noted.

Eskimos traditionally had a diet extremely high in fat and low in carbohydrate. European explorers found this diet quite unacceptable; there is, however, some laboratory evidence that fat intake can be gradually raised to high levels. Whether Eskimos do, in fact, digest fat and metabolise fatty acids more efficiently than other populations has not been established.

The second possibility concerns steatopygia, frequently found amongst Hottentot, Bushmen and Andamanese, particularly the women. This character is, in fact, a very variable one in these populations, and by illustrating the most extreme examples racial typologists have given a misleading impression of the prevalence of this character. Moreover its incidence in neighbouring peoples has yet to be investigated. The fat deposits in steatopygia have been shown (Krut and Singer) to be identical in fatty acid composition to that of buttock fat in Europeans and Bantu. There is also evidence that the fat is reduced during lean seasons. Steatopygia may, in fact, be a specialised manifestation of a much more widespread character and confer some selective advantage against food shortage by providing rather more than the usual body fat deposits. Its survival value to the pregnant woman seems very likely.

The high degree of nutritional adaptiveness of modern man

is clearly a fundamental and long-standing species property. Any genetic deviations are invariably very serious. Thus, the abnormal genes which lead to disordered amino-acid metabolism (e.g. phenylketonuria, or alkaptonuria) are present in very low frequencies, indicative of the action of strong selective pressure towards their elimination.

Climatic adaptation

Man's relative hairlessness (as Darwin noted) is a feature in which he diverges from other Anthropoidea. Modern man carries hair at an average density of about sixty per sq. cm; in tropical peoples the hair follicle density and distribution is much the same as that of temperate dwellers, but the thickness and length of the hairs are less; in the Bushmen, for example, the hairs are extremely fine. In arctic animals, for example the caribou, or domestic animals such as the sheep, the density rises to about 1,000 hairs per sq. cm.

The reduction of hair in man is clearly connected with the need to lose heat rapidly when the bodily heat load rises to high levels, as it does during strenuous and sustained activities at high air temperatures in the sun. Now, this loss of heat is, of course, brought about by sweating; if this evaporative heat loss is to be maximally effective, it is of great advantage that hair should be absent or sparse. A hairy pelt with a layer of trapped still air will greatly reduce evaporation even in windy conditions. The superiority of man in this respect is shown in Fig. 40. In hot dry conditions (with a large water vapour pressure gradient between skin and air) evaporation will be only one-quarter or one-fifth from a hairy skin in which air is kept immobilised, compared with a 'smooth' skin; and the evaporative loss will be even more reduced in humid conditions, that is when the vapour pressure difference becomes small. Moreover, the still air layer next to human skin can be reduced from ½ cm to ⅕ cm or less by a wind-speed of 5 mph (2 m/sec), whereas in a hairy animal the still air layer may remain as high as 1 cm or more.

The relative hairlessness of man is, in fact, inseparable from the development of the eccrine sweat glands (Fig. 41) man is physically of the order of 600 kCals. Thus the sweat gland capability is closely adjusted both to the size and peak activity of the tropical hominid.

Another physiological pro... ... gland testifies to its adaptive ...dual exposed repeatedly to hot climates ...anced sweat response, so that a greater heat ...a can be endured, the output of work greatly increased and the risk of heat disability diminished, while the body temperature rise is decreased (Fig. 42). The state of acclimatisation to heat is demonstrably present in tropical and desert dwellers; without it the hard work of the peasant in

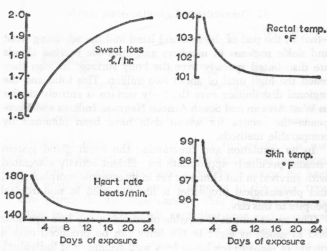

42 Physiological changes during acclimatisation to heat

jungle and swamp, in monsoon and hot summer climates, could not proceed efficiently. It is a property also readily evoked in temperate climate dwellers, when exposed to heat stress.

For them it makes possible an even greater output of energy; the full sweat loss capacity can be used (except in hot summer conditions) for dissipating the heat load of work, since heat loss in cool temperatures by convection and radiation is rapid. This means that the energy output of neolithic peasants clearing the forests of temperate Europe could have reached levels as high as those of today's Canadian or Scandinavian lumberjacks, twice or even thrice that of the tropical dweller. Muscle work of these intensities must in its turn have exerted a selective action in favour of a burlier physique and larger body weight. Against the gain in energy output made possible (or necessitated) by life in cool climates, must be set the higher food requirements. Even at rest the metabolic rate per kilogram body weight tends to be higher.

Thus, the development by the tropical hominid of the eccrine evaporative heat loss system has constituted a pre-adaptation of major functional importance for the subsequent world-wide spread of *Homo sapiens*. Little, if any, modification in the structural and physiological basis of this system has occurred in any regional or racial group, though its exact functioning will vary to some extent with variation in other bodily characters, such as skin colour and bodily physique. There is some evidence that the more lightly built tropical dweller with his relatively greater skin surface area can sweat more efficiently and economically. The fact that light-coloured skin reflects more and absorbs less radiation, at all wave lengths, than dark skins, means that in conditions of intense sunlight, dark-coloured individuals will (for a given posture and bodily surface area) absorb about ten per cent more radiant energy. They will, therefore, need to sweat that much more—an increase of little importance to the acclimatised subject. Naturally, in shade conditions this difference will disappear. Since darker skin colour is so universal in hot sunny regions, the fact that its possession adds somewhat to the outdoor heat load strengthens the view that it must carry a specially important advantage for life in equatorial regions. This advantage, as discussed below, resides in its protective action against ultra-violet light.

The original condition of 'hairlessness' has, with the later geographical diffusion and differentiation of human populations, undergone some secondary modification. Although much play has been made with 'hairiness' as a 'racial' character, our information about this simple attribute is remarkably deficient and uneven, and most judgements are made in impressionistic terms, e.g. 'northern Australian aborigines are more hairy than southern'. The information suggests that greater hairiness is evident in central Europe (Alpine areas), the Balkans, and western Asia, also among north Australian aborigines, the Ainu and some Indians (Brahmins). It seems the case that some human populations, at least, have undergone some increase of hairiness in cooler climates. It must be admitted that the significance of variation in this character remains obscure. The present distribution presumably reflects in some degree the hybridisation by 'hairy' populations with basically less hairy ones.

A climatic significance has also speculatively been attached to variations in the amount of facial hair and in the form of head hair. The springy 'peppercorn' hair of Africans has been thought to provide useful insulation against solar radiation without impeding sweating or evaporation. There is, in fact, a gradation of hair form throughout African peoples from 'frizzy' to 'wavy' and outside Africa from 'curly' and 'wavy' to straight. Geographical clines probably exist, but these remain to be delineated and to be elucidated in genetic and functional terms.

Man's tolerance to cold is based on physiological processes common to mammals as a whole, but limited in ways characteristic of tropical animals. Exposure to cold induces the usual constriction of skin blood vessels and this has the effect of reducing the blood flow through the skin and hence the heat loss from the body surface. This decrease in skin thermal conductance ('insulative adaptation') cannot of course be assisted materially by the erection of hair which in furry, true cold climate animals increases the thickness of the layer of trapped air; in men this response takes the quite rudimentary form of 'goose-flesh'. Exposure to cold evokes another usual mammalian response, namely an increase in heat production ('metabolic adaptation') brought about mainly by the muscular effort of shivering, with probably some contribution by 'non-shivering' thermogenesis involving an increased heat liberation principally from the liver. An increased output of adrenalin is involved in these responses as it is in mammals generally.

Now for these metabolic adaptations to cold, man has a high 'critical' temperature, that is, the air temperature at which the naked body responds by an increase in metabolic heat production is high, about 28°C. This contrasts greatly with arctic animals which are able to maintain their internal body temperature without an increased metabolism down to 'critical' temperatures as low as 10°C or lower. Their ability to do this rests mainly on their possession of a high insulation in the form of fur and subcutaneous fat. It is in these respects that tropical man is so conspicuously lacking. Indeed it is probable that some Anthropoidea are less 'tropicalised' than man. The mountain gorilla lives at fairly high altitudes enduring cold in the winter with little shelter.

Man does, of course, lower his critical temperature artificially, simply by maintaining a microclimate at a 'tropical' temperature by clothing himself with extra insulation and by warming his living space. He relies also on his large output of energy, and whenever necessary on working at levels high enough for skin temperature to reach the sweating threshold.

For his penetration into cool habitats, or survival during cold winters, man has depended on a combination of technological, behavioural and physiological processes of adaptation. Populations of *Homo* at every stage of evolution of the genus have been able to adapt to cold environments (Fig. 29). The first decisive achievement is to be credited to *Homo erectus* at Choukoutien where we have evidence of the use of fire. The neanderthal hunter-gatherer populations were in possession of northwestern and continental Europe throughout the first cold phase of the last glacial period some 70,000 years ago. There is abundant evidence for their use of fire and cave shelters in central Europe. We are not as sure about their garment-making activities as we are for the later Aurignacian and Magdalenian *sapiens*, populations who were able to withstand cold conditions with great success. Modern *sapiens* has had a long history of colonisation of the Arctic; in fact, Eskimo communities established their circumpolar cultures before the end of the pleistocene period.

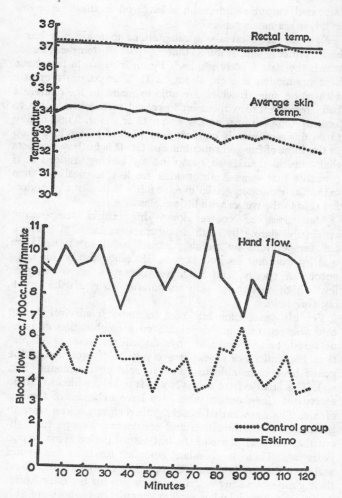

43 (A) Cold adaptation, to show the higher skin temperature and hand blood flow of Eskimos

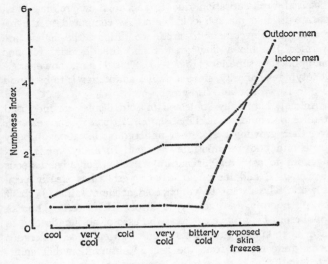

43 (B) Cold adaptation, to show the greater skill of individuals spending much time in the cold (from Mackworth)

The animal fur clothing of circumpolar peoples of today is of a high order of efficiency. Eskimo clothing attains an insulating value of eight to twelve clo, i.e. comparable to the insulation of about eight to ten light suits; it enables extremely low air temperatures to be borne with comfort. This 'natural' clothing possesses the properties of waterproofing and of resistance to compression, as well as thermal insulation, not equalled by the assemblies of modern explorers. The skin and rectal temperatures of Eskimos doing light work for five hours in a twelve mph wind at 24°C remain at levels little different from that measured indoors. The gloves, footwear and headwear of Eskimos are all efficiently designed and made. Their shelter conditions are also maintained at high temperatures.

Even the well-protected Eskimo does not escape the necessity for calling into play some biological adjustment to cold. There is evidence that the hands undergo a 'hardening' or localised acclimatisation due to repeated or prolonged exposure to cold air and cold water. As compared to the responses of newcomers to arctic conditions, the hands are warmer, the blood flow greater and the dexterity for fine manipulation superior (Fig. 43). This is not, however, a genotypic peculiarity, since a similar adaptation is to be found also in Newfoundland fishermen.

Animals habitually subjected to cold display an increased state of resistance or acclimatisation; if this exposure extends over their growing period they undergo modifications in body shape and body composition as well. In many animals indigenous to cold regions natural selection for advantageous physiological and morphological properties has clearly been at work. The extent to which cold acclimatisation, both at the phenotypic and genotypic levels, characterises human populations is not as clear as is the case of acclimatisation to heat. That human groups do acquire an enhanced tolerance seems quite certain from the general observation that habituated individuals sleep much sounder at low temperatures (with a minimum of covering or shelter) than do newcomers. This is spectacularly true of the hunter-gatherer peoples of central Australia (Pitjandara), of Kalahari Bushmen, Alacaluf Indians of Tierra del Fuego, and of the Alpaca and Vicuna Quechua Indian shepherds of Peru. But Europeans can also be 'hardened' and Antarctic explorers learn to do with progressively less bedclothing as time goes by.

Animals well adapted to cold when examined under thermoneutral conditions are characterised by a raised metabolic rate and some increase in extremity temperatures as compared to newcomers. These same adjustments seem to hold for the Eskimo (Fig. 43). European groups in Antarctica or in sub-arctic conditions in Norway also exhibit raised metabolic rates. When acclimatised, various species of animals tested under acute and severe cold conditions are able to adapt with much less shivering than in the unacclimatised state. This is true also of Australian aborigines, Andean and Chilean Indians and artificially exposed Europeans and this seems to be the reason why they sleep better than newcomers. But, Australian aborigines are surprising in that their heat production falls slowly but steadily, whereas in other groups it is maintained or even increased (Fig. 44). Also the cooling of the extremities is more rapid in the aborigines. Thus, the aborigines when chilled maintain a steady 'core' temperature by intense peripheral vasoconstriction without increased heat production (Hammel *et al.*); the other ethnic groups maintain a steady inner temperature by increasing their heat production while undergoing a lesser degree of vasoconstriction.

The peculiarity of the aboriginal response has been claimed as the outcome of true genetic selection; even during the hot season tests on aborigines in cold chambers have yielded similar results. The question remains *sub judice* since there is some controversy amongst physiologists on the comparability of the various test procedures. It does seem the

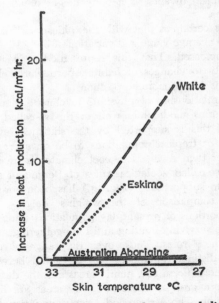

44 To show that in white and Eskimo subjects, metabolism (shivering) increases as the skin is cooled, whereas this is not the case with Australian aborigines

case that different modes of life in the cold can bring about different patterns of physiological response. This may be a peculiarity of man since the biological, behavioural and technological responses to the challenge of cold can take quite different forms in his exploitation of colder regions in different parts of the world.

Body and facial form

We do not know in any detail what the physique of the hominids in their first tropical phase was really like. All we can say is that these groups, judging from their skeletal remains, comprised quite small-statured individuals. *Australopithecus* is estimated to have been not much more than four feet high. The estimate for the later *Homo erectus* of Java, still a tropical dweller, is a body height of about five feet four inches.

What is certain is that with the widespread dispersion of *Homo* the average value and variation of body size and shape greatly increased. That this represented a developmental adaptability to changes of habitat, particularly climate and nutrition, is a reasonable supposition.

In the relationship of physique to climate man, even today, conforms moderately well to the so-called ecological rules, and this is supported by the statistical evidence. A tendency for tropical populations to be on average slighter and lighter than dwellers in cool climates is in accordance with the so-called zoological rules of Bergmann and Allen; evidence to support this (Fig. 45) has been adduced by a statistical comparison of the weights, heights, limb and trunk proportions of present-day populations (Roberts, Newman). The surviving hunting and food-gathering groups conform to these rules. Thus, over the range of climate of Australia, distinct differences can be noted between those living in the uniform hot, humid areas and the desert groups and southern groups. Those in hotter areas are lighter and longer of limb. The African and Asian pygmy populations are all tropical dwellers. *Homo erectus* at Pekin living in a cooler climate was taller than the Javanese representative.

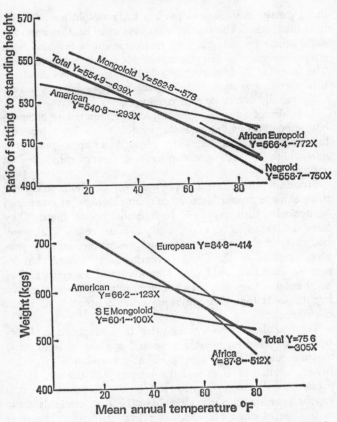

45 Relation between mean annual temperature and body weight (below) and body linearity (above)

For physical and physiological reasons there would seem to be advantages for people living in predominantly hot climates to remain either of light body weight or linear in build, or both. Where heat is gained from the environment, this gain per unit area of skin is at the same rate for individuals of different physique. The heat produced by metabolism is the same per kg. body weight, but the smaller individual has a greater surface area per kg. body weight available for heat dissipation. The smaller man thus loses heat by sweating more efficiently and his total loss of sweat is less and used more economically. His water and salt requirements are less. The fact that he is physically relatively small is no handicap in enterprises such as hunting which, as we have seen, develop rapidly as a co-operative enterprise.

It is also of advantage for tropical hunters not to accumulate subcutaneous fat and the evidence we have supports this. In 'Sheldonian' terms the physique of these peoples is fairly high in both ectomorphy and mesomorphy, low in endomorphy.

Hunting groups, being heavy meat eaters, are in no danger from chronic protein, iron or calcium shortage, as compared to agriculturalists on their high carbohydrate diets. They have no reason to be undersized on these counts. Yet small body size is characteristic of many present day hunting peoples. Pygmies of the Congo, Negritoes of Malaysia, Andamanese Islanders, Philippine Negritoes and Papuans are all meat eaters. They are not phenotypically small and the best hypothesis is that their physique is an adaptation to warm environments.

There is also some suggestion that the configuration of certain facial features, notably nose and eye shape, is in some measure related to the climate. That a correlation exists between breadth of nose and the humidity of the air, as expressed in the mean annual wet bulb temperature or the vapour pressure, seems undeniable. The first hominids show in this, as in other respects, their tropical origin. The nose aperture is notably large in *Australopithecus* and *Homo erectus* in Java. Whether it is any smaller in Pekin man living in cooler climates has not been established. The first Neanderthalers lived during a period of warm climate, but it does not seem that nose shape altered when the climate cooled during the final phase of the last glaciation. This question also awaits a reappraisal. Certainly, in modern man distribution of nose-shape is such that very dry areas (desert or cold) are associated with the appearance of narrow nosed peoples. This would seem to carry the functional advantage that the very dry inspired air is easily and quickly moistened (and dust particles trapped), since the lining of the respiratory tract must be kept moist.

Work capacity

The bipedal physique of the hominids is admirably designed for the efficient performance of long-sustained muscular activity, particularly running, as well as for short bursts of intense exertion. The performance of hard physical work, of course, calls for an increase in oxygen utilisation, in respiration, in the output of the heart and the circulation to the active muscles.

The work of hunting demands patient day-long tracking, attacking the game at short range and relentlessly pursuing a wounded quarry. For these activities the hominid is well suited. The proportion of muscle mass and lung volume to body weight is high and the capacity of the lungs and heart allows a large increase in oxygen intake and transport to the muscles. With so efficient a heat loss system, a long continuing steady-state of work output can be sustained. As the bipedal hunter can carry his own food, he can pursue his game without losing the trail. The biological endowment of a high work capacity, combined with cunning hunting technologies—spears, darts, arrows, slings, traps, snares and blinds—gave the hominids an almost absolute mastery over other animals. Hunting peoples of today, for example the Kalahari Bushmen, employ a wide repertoire of hunting skills. In well chosen spots they will construct ingenious traps for small game and visit them two or three times daily. But they cannot escape the harder work of tracking, and as is often the case they must 'run down' the poisoned, slowly weakening buck, antelope or giraffe.

Muscle activity, being an adaptive function, is susceptible, like other adaptive processes, to further improvement; like adjustments to heat and cold, it can be improved through training. The difference between a physically fit man, such as an active hunter, and an untrained subject shows itself in the more efficient circulation (the smaller increase in pulse rate), and the more efficient utilisation of oxygen by the muscles (as evidenced by the lower lactate production). The muscularity and the chest size undergo some increase. Among hunting peoples many of the active young men are found to be in a well-trained condition as measured by fitness tests. Eskimos have been reported to maintain a continuous run of twenty miles behind the sledge. The load carrying ability of the New Guinea highlanders, or of Sherpas in the Himalayas, is well known. The extraordinary achievements by athletes are another pointer to the strong selection of genotypes in favour of high muscular capacity, so necessary in the past for primitive hunting.

The capacity for hard physical work, acquired of necessity in the hunting ecology, operates as an important pre-adaptation for the type of activity needed for survival in totally different habitats at later stages of hominid evolution. Without this endowment agriculture with its many tasks demanding a high energy expenditure could never have been undertaken.

For man to spread up to high altitudes, rather similar physiological changes to those of muscular exercise are involved. Since the introduction of agriculture the population at, say, above 10,000 feet, where the oxygen tension is markedly reduced, has reached quite large numbers. The responses to the lowered oxygen tension are rather similar to the responses elicited during exercise when oxygen requirements are increased. A major pre-requisite for successful survival at high altitude is an improvement in the capacity of the oxygen transport system. It is not enough that the newcomer should breathe deeper, as he does because the lowered arterial O_2 tension stimulates his respiratory centre. For colonisation there has to be a much more complex process of acclimatisation and this involves lungs, circulation, muscles and tissues. In these respects there is no doubt of the superiority of the indigenous people—a superiority comparable to that of the trained athlete. Just as the trained athlete has an enlarged chest expansion and chest size, so too have the natives of the high Andes, Ethiopia, and the Himalayas.

When we consider (Plate 22) those strange people the Ama of Japan, who exploit a most difficult ecological niche

—they spend so much of their working lives not at low but at high pressure—we find that the adaptiveness of the respiratory system has much to do with their success in the diving profession. Like the high-altitude dweller, the Ama are superior in their breathing capacity, in their vital capacity and in their chest development. Adaptations developed long ago for hunting life would seem to provide the key to the performance of this extraordinary task.

Pigmentation

We shall probably never know what the skin or hair colour of the first hominids was, nor its range of variability. The possession of a darkish skin colour—and this is not unique to man—seems to be an essential adaptation of tropical and equatorial regions. The later history of the hominids has clearly been attended by great variation in pigmentation, very probably related to climatic factors.

It is necessary to emphasise that the mere visual appraisal of skin colour is not very informative and may often be misleading. An objective study of the colour properties of the skin (by reflectance spectrophotometry), as well as by chemical analysis of the pigments themselves, shows that three main components are always involved—the brown pigment melanin (and this is the most important component, in the lower layers of the epidermis), the red pigment haemoglobin in the skin circulation, and a yellowish pigment called carotene.

The melanin-making system of the human epidermis is a universal property of all varieties of mankind. Genes which suppress this faculty—the genes for albinism—are found in all populations, but albinos are quite rare. Human beings differ genetically in the extent to which melanin is found in the skin, but they are all alike in that melanisation can be intensified by exposure to various agents, of which the most important is the ultra-violet rays of solar radiation. The regional distribution over the skin surface of melanophores (like the distribution of sweat glands), is similar in dark and light skinned people.

The familiar phenomenon of sunburn extends through the stages of reddening of the skin to severe blistering followed by desquamation. The wavelengths provoking these responses are in the ultra-violet range of the spectrum in a region invisible to the human eye. It can be accepted that a certain intensity of melanin pigmentation is universally necessary as a protection against the damaging effects of ultra-violet. An intensification of exposure to ultra-violet brings about further tanning and added protection. This is a true 'acclimatising' process. The melanin is produced in the lower layers and the granules move into the upper layers as tanning proceeds.

There is not only more pigment in dark skin; it is distributed more uniformly throughout the epidermis. It is probable that ultra-violet exposure also increases the thickness of the stratum corneum. Albinos derive their protection against ultra-violet light because of hypertrophy of this skin layer.

Negroes, southern Indians and other dark-skinned people are less sensitive to sunburn. A dose of ultra-violet light which damages light coloured skin to the extent of putting the sweat glands out of action (Thomson), has very little effect on moderately dark or tanned skin.

In sufficient intensity ultra-violet light of the wavelengths that cause sunburn can induce cancers of the skin of albino mice or albino rats. Europeans in northern Australia suffer an incidence of skin carcinoma far in excess of that in Europe. Moreover, those Europeans who tan very poorly are more prone to suffer skin carcinomas early in middle age than those who tan well.

Cancer of the skin is very rare in Negroes in the United States and in South Africa. When cancer of the skin does occur in Negroes it is to be found as often on unexposed as exposed skin, contrary to the finding in Europeans. The incidence of epithelioma in Cape-coloured (White-Hottentot hybrids) groups (Fig. 46) is much less than that of the European. In the Argentine nearly all cases of skin cancer occur amongst immigrants, very rarely in Indians or Negroes.

The protective value of melanin against the carcinogenic action of ultra-violet light must have played an important part in the regional differentiation of skin colour.

The selective significance of basal-cell carcinomas is not easy to assess, since they rarely cause severe debility and typically only develop later in life. The melanomas are much more rapidly fatal and a high proportion occur in the reproductive period. The late development of basal-cell carcinomas, however, is no doubt partly due to the protection usually afforded by tanning and clothing and in any case can only be said to characterise the disease in temperate and sub-tropical zones. If naked light coloured people were exposed to strong ultra-violet radiation, it seems likely that selection would strongly favour the darker individuals through their lower susceptibility to skin cancer. Nor must the immediate burning effect of solar radiation be neglected. Under natural conditions severe sunburn would be extremely disabling.

46 The extent to which Europeans are more susceptible to carcinogenic action of ultra-violet light compared to Cape-coloured individuals

Geographical variations in human skin colour seem to be plausibly related to the intensity of ultra-violet. The Sudanese regions of Africa are exposed to the most intense solar radiation and here is found the heaviest pigmentation. Other hot-desert and savannah peoples, such as the aboriginal Australians, who do not possess clothing or have acquired it only recently, tend also to be very dark skinned. Where less heavily pigmented peoples are living under comparable conditions, there is usually evidence that they are relatively recent immigrants, as, for example, in the hot deserts of the New World. The clouded western seaboards of continents in temperate latitudes have the least sunlight. In the Arctic the open dust-free skies of summer and reflection from snow and ice expose the individual to strong ultra-violet radiation. As already mentioned, arctic peoples tend to be darker than temperate ones.

Thus, the geographical relation between ultra-violet light and skin colour would appear to be determined by the protective effect of dark pigmentation; darker-skinned varieties on the whole are found in regions of higher ultra-violet light intensity. Even in tropical zones there seems to be a difference between jungle-shaded and non-shaded peoples, e.g. African pygmies are lighter coloured on the whole than the surrounding Bantu.

The sun-tanning which is acquired by lighter-skinned individuals as a protective character may be regarded as a 'phenocopy' of the genetically determined darker colour of peoples in tropical and equatorial countries. Dark pigmentation must have arisen independently more than once, namely in the dark Europeanoid peoples of south India and Arabia, among Oceanic Negroes, and in Africa, since these peoples do not show close affinity in many of their genetic characters. Relaxation from intense natural selection in the modern era has no doubt permitted the appearance of lighter-skinned populations in parts of southern Africa, in Europe and elsewhere.

While the development of heavy pigmentation in regions of strong insolation can be explained in terms of the protection against the carcinogenic and burning effects of ultra-violet radiation, is there some positive advantage in being light-skinned in regions of low ultra-violet incidence? The nature of this advantage if any is not certainly known.

One theory has it that loss of melanin pigment would have facilitated the manufacture of calciferol (Vitamin D), so

important in bone development, which requires ultra-violet
light for its synthesis from ergosterol precursors in the skin.
Reduction of melanin would facilitate the penetration of
ultra-violet radiation into the epidermis in light-skinned people living in regions of low sunlight intensity. This factor
might conceivably be critical for growth and survival of
those infants where the dietary supply of Vitamin D is very
low.

Dark hair colour and the pigmented iris seem plausibly
associated with dark skin colour as advantageous characters
in regions of strong sunlight, intense ultra-violet radiation and
glare. But with the spread of populations to new habitats,
diversification in the form and colour of hair and in eye colour
has followed. Thus, peoples of both dark and light coloration
are now to be found in association with all varieties of body
forms, facial features, blood group and other sero-genetical
characters.

Genetic differentiation

The phenomena of adaptation and variation, evidenced in
functional, morphological and development characters, have
so far been considered against the changing ecological background in the development of *Homo* as he emerged from a
relatively uniform and restricted tropical environment into a
variety of new and challenging conditions. For a most exact
understanding of the biological changes overtaking the human species in these evolutionary phases, the analysis should
ideally be pursued in genetic and selective terms. As applied
to the differentiation of early human populations of hunters,
fishers and food gatherers, such an analysis becomes feasible
only when the precise genetic and demographic observations
on their present day representatives are obtainable. But the
processes at work are fully applicable, in principle, to bygone
palaeolithic groups. In so far as they are concerned with the
genetics of small, more or less isolated populations, it is justi-
fiable also to use data obtained on present-day simple farming or nomadic communities to illuminate man's differentiation throughout the palaeolithic and neolithic periods.

We cannot, of course, reconstruct in any detail for past populations, and barely for present-day populations, the exact course of transformation of particular characters, or the changes in their frequency of occurrence or degree of expression in different circumstances. We can, however, take into consideration the relevant factors of the hunter-gatherer life, the ecological condition of food supply and climate, the population characters and the time element involved and see how plausibly the observed effects are explicable in terms of basic evolutionary processes.

In the simplest terms evolution means the replacement of one set of genes by another. At any stage of the existence of a species every one of its constituent populations displays considerable diversity. The fossil record shows this clearly whenever a reasonable sample is available, as we see for example in the *Homo erectus* population at Choukoutien, or in 'archaic' *Homo sapiens,* or among the groups at Krapina in Yugoslavia and Mount Carmel in Palestine, or in the 'modern' Cromagnon *sapiens* in France. In every population much of the variability is inborn, but some of it is attributable to developmental, nutritional and functional factors operating irrespective of the genotypes concerned. Inborn differences between individuals affect every character, morphological, physiological, psychological, in greater or lesser degree.

Of the characters of the cranium and skeleton (which is all the direct evidence we have of the biological constitution of bygone populations), forty to eighty per cent of the variability within and between populations is genetically determined, depending on the character and its environmental interaction. (Such estimates come largely from modern twin studies.) Of course, when we come to surviving hunter-gatherer groups, many more morphological characters and their range of expression are known to us and we can take into account explicitly in genetic terms the diversity of such features as skin colour, blood group and serum protein systems, haemoglobin variants, various blood enzymes, colour vision and taste sensitivity. Table 7 summarises the genetical characters of particular value in studies of affinity and differentiation. To some extent 'multifactorially' determined (polygenic) characters can be used for this purpose, and Table 7 also lists features of the face, head, hair and physique of anthropological value.

Table 7.   Characters of Genetic Significance in Population Comparisons

System	Alleles	Description of character
	A: Single loci	
ABO	$I^A : I^B : I^C$	Red cell antigens corresponding to I^A, I^B detected
Diego	$Di+ : Di-$	Red cell antigens corresponding to Di+ detected
Lutheran	$Lu^a : Lu^b$	Red cell antigens corresponding to alleles detected
Kell	K : k	Red cell antigens corresponding to alleles detected
Duffy	$Fy^a : Fy^b$	Red cell antigens corresponding to alleles detected
Gm groups	$Gm^a : Gm^b$	Variations in serum gamma globulin detected
Haemoglobin variants	$Hb^C : Hb^D : Hb^S : Hb^O$ etc	Variations in haemoglobin structure detected
G–6 PDD	Normal: deficient.	Enzyme anomaly in the red cell (glucose–6 phosphate dehydrogenase deficiency)
Haptoglobin	$Hp^1 : Hp^2$	Variation in (serum protein) haptoglobin structure
Transferrin	$Tf^C : Tf^{D_1}$	Variation in (serum protein) transferrin structure
Taster factor	T : t	Ability to taste phenylthiocarbamide (PTC)
Colour blindness	C : c	Red-green colour blindness (allele c)
	B: Multiple loci	
MNS	$Ag^M : Ag^N$ S : s }	Red cell antigens corresponding to alleles detected
Rh systems	C : c D : d E : e }	Red cell antigens corresponding to alleles detected
Skin colour	Probably three loci additive	Reflectance of light in the visible spectrum from the skin surface compared to that from a white surface
Dermatoglyphics	'Small number interacting'	Number of ridge counts

C: Continuous characters—multifactorial, with fairly high heritability

Stature
Cephalic index
Arm length
Leg length   Hair colour
Nose height   Hair form
Upper facial height Eye shape
Bigonial (jaw) width Eye colour

Causes of genetic diversity

The genetic diversity displayed by a population at any time represents the outcome of the interplay between two sets of factors—one set concerned with the supply and source of genetic variation; the other influencing the direction of change, and the two working together determine the final composition of the genetic constitution.

The *supply* of genetic variation can be influenced by three agencies which can act singly or in combination. They are (i) mutation at genetic loci introducing novel genes into the gene pool and hence novel genotypes; (ii) genetic recombination bringing about, by reshuffling of alleles, new combinational possibilities within each genotypic system; and (iii) hybridisation or admixture introducing new genes from outside.

Of the agencies capable of determining the *direction* of genetic diversity, natural selection is the most powerful process of evolutionary adjustment. Novel or unusual genotypes may endow their carriers with characters specially favourable to them in the face of particular stresses, enabling them to reproduce a sufficiently greater number of offspring than the bearers of less favoured genotypes. Genetical differences are therefore reflected in differences in the prospective contribution made to posterity. The action of environmental or other agencies in favouring or eliminating characters—and therefore their genotypes—according to their fitness, is natural selection.

The other agency which may bring about short-term alterations in genetic variability operates through 'chance' effects. These include the breaking away of a small number of mating couples from a larger group—the 'founder effect'; and the accidents of sampling in a small breeding group—the 'drift effect'. The latter would also include the bias introduced by the disproportionate contribution which a chief with many wives may make in a very small breeding group. As a result of these chance effects the new group or generation starts with a complement of genes which in some respects is quite unrepresentative of the earlier breeding group.

A number of important ancillary factors influence the intensity of the action of both natural selection and chance effects. These are the size of the breeding population, the average family size, the degree of isolation measured by 'mating distance' and the features of the mating system itself.

The interplay between the agencies of selection and of

variation constitutes the fundamental evolutionary process; the basic thesis of its operation has been formulated by Mather as follows:

> If either the agencies of variation or the forces of selection are altered the genetical constitution will alter accordingly, but once an adequate genetical adjustment has been achieved selection will act towards stabilising that adjustment. Insofar as equilibrium is approached or attained it is because a balance is achieved amongst the agencies of variation—especially mutation and recombination—and the forces of selection.

This is a restatement in genetic terms of Dunn's postulate:

> Evolution can be viewed both as a process by which species and higher categories differentiated and developed in the past, and as a continuous and continuing process acting today to produce and maintain the adaptation of populations to their environments, which is so marked a feature of successful species.

As long as there are no disturbing influences, and in the short term this is usually or approximately the case, the genetical composition of a population remains intact. This stability of the gene frequencies for particular gene systems enables the application of the Hardy-Weinberg equation for estimating population gene frequencies.

Over the long term, genetic constitution will change. Three important equilibria between natural selection and the agencies of genetic variation need to be considered: (i) the interplay between natural selection and mutation; (ii) natural selection holding the balance between the variant forms of a genotype, that is, maintaining the polymorphisms so characteristic of much of the population diversity of man; and (iii) natural selection operating on the polygenic systems responsible for characters showing continuous variation.

(i) Mutation and selection

The only source of new genes, new heritable variation, is mutation. Mutation is the inception of a heritable variable by a chemical change whose nature is still unclear but which produces a mutant gene, or mutant chromosome, which gives rise to a mutant character. A mutant gene will reproduce itself with self-copying precision; it usually affects the same character system as does the gene from which it arose. The mutant character may be only slightly altered, but a mutation may influence the rate of a development process in such a way as to bring about a large effect in the fully grown adult. The persistence and spread of mutations of these kinds (along with the spread of novel or rare recombinations) have clearly been responsible for the modifications of characters we see as evolutionary adaptations. For example, we may certainly accept that mutation has been responsible for the appearance of the haemoglobin variants (Table 7), that is, an alteration in the gene produces a change in the haemoglobin molecule, since the protein constitution is precisely determined by the gene molecule. By mutation, the variants of haemoglobin called S or C and others have arisen *de novo* probably in more than one population group. Similarly we may be reasonably sure that the genetic difference in stature between Congo pygmies and the Tursi results from the appearance of mutant genes in one or both of these groups, as compared to the geographically intermediate populations, since recombination alone is not likely to bring about pygmy or even the tall stature genotypes. Some degree of subsequent intercrossing no doubt has occurred.

It is easy to postulate or assert that many genetic differences between populations in time or space may have arisen by the appearance, persistence, multiplication and spread of a mutant genetic change. But, because of its relative rarity, the recurrence of a mutation does not by itself guarantee that its frequency will rise to the levels actually observed in different populations or during evolutionary succession. Even when, as will occasionally happen, the mutant gene is not disadvantageous in its effect, its frequency under recurrent mutation will increase extremely slowly, since mutation is not only a rare phenomenon but also a reversible one. For a gene to spread effectively within the time scale of evolutionary change it must be subject to favourable natural selection. It depends on the Darwinian fitness of the individuals displaying the effects of the mutant gene whether those individuals (and the genes with them) will be eliminated or preserved.

The extent to which a mutant gene will become established depends on a balance between its rate of recurrence and its 'fitness' or survival power relative to the gene it is replacing. The fitness conferred by a gene relative to another is simply expressed in terms of reproductive performance. If an individual possesses some character which confers a greater viability or fertility on him compared to other individuals in the population, he will tend to have a greater number of offspring. He will be more fit in the prevailing environment and the character can be said to be adaptive.

Darwinian fitness covers not only biological infertility but unviability or infertility from any cause, social or psychological—the genes are lost whatever the cause. Darwinian fitness is measured as the ratio between the reproductive performance (in terms of viable offspring) of individuals carrying a particular character as compared with others without it. As applied to the representation of genes from one generation to the next, we estimate the fitness of gene A_m compared to A_n where the gene A_n has a fitness of unity and the less fit gene is A_m. If gene A_m is represented in 999 gametes while gene A_n is represented by 1,000 then the fitness (f) of gene A_m is 0.999. Natural selection (s) in favour of A_n or against A_m is 1 gene per 1,000 produced: i.e.

$$s = \frac{1,000 - 999}{1,000} = 0.01 \text{ or } s = 1 - f.$$

When new genes are appearing in a population by mutation (rate = m) and are being either favoured or eliminated, the proportion (p) of the population possessing the gene after a number of generations will be at a balance struck between the rate at which mutation is occurring (or displacing the normal gene) and the rate at which it persists due to its fitness:

$$p = \frac{km.}{s}$$

The equilibrium value and the time it takes to achieve it will be shorter if m is greater or s is smaller. (The constant k is 2 (and equilibrium is reached faster) for a gene with dominant expression and 1 for a recessive gene.) From an evolutionary point of view the equilibrium time for the establishment of a favourable mutation may be measured in hundreds or thousands of generations. Mutation rates are of the order of 1 to 4×10^{-5} (i.e. 1 to 4 gametes carrying the new gene in 100,000) while the change of fertility can vary widely and with it the selective value of the gene. But even a change of fitness (f) to 0.999 or a selection pressure (s) as little as 0.001 will lead to the establishment of a new gene in something of the order of 500 to 1,000 generations, say 100,000 to 200,000 years. This must be viewed against a time span of some 4–500,000 years for *Homo erectus* and 300,000 years for *Homo sapiens* (of all varieties).

The interaction between mutation (m) and natural selection (s) will be more effective in a population which is subdivided into many partially isolated local breeding units. From what we know of modern hunting and gathering groups and from the archaeological evidence this seems to have been the situation generally throughout palaeolithic times.

The gene for colour blindness (a sex-linked Mendelian gene) illustrates the working of some of the processes just described. Since normal colour vision is so important for food gathering and hunting (Polyak 1957), the colour blind would be placed at a clear disadvantage.

'The red-green blind often cannot distinguish over-ripe or rotten from ripe, or ripe from unripe fruit by colour or ripe fruit such as cherries or gooseberries from the leaves of the trees and bushes' (Pickford). As fewer colour-blind children or young adults died of food poisoning or gastro-enteritis, the intensity of selection against them would diminish. The frequency of colour blindness in different groups is in accordance with these postulates (Table 8).

Hunters and food gatherers show the lowest rate, populations far removed from hunting and food gathering the highest; intermediate are the groups still directly dependent on agriculture and also those directly descended from hunters and gatherers. The numbers of the colour blind (m) would

Table 8. Rates of colour blindness in different groups (from Post)

A. Hunters and gatherers	0·02
B. Economies somewhat removed from A	0·033
C. Economies most removed from A	0·051

tend to increase by recurrent mutations if the screening action of natural selection (s) against them was relaxed.

The allelic system of today represents the outcome of selection acting over long periods, in favour of or against mutations which have appeared repeatedly in the human gene complex. In view of the time span of hominid evolution, entirely new advantageous mutations which will be incorporated in the gene complex must be very few. The vast majority of mutations as they continue to recur will be cases of familiar type. As selection pressures change the equilibrium values of mutant genes will change accordingly. The major type of genetic change still going on will be in the shifting of gene ratios of existing allelic or polygene systems.

(ii) *Selection of alleles*

Not only the new genes produced by mutation, but those introduced by hybridisation will come under scrutiny by natural selection leading to either acceptance or rejection. Moreover, the existing genotypes will display a corresponding change in fitness if an alteration in environment circumstances (e.g. in climate, or disease or nutrition) brings a change of selective forces into play. Some existing genotypes will now possess an enhanced fitness (or adaptive response) and others less. One result will be to change the frequency of the alleles so that the proportion of individuals with qualitatively different features (and falling into distinctive categories) will change.

These results follow from the basic equation that two alleles, say A_m and A_n, are reproduced according to their relative fitness ($f = 1 - s$) in each generation in the ratio $\frac{A_m}{A_n} = k(1 - s)$.

Selection even as slight as $s = 0.01$ or $s = 0.001$ can act effectively to shift existing allelic ratios from one extreme to another and thus lead to the predominance of previously rare genotypes. Thus for s = 0.01 very large alterations in gene frequency will take place over a period even of 500 generations. Even with selection as small as s = 0.001 in a period of 5 to 8,000 generations large changes will occur (Fig. 47). Where the less common gene is already present at a frequency which is not too low a marked change in allelic ratio will be achieved in periods of 1,000 generations or so.

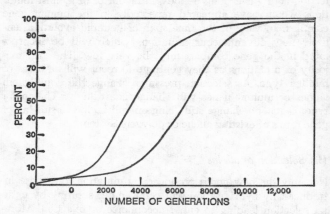

47 Change in gene frequencies under natural selection

In the modern species of man different populations, whether they are hunters or agriculturalists, urban or industrialised, possess alleles (of a given system) in very different frequencies. This means that the genotypes to which allelic pairs give rise are also present in different proportions. The table illustrates the values for a few selected populations of some of the extensive differences found in a number of gene systems. The systems illustrated here are 'polymorphic'. In these the character determined by any locus will exist in two or three forms, but even the rarest of these genotypes is in too high a frequency to be maintained by recurrent mutation. It can readily be shown that these polymorphisms can be maintained by a balance between opposed selective pres-

Table 9. Blood group (allelic and chromosome) frequencies (percentage to nearest whole number)

	ABO system			MNS system				Rhesus system						Duffy		P system	
	p	q	r	MS	Ms	NS	Ns	CDE	CDe	cDE	cDe	Cde cdE	cde	Fy^a	Fy^a+Fy^b	P_1^a	P_1^b
South African Bantu (from Mourant)	19	12	69	9	49	4	38	0	14	1	60	2	23	6	94	72	28
Nuer of Sudan (Roberts)	16	13	71	15	42	8	35	0	0	2	81	0	17	—	—	69	32
Hottentots (Zoudendyk, Mourant)	21	16	62	12	62	2	24	0	19	6	68	0	7	15	85	13	87
Xavante Indians (Brazil) (Saszano, Neeletal)	0	0	10	37	41	9	13	4	59	33	0	0	4	54	46	64	36
Carib Indians (Harvey, Mourant et al)	4	1	95	33	43	6	18	1	55	28	16	0	0	59	41	54	46
Eskimo (from Mourant)	25	2	73	19	62	0	19	3	73	22	2	0	0	75	25	18	82
Chinese (from Mourant)	20	24	56	4	57	1	38	0	71	18	3	0	8	90	10	15	85
Australian Aborigines (Simmonds et al and Mourant)	37	0	63	0	46	1	53	0	79	18	3	0	0	100	0	36	64
Micronesians (Simmonds et al)	20	10	70	0	14	0	86	0	49	47	4	0	0	100	0	55	45
Brahmins (Uttar Pradesh) (Tiwari and Bhasin)	25	20	55	31	30	8	31	3	51	12	9	4*	22	—	—	—	—
Afghanistans (Woood-Walker et al)	21	25	54	17	49	10	24	0	60	24	2	0	14	58	42	39	61
English (from Mourant)	25	5	70	25	28	8	39	0	41	16	1	2	40	43	57	49	51
Bedouin (Maranijian et al)	17	0	73	37	41	7	15	0	41	17	14	0	28	26	74	42	58

sures. A new balance between the polymorphic characters will follow if there is a change in the reproductive fitness of the genotypes concerned, that is, by a change in the balance of selective forces.

An illuminating example of a balanced polymorphism is that of the gene system governing the production of haemoglobin in the red cell. The 'normal' gene Hb^a produces in the homozygote Hb^aHb^a red cells carrying normal haemoglobin Hb–A. The allele (the sickle-cell gene) Hb^s produces in the homozygote Hb^sHb^s a cell deficient in haemoglobin Hb–A and containing the abnormal haemoglobin Hb–S. Homozygous individuals suffer from a haemolytic sickle-cell anaemia. The heterozygote Hb^aHb^s is healthy and the red cells look normal but can be shown to contain the abnormal haemoglobin. Sickle-cell anaemics generally die prematurely and, in tropical Africa where poor nutrition and various infections increase the difficulties of survival, the homozygote is virtually lethal. Each sickle-cell anaemic carries two Hb^s genes which are eliminated from the breeding population by his premature death. If this loss were not compensated the gene frequency would be expected to fall to fairly low levels in ten to twenty generations. Replacement of the lost genes by mutation would need an improbably high mutation-rate and the most likely mechanism is by heterosis. For this to be effective the heterozygotes (Hb^aHb^s) must be fitter in the Darwinian sense than either homozygote (Hb^sHb^s or Hb^aHb^a), that is, they must be more likely to pass on their genes to the next generation. Under these conditions we get a state of balanced polymorphism. The gene frequency reaches an equilibrium value which depends on the relative fitnesses of the three genotypes and this equilibrium is stable, tending to return to the same value if disturbed by some temporary change.

There is evidence that the sickle-cell trait does in fact confer some selective advantage in certain environments. There is a general consensus of opinion that the trait confers some degree of immunity to malaria and that this is particularly important in the first three years of life before other mechanisms become effective.

The geographical distribution of sickling is on the whole consistent with the malaria-selection hypothesis, since it is most frequent in areas in which malarial endemicity is high or was so until quite recently. In the absence of malaria we should expect the gene frequency to fall to low levels quite rapidly and this may be one reason for the relatively low values in many New World Negro populations, though intermixture with Europeans and American Indians complicates the picture.

It is likely that many human polymorphisms (such as those in Table 9) are maintained by heterozygote advantage, though the responsible selecting agencies have yet to be found.

(iii) *Polygenic characters and selection*

Much of the variation within and between populations of a species at any one time, or over the course of time, arises from bodily characters which differ only quantitively, i.e. in degree from one individual to another. Such characters display a continuous distribution within the population. The whole range of morphological features are of this kind—bodily shape and size, the dimensions of the skeleton, the amount of muscle and fat, the shape and size of facial and cranial features, variations of hair form, the intensity of skin and hair colour. These quantitative features present a characteristic distribution when assessed on samples representative of a population (Fig. 48) such that the most common values are clustered round the mean, with extreme values lowest in frequency. This 'normal' or 'gaussian' distribution is shown for skin colour for a number of populations in Fig. 48.

Not only is there continuity within any population, there is also overlap between different populations. The recurrence of features similar in shape and size amongst widespread populations within the human species is far greater than is usually realised. If a 'gaussian' curve is drawn for mankind as a whole in respect of some quantitative feature, using the most frequent values (i.e. the mean) for each population, the dispersion, large though it is, is not in fact as large as

REFLECTANCE: Filter 9. Upper arm

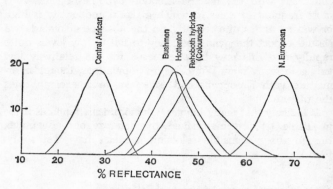

48 Skin-colour variation

that found within the different populations (Table 10). The between-populations variability (expressed as the standard deviation) is less than the within-populations variability for most characters both on the skeleton and the living; this is shown in the table for some 400 populations. This situation is not at all surprising in the light of the 'spectrum' differentiation of *Homo* throughout its evolution (Ch. 3).

Selection acts of course also on the complex of genes, the polygenes, which constitute the genotypes determining those continuously varying characters. As in the cases already considered—mutant genes, allelic ratios, polymorphic genes—selection may act on polygenes either to maintain an existing situation or if selectional forces alter, to shift the mean expression to a new value.

In 'stabilising' selection, the forces of selection favour the central expression of the character at the expense of the extremes. The mean value is thus the optimum expression and suffers the least action of selection; the action of selection is to narrow the range of expression. In each generation the genotypes produced by recombination and producing the extreme values are less fit and suffer elimination. Thus individuals grossly deviant from the mean or 'normal' will be

Table 10. To show the extent of inter-population variation compared with intra-population variation (from Tildsley)

Character	Inter-population mean (mm.) with numbers in brackets	Inter-population Standard Deviation (σ_{ie})	Mean Intra-population Standard Deviation (σ_{ie}) with number of groups in brackets	$\dfrac{(\sigma_{ir})}{(\sigma_{ie})}$
Breadth of nose	37·1 (370)	3·7	2·8 (217)	·774
Max. head breadth	150·4 (441)	5·4	5·209 (314)	·953
Sitting height	864·3 (266)	31·93	33·44 (129)	1·047
Nose height	53·4 (255)	3·367	3·818 (177)	1·134
Stature	1652 (573)	49·75+	58·87 (296)	1·183
Span	1740 (147)	59·85—	71·81 (102)	1·200
Head length	187·9 (478)	4·895+	6·323 (326)	1·292
Hand breadth	87·4 (65)	6·183	4·467 (41)	·722
Hand length	187·4 (71)	9·573	9·376 (42)	·961
Acromial breadth (shoulder width)	370·2 (94)	19·022	18·865 (80)	·992
Width of mouth	54·3 (82)	3·605	3·728 (34)	1·034
Breadth of ear	34·5+ (109)	2·181	2·661 (63)	1·220
Chest girth (at rest)	887·9 (76)	38·02	49·89 (39)	1·310
Arm length	742·5— (63)	25·12	32·90 (33)	1·311
Head girth	554·1 (97)	10·643	14·446 (56)	1·357
Ilio-cristal br. (hip width)	280·3 (71)	11·632	16·325+ (55)	1·415
Length of ear	62·3 (120)	3·094	4·428 (65)	1·431
Upper face height (to nasion)	71·9 (56)	3·275+	4·949 (51)	1·511
Breadth between inner corners of eyes	33·1 (104)	1·605—	2·665— (44)	1·650
Physiognomic face height	184·4 (101)	5·316	8·936 (46)	1·681

eliminated during development or reproductive life. For example, three-fifths of all early post-natal deaths can be regarded as resulting from selection for an optimum weight (Fig. 49), a selection effect calculated as nearly 0.03.

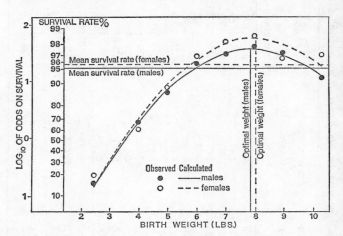

49 Optimum birth rate associated with lowest neo-natal mortality

In 'directional' selection, the optimum is located away from the existing mean expression and selection acts to shift it toward the new optimum—which in due course becomes the new, preferred, mean value. Directional selection is commonplace in experimental breeding, in the domestic breeding of plants and animals and in evolution. This shift is seen in many features in the fossil material, for example in the enlargement of the cranial capacity, the reduction in frontal and occipital cranial ridges, the shift upwards of the maximum cranial width, the narrowing of the angle of the basi-cranial axis, the appearance of the chin eminence and so on.

At each of the successive stages there exists a range of variation such that, by selection, a new optimum can be achieved.

In addition to these evolutionary successional trends, directional polygenic selection has often acted, within a species, as a major interpopulation or geographical differentiating force. The increase in average body weight and shortening of limbs relative to trunk (so far as they are genetically determined) associated with a change from hotter to cooler climates, the geographical gradients of skin and hair colour, the alteration in hair form from frizzy to curly, wavy and straight, are all expressions of directional selection.

We must, however, bear in mind that to some extent the phenotypic range of many multifactorial characters will be adjusted to particular circumstances as a result not of genetic change but of modification during the growth of the individual and by physiological responses. Acquired variation of this kind affects, for example, those characters susceptible to change by nutritional deficiencies. Moreover, shift in mean values between neighbouring populations can also occur as a result of recent hybridisation. The hybridisation, for example, between Europeans and Hottentots to produce the large 'Cape-coloured' population of south and southwest Africa is well illustrated by the intermediate skin colour of the off-spring, as shown for the Rehoboth people (Fig. 48). Thus in attempting to assess the genetic relationships of 'affinity' between human groups the factors of regional selection, of acquired modifications and of hybridisation have to be taken into account as well as the operation of random changes.

These considerations apply very clearly as we shall see when we try to assess the extent of the differentiation which marks off present-day isolated or semi-isolated groups, such as the 'fringe' populations of hunters, gatherers and simple agriculturalists, from their more numerous, more technologically advanced neighbours; or, to put this another way, in attempting to decide how far these latter populations are related to or descended from the still existing simpler groups in their vicinity.

(iv) *Chance differentiation*

We come finally to a number of processes which in the short run account for some of the interpopulation variation seen in the human polytypic species. These processes are particularly operative where populations comprise quite small bands or family groups such as those which characterised man throughout his hunter-gatherer period, isolated settlements, and religious, social, linguistic and other 'isolates' at the present time.

When the sample of germ cells or gametes from which the next generation is formed happens to be a small one, the proportions of the alleles it contains may not be at all representative of all the parents' gametes. The frequency of alleles may by chance deviate strikingly from the expected frequency. In successive samplings the deviations may be such that eventually only one type of allele may occur in the sample—of an allelic pair one gene may thus be lost and one fixed by chance.

Calculation of the change in the frequency of an allele as a result of genetic 'drift' shows that the effective breeding size of the community needs to be very small, even less than one hundred, for significant shifts to occur. 'Sampling error' may well have been of some importance in the past among very small hunting bands or agricultural isolates. Evidence for its operation has been adduced for Swiss alpine communities, Sicilian villages and religious groups such as the Hutterites. Unless there is a high degree of breeding isolation, genetic drift must be reckoned a minor differentiating force. For example, as one ascends the Chilean highlands, and the settlements become smaller and more isolated, the evidence points to the fact that only in the most inaccessible settlements would local evolution by random drift be operative (Cruz-Coke).

The interaction of genetic drift with natural selection is complex. In the short run, and in small populations, drift may conceivably allow an allele of negative selective value to be fixed, or an allele of positive selective value to be lost, before selection can operate. But selection will come into action since it is unlikely that the replacement of one allele by another will ever have a neutral effect on survival. Large variations in a gene system from one community to the next may mean that the selecting agent controlling the system is only intermittent in its action and drift may well be operative.

More important than genetic drift, there is in human history one situation in particular where 'chance' differentiation must often have played a major role in producing local variations in gene frequency and in the distributions of 'polygenic' characters. This is the 'founder' effect—the colonisation of a new territory by a small group of individuals not genetically representative of the original population. As a sample of the parental population such a migratory group may possess allelic frequencies quite different from those found in the parent group, indeed some genes may actually be absent or in such low frequency as to be easily lost. Unless mutation reintroduces these genes, all the descendants will also lack them and the gene complex will become adapted to their absence. A plausible illustration of this is the absence among American Indian communities of the gene for blood group B. It has been argued that the first migrant groups moving into and over the Bering Straits had the B gene either absent or in such low frequency that it suffered elimination by natural selection. The often surprising differences in frequency of blood groups and other traits between small subsistence farming groups, as in the Malayan jungle, groups which are clearly related in many other respects, may well be best explained as the outcome of the founder effect. The ABO blood groups of ten ethnic groups of Kivu Province, studied by Hiernaux, show a rather uneven distribution whereas in physical characters (e.g. in the body height to weight ratio) a clear relationship to the habitat appears. This situation is to be explained as the result of relatively recent common dispersion from a few biotopically distinct centres. The fact that of the present Tristan da Cunha population numbering under 300 four persons are homozygous for the gene of *retinitis pigmenatosa* is due simply to the chance that one of the original fifteen founding ancestors must have been heterozygous for this condition. The seventeen-fold increase in the population since then accounts for the present four homozygotes (eight allelomorphs) and the nine heterozygotes—the parents and children of those affected—a total of seventeen allelomorphs (Roberts).

The curious patchy distribution of many diseases may be accounted for in terms of the past history of migration. Berry offers such an explanation for the high frequency of multiple sclerosis in Shetland and in Orkney compared to the much lower rates in the Faroes and Iceland. His hypothesis is that the ancestors of the present population of Orkney and Shetland carried by chance more of the disease-producing genes than average, whereas the ancestors of the Faroe Islanders and the Icelanders were more typical of their Scandinavian ancestors and hence did not carry so many genes of this sort.

(v) *Hybridisation*

Hybridisation represents a means whereby genes already present in some populations within a species are introduced into other populations. The population structure of the human species throughout most of its history, that is until large breeding aggregates were established, has been that of small isolates existing discretely for long periods and giving rise to small breakaway units, living as virtually isolated demes. Nevertheless, if we may judge from the situation existing amongst Bushmen, indigenous Australians (Tisdale) and many other groups, hunting bands are genetically part of a continuous network maintained by well established and well recognised practices of clan exogamy. Isolation then means that the major gene flow is within a certain regional grouping, with barriers restricting gene exchanges with particular neighbouring groups, the number of matings falling off exponentially with distance. This situation has persisted till very recent times, as the well analysed examples in Sicily (Cavalli-Sforza), Hungary (Nemeskiri) and a rural Oxfordshire village (Harrison) illustrate.

Hybridisation brings about the substitution of a new and major inflow of genes into a hitherto partially closed breeding network. With the establishment of large human aggregates, the scale and the relative proportions of the mixing groups have varied within wide limits. The change in frequency of a gene (e.g. a blood group or haemoglobin variant gene), or a change in the mean and range of a polygenically determined character (e.g. skin-colour or body height), obviously depends on the number of immigrants,

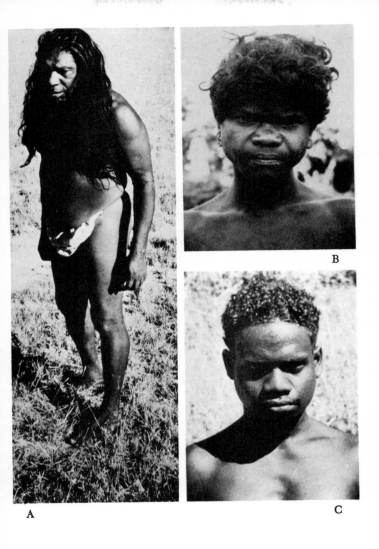

12 Populations still in the hunter-gatherer stage: (A) Vedda; (B) Paniyan; (C) Kadar

13 Philippine Negrito: Aeta of Luzon, Philippines

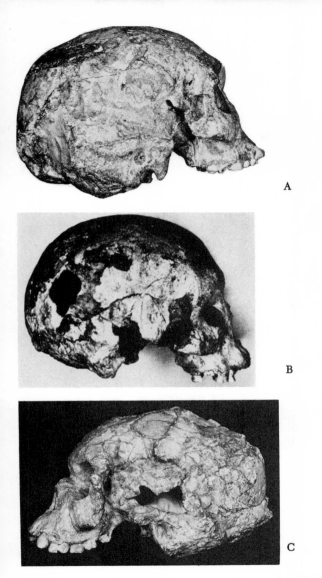

14 Fossil skulls from (A) Wadjak (Java); (B) Keilor (Australia); and (C) Talgai (Australia)

15 Implements of Australian aborigines

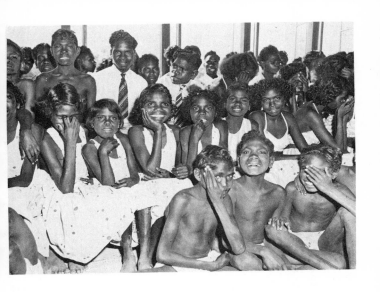

16 The physical characters of Australian aborigines: (above) school children at Millingimbie Mission in the Northern Territory; (below) Typical young adults of the Njalia tribe

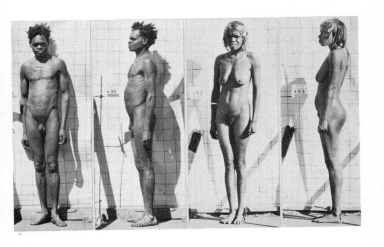

17 Present-day hunter-gatherers in Africa: (opposite) Congo pygmy; (above) Bushman mother and child

18 Circumpolar people today: (opposite) Alaskan Eskimo and
(above) Yakut hunter

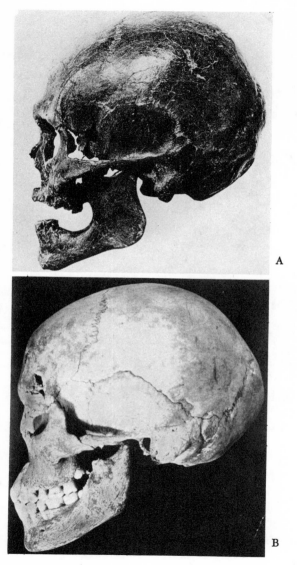

19 Fossil man in America: (A) Tepexman; (B) Minnesota

20 Dinka

21 Xavante Indians

22 Different types of body insulation among the Ama of Japan: (left) Hekura Island; (centre) Shima Peninsula; (right) Boso Peninsula

colonists or invaders, the frequency of the gene amongst them and the quantitative value of the multifactorial character each immigrant carries. When mixture is complete the calculation of the degree of admixture (m) can be made quite simply from a knowledge of the allele frequencies of the mixed population (q_3) and of the contributing parental populations (q_1 and q_2):

$$m = \frac{q_1 - q_2}{q_3 - q_2}.$$

Such calculations have been made for a number of contemporary populations where gene frequencies are known for all three groups involved. But two diverse populations brought together do not rapidly or necessarily become a panmictic (or Hardy-Weinberg) population. Barriers to gene flow are present in the form of religious, cultural, caste, economic and class barriers and many closed breeding groups persist long after migration, so that their links with their parental populations can be traced centuries after their original dispersion. The gypsies, for whom quite adequate genetic data exist, are well-known examples of this persistence. Physical anthropologists rely in principle on the diffusion and persistence of similar patterns of genetic and other traits in tracing affinities over large distances. Clearly many factors operate to modify and interfere with the maintenance of similar gene pools in dispersed populations derived from the same origins. As we have seen, mutations, chance effects, and hybridisation, interacting with natural selection as well as acquired variation, all serve to produce diversity though not with complete obliteration of the original relationships.

The biological consequences of admixture between populations may not be panmixis within a circumscribed area, but may take the form of interpenetration. Thus two genetically different populations will be geographically some distance apart; between them a series of interconnected populations may form to produce gradients in gene frequency known as 'genoclines', while the gradients in character variation so produced are 'phenoclines'.

Whenever a territorially contiguous series of communities

can be specified and compared in genetic terms there is a strong likelihood that clines of shorter or longer extent will be revealed. There is for example a B-gene frequency cline extending from Central Asia into North American Eskimo populations comparable to that running westward into Europe. Blood group gradients of increasing frequency of both A and B genes and a decrease in O can be traced along the southeastern regions of South Africa into the Cape Province and Namaqualand indicating a region of gene flow between Bantu and Hottentot. Haemoglobin C occurs along a gradient of decreasing intensity in West Africa. Altitudinal clines are also known, for example, in New Guinea there is a decreasing frequency of G6PDD (the genetic enzyme deficiency—glucose–6 phosphate dehydrogenase deficiency) with increasing height.

The interpretation of these clines can be very difficult, and they may in fact be the outcome of relatively recent hybridising gene flow. There is no doubt, however, that many clines are an expression of geographically determined differential selection, particularly so when genoclines and phenoclines for different characters do not run on parallel gradients.

The immediate consequences of mixing go beyond the production of hybridised individuals and the arithmetical changes of gene frequency or bodily dimensions. The changes in the genotype may affect the viability, development and fertility of the new crosses. Such effects are best understood by considering the genetic contrasts of inbreeding and outbreeding.

Inbreeding 'depression' is a phenomenon well recognized among plants and animals in which rarer homozygotes are deliberately allowed to accumulate, since homozygotes due to their natural rarity are less efficient and conform less closely to 'optimal' phenotypes. Among plants and animals that have suffered inbreeding depression, growth rate and adult body size are typically reduced, but when the parental homozygous strains are crossed, the hybrid offspring are more vigorous and grow faster than the inbred parents. Second generation hybrids between inbred lines are less vigorous than first generation hybrids because as a whole they are less heterozygous, but they are still more fit than their inbred parents.

How far this situation has relevance to man is by no means certain and indeed it may be applicable only to a very limited extent. Inbreeding effects have been looked for in many studies of close consanguineous matings. A few have been detected, such as a slightly greater prenatal mortality or a slightly smaller body size in the offspring. C.D. Darlington has in fact argued that people in longstanding isolates may have become adapted to some extent to homozygosity and suffer no obvious disadvantage from the inbreeding. Homozygosity due to inbreeding exposes a recessive gene with deleterious effects to more stringent selection, and even a small advantage of the heterozygote carrier might be inadequate to prevent its local extinction.

When hitherto separated groups hybridise the parental populations are in the vast majority of loci highly heterozygous already, even though the allelic combinations for some characters are different in the two lines. New heterozygotes are formed, but they do not necessarily confer greater fitness or vigour than the parental heterozygotes. There may be cases where the hybridisation results in the appearance of some new heterozygous genotypes replacing homozygous forms in one or both the parental strains. Thus in interracial crosses, as far as the evidence goes there is sometimes a heterotic effect, but as often it is merely a dominance effect. A most interesting case of a possible heterosis effect is the acceleration of growth and larger body size (the 'secular' trend) in modern communities over the last thirty to fifty years. This has been thought to be in part at least the results of the breakdown of isolates which is now going on rapidly and the increase in heterozygosity which follows.

Population control

Every community suffers a continual struggle for existence—an ecological struggle engendered by demands for food, by climate stress, by pathogens, by danger from predators or by accidents; the struggle is played out in biological terms as adaptive success or its lack, as preferential fitness or elimination, and is finally registered as the demographic experience of the community—of births and deaths, population size and density and composition; in fertility, growth and longevity.

Evidence from many animal communities, including primate bands, shows that natural populations tend to attain a viable density over a recognised territory without actual interterritorial conflict or warfare. This density is in fact a series of up and down fluctuations around an equilibrium value set by ecological circumstances and resources.

The movement and territorial range achieved by hunting-gathering groups during the terminal phase of the pleistocene period, culminating, as we have seen, in the penetration of vast new areas—North, Central and South America, the southeastern Asian archipelago, Australia and the circumpolar regions—indicate that the expansion of the *sapiens* species went on slowly and inexorably. To be sure, the densities attained remained uniformly low if we may judge from the meagre data on present-day surviving groups. A density higher than one-half square mile per head (two persons per square mile) was probably not often reached. For Britain in the Upper Palaeolithic a value of two hundred square miles per head of population has been estimated—comparable to that of Eskimos and Indians of the northwestern territories. The densities for present-day Australian aborigines is roughly twenty-five square miles per head. In the mesolithic densities were probably higher, about ten square miles per head, and amongst successful hunters such as the Indians of the pampas or British Columbia it reached roughly about one square mile per head.

So slow was the expansion of pre-agricultural populations, and so generally low the density, that it seems reasonable to suppose that the populations must have been subject to control forces. These enabled them to keep in approximate equilibrium with the local 'food-chain' whenever further migration and the splitting off of families or bands become impracticable owing to the occupancy of surrounding territories.

The existence of control forces must mean that pressure on resources, and hence the forces of natural selection (despite the countervailing processes of adaptation), were always at work.

For communities so exposed to the natural environment as primitive hunters and gatherers, multiple natural control processes would operate as they do in animal communities, with the addition of social measures of birth and death control. It is true we have little direct evidence of the way in which these different kinds of control actually operated to determine the population size, composition and longevity, of particular communities. There are, however, a number of pointers, apart from the indirect evidence drawn from animal population ecology. Of particular significance are the reported values for the total fertility, that is, the number of children per completed family. The most frequent figure of four children per mother for hunters and gatherers seems lower than that for advanced agriculturalists, with six or more. Of the four or five actually born in pre-agricultural families, only two or three actually reached maturity. The widespread occurrence of this small family size has been abundantly documented (Carr-Saunders). The family as a whole tended to be small since survival beyond forty years of age was rare. In keeping numbers down, there would appear to have been elimination at all stages in the numbers conceived and born, in the infant and childhood groups and in late maturity.

For the slowing down of the rate of reproduction a combination of biological and sociological factors would operate effectively in primitive society. The intervals between pregnancies are deliberately spread out by prolongation of the breast feeding period aided by restriction on intercourse. As the expectancy of life is short, often as little as twenty-five years, the woman's reproductive period is shortened, so also reducing fertility. A variety of diseases may act as additional causes of infertility, for example, hookworm, anaemia, and malaria. Another factor is genetic, arising from the increased frequency of consanguineous marriages in small inbreeding groups. Due to the increase in homozygosity, the risks of stillbirths and of abortion associated with congenital defect are sensibly increased. Finally, there are accounts of measures to induce abortion deliberately, of which the best known is the report that the Nevada Indians used the herb *Lithospermium ruderale* to prevent conception. How effective the extracts, which can be taken by mouth, really were remains unclear. The fact that claims for many antifertility 'bush-tea' preparations have been advanced by primitive peoples indicates a clear realisation of the necessity for population control.

Reduction in the numbers of those born is again the object of both unconscious and deliberate measures. Deliberate infanticide is known to have been practised regularly by communities of hunters in aboriginal America, Australia, Bering Straits and tribal India, and occasionally by many others. Yet for effective reduction of numbers in infancy the usual hazards of disease and malnutrition would ordinarily have been sufficient. Mortality at the weaning period, especially after prolonged and inadequate breast feeding, notoriously makes a major contribution to infantile elimination.

Infectious disease remains the overriding cause of high mortality at all ages; it operated to a much greater extent when man began to crowd into large permanent settlements with the attendant pollution of drinking water, poor sanitation, and easy cross infection between individuals or by insect and other vectors. But even in the pre-agricultural era, men were as susceptible as they are now to infections by viruses responsible for respiratory disorders, influenza, common cold and others; amongst modern hunters and collectors there is a world-wide distribution of identical viral antibodies from Pacific Islanders to Kalahari Bushmen. Because of the multiplicity of viral strains and their repeated modification, mortality would have been high whenever a new pathogen was encountered. The susceptibility of remote communities to diseases like measles, smallpox or tuberculosis, brought in by invaders, migrants or colonisers, has played a large part in the destruction of these societies.

In Africa infection from malaria would seem to have afflicted man from the earliest times. The association of plasmodia with both apes and monkeys makes it likely that man's plasmodia have an anthropoid source, but the exact relationships are still far from clear. This long association led to the establishment through natural selection of a number of haemoglobin variants which in the heterozygote, as we have noted, confer some resistance to malaria. Nevertheless the protection so afforded has been limited and at the present time malaria remains the major killing and debilitating disease.

In primitive society particularly high risks are run by the women during delivery. Under conditions of chronic food shortage, deficiencies of calcium, iron and vitamins will all affect the females especially during the vulnerable periods of puberty and pregnancy. This in turn will adversely affect reproductive performance.

While the composition of the hunters' diet is a very satisfactory one, it is by no means a secure one, whether he be fisherman, hunter, gatherer or all three. Sudden failures through drought, disease, or excessive exploitation of resources must have occurred often as a 'control' factor on population numbers, as we may judge from our knowledge of the fluctuation of food supplies of present day hunters.

The net result is that expectation of life throughout the hunter-gathering era was, and still is, very low. Estimates of the age of death have been made for human communities of the Upper Pleistocene and later prehistoric times by means of the stage of tooth eruption, the stage of ossification of the small wrist bones, the degree of union of the epiphyses, and the degree of closure of the cranial sutures. It is possible to group skeletal remains into four or five age-categories: childhood (0–12/13 years), youth or adolescence (12/13–21 years), adults (21–40 years), mature or middle-aged (40–59 years), and aged (60+). Approximate as these estimates are they show that for the most of the period of man's existence the age of death was very much earlier than it has become in recent times in conditions of Western civilisation. Survival beyond the age of forty was a lot of not more than about ten per cent of the population, and about half only lived beyond the age of twenty. According to Vallois, only one of some forty known neanderthal individuals passed the age of fifty; of some seventy-six upper palaeolithic *Homo sapiens* only two did so; of sixty-five mesolithic individuals also only two; amongst ninety-four Silesian neolithic skeletons, only four were over fifty years old. Mortality of this order seems characteristic of food-gathering, hunting and simple agricultural communities of recent and present times. For the

Indian Knoll people, a pre-agricultural tribe of the Indian settled community at Pecos, deaths before the age of twenty-one number fifty-seven per cent.

The demographic feature that stands out is the smallness of the family group, particularly the restriction on the number of children coming to maturity. It may be that the incessant need to transport essential household possessions by a man and wife in the nomadic condition of the hunting-gathering life makes it very difficult to carry or tend more than one very small child at any one time. That the groups can persist with reduced fertility may reflect the relatively more favourable living circumstances—less overcrowding, less pollution of living space, more balanced diet—as compared to the denser, more static way of life of later agriculturalists.

With a relatively simple and stable ecological situation, as in the case of hunters and gatherers, it might be expected that quantitative relationships between population density and some function of the environment would be discernible. A rough calculation, based only on energy balance, shows that a food collecting group is bound to occupy its territory at a density of the order of one head per square mile. (Assume that the individual has to move continuously every day in a yearly cycle over a piece of ground in the search for food, obtaining and expending say 1,600 Kcals per day. During active periods he might cover, say, eight miles per day at an average cost of 200 Kcals/mile/hr. If he 'explores' a yard width, this represents a coverage of $\frac{1}{220}$ square miles per day, i.e. a population density per food collector of $1\frac{1}{2}$ square miles a year.) In fact, food availability for the hunter collector varies very widely from place to place and season to season, and a simple relationship based on continuous slow exploitation of the environment is not likely to hold except in a very general way. Thus, coastal and riverline food collectors tend to be more numerous than inland groups. An overriding population determinant in arid habitats must be the water supply. In Australia, as Birdsell has shown, there is an overall correlation of $+0.8$ between mean annual rainfall and tribal population density, and he has found a simple equation which gives a relation of density to tribal area and to rainfall.

The rough calculation given above also indicates that if the 'extractive' ratio, i.e. ratio of energy needed for food production to energy used per day, is of the order of seventy-five per cent, the density of population will remain at the order of one per square mile. As the ratio falls, so will the density rise. It falls to about twenty-five per cent in simple agricultural communities and today is of the order of three per cent.

CHAPTER 5

THE LAST HUNTERS AND THE FIRST AGRICULTURALISTS

From Palaeolithic to Neolithic

The last 10,000 years of the Pleistocene, ending about 5,000 years BP, was marked both by a peripheral expansion and an inner contraction of the old stone age hunting life. It was an extraordinary episode in the ecological history of feral mankind. Some time before the recession of the northern ice-sheets, there began at the perimeter of the old hunting cultural area the slow but continuous infiltration across the Bering Straits into the New World, probably from 15,000 BP. An even earlier movement, probably 20,000 years BP, brought *Homo sapiens* right through southeast Asia and the Indonesian archipelago (Fig. 28) into Australia. This great outward spread of hunter-gatherers and fisher-hunter-gatherers continued for some thousands of years, ending with the colonisation of the whole American continent, Australia, Tasmania and into quite recent times, of New Zealand and the rest of Polynesia. As the ice-sheets receded the area of occupation by the hunting folk in the northern hemisphere moved northwards. With the ending of the Pleistocene, the palaeolithic cultures continued in the modified form known as the mesolithic stage. The hunter-gatherers of today may be regarded as mesolithic survivors who have undergone local modification.

In the central and older core of this vast hunting region the mesolithic culture quite soon, perhaps 10,000 years BP, began to be replaced permanently by the farming system. The farming culture of the neolithic phase in its turn gradually moved outwards, was taken up in peripheral areas and displaced the hunter societies more and more. But a remnant of the hunter-gatherer mode of existence continued to exist side by side with the Neolithic and the later metal-using cultures.

These last remnants of the pre-agricultural world provide us with the only direct information we can hope to obtain of the biology of hunter-gatherer populations exposed to the multiple hazards of the natural environment. The mesolithic state of culture was basically the continuation of the age-old hunting, fishing and gathering economy into post-Pleistocene times. The microlith, the characteristic tool-form of the Mesolithic, had many prototypes in the Upper Palaeolithic. In the Near East the Neolithic commenced within a few hundred centuries of the conventionally agreed termination of the Pleistocene—10,000 years BP—and in this area the mesolithic period was extremely short. In Britain, as in central and western Europe generally, the Mesolithic lasted from about 8,000 to about 5,000 years BP. The farming life began about 8,000 years BP in southeast Asia, and about the same time independently in Meso-America. It began about 5,000 years BP in east Africa; in southern Africa its start was delayed till near the Christian era.

It is now accepted that both in the Near East and in Meso-America the transition to a full agricultural economy was in fact protracted. There was no sudden Neolithic Revolution. Where the mesolithic way of life survived, elements of the Neolithic and later the Bronze and Iron Ages obtruded. In many parts of the world the hunter-fisher-gatherer economy went on at an essentially mesolithic level. This was (until very recently) true of the Australian aborigines, the Eskimo and Siberian circumpolar peoples, some tribes of New Guinea and South America, the Andaman islanders and southeast Asian Negritos, Kalahari Bushmen, Congo pygmies and of a few Bantu-speaking tribes of east Africa.

The development of the different cultural phases of mankind has been so uneven that in the mid-twentieth century world today every phase is still represented. In Europe, of course, the subsistence hunting or fishing life has been extinct since about 3–4,000 BP; but in Africa, Asia and America it persisted alongside both simple and advanced agriculturalists and in Australia until recently the Mesolithic was the only culture.

(i) *Europe*

In Europe the micro-environments exploited with success in mesolithic times were very diverse and included shore lines, lake margins, forest fringes and heathland. In detail the ecological adjustments achieved by some of the mesolithic societies are very impressive. The Maglemose culture, over the period from about 10,000 BP to 5,000 BP, prevailed in northern Europe all the way from Britain to the east Baltic. Some of the equipment—axes, adzes, chisels—was well designed for woodworking and treefelling and some for fishing and fowling (Fig. 50). The tools in bone and antler included small and large barbs for fish spears and fowling weapons. Wooden implements included arrow shafts and bows, picks and throwing sticks. Inventions of note were the paddle-rudders of wood, an ice-pick of bone, fish nets and fish traps. 'The extreme skill and thoroughness with which they exploited their difficult environment was worthy of the successors of the gifted upper palaeolithic societies' (Jacquetta Hawkes). The related and later development, the Ertebölle culture of Denmark and northern Germany, known from the large kitchen midden remains, shows the beginnings of contact with incoming neolithic peoples, for instance, the presence of pottery. In neighbouring regions of south Sweden, Denmark, Poland and north Germany lived other neolithic peoples exploiting the forests and using heavy reindeer antler axes and adzes. The people of this Lyngby culture made the earliest true handled axes.

Other achievements of this period were the domestication of the dog both in northern Europe and the Near East, and the construction of skin boats and dug out canoes. The mesolithic peoples in northwest Europe were able to make their settlements on coastlands now freed of ice and to travel large distances over newly flooded areas.

Poorer versions of the mesolithic culture developed on the north coasts of Spain and Portugal and the northeast coasts of Ireland.

These last European hunters and fishermen, as we know them from their scattered and sparse skeletal remains, dis-

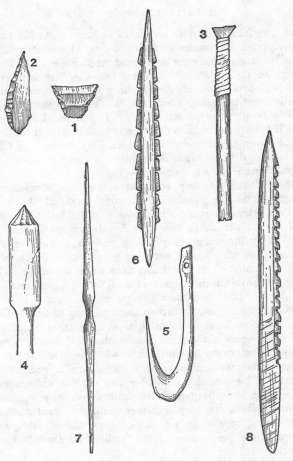

50 Some implements of the mesolithic cultures of Europe: (left to right, top) Azilian point, Mas d'Azil (Oakley, after Piette); Tardenoisian trapeze, Tardenois, Aisne (Oakley); bone fish spear with microlith barbs, Maglemosian, southern Sweden (Oakley); microlith hafted in wood with sinew binding, found in peat, Kitchen-midden culture, Denmark (Oakley); (bottom) blunt-ended wooden arrowhead for shooting birds and small game (Clark); elm-wood bow found in peat, Holmegaard, Denmark (Clark); bone fish hook, Maglemosian (Clark); bone leister prong, Maglemosian, from bed of the North Sea (Clark)

play a variability of skull and facial features quite like that of many population groups of the preceding Upper Palaeolithic. The late mesolithic peoples in eastern Europe as in Britain merge in their physical character into the first farmers. At this period of about 6,000 BP the people are usually more lightly built than their predecessors. The skull is less rugged and its range of shape more varied. The material is so sparse that it is only possible to describe it in this general way. One major group of thirty skulls is known from the cave of Ofnet, Bavaria, and these are quite similar to those of present-day populations in the Alpine regions (Plate 11).

It is difficult to say to what extent the Maglemosian-Lyngby-Ertebölle population complex provided the source for the later enlarged continental populations of neolithic and bronze age times and how far they were in fact supplanted by incoming groups. Both processes could have occurred. The adoption of neolithic practices by fisher folk is well documented; at the same time there are clear indications of physical movement of neolithic peoples from the Middle East into Southeast Europe and along and from the Mediterranean coast. In Britain the transition to the Neolithic resulted more from invasion than from cultural transformation on the part of the pre-agriculturalists. Of course in many areas the migratory neolithic folk who displaced the mesolithic natives were already of a rather similar genetic constitution. This would account for the relative uniformity of the modern gene frequency distribution over large regions of Europe. Where the map indicates marked discontinuities or even strong gradients, we cannot now tell whether these represent the persistence of the earliest hunter-folk turned farmers.

Nevertheless, despite the long history of invasion and migration, there remains in Europe clear evidence of strong autochthonous strata in some regions. The Basques, the Lapps and the Sardinians, and a number of smaller isolates, remain as relatively distinctive groups even though there are now also some genetic gradients extending into their neighbours and showing that isolation has not been complete. For example the finger-print patterns of French and Spanish Basques are very similar to those of their Spanish and Portuguese neighbours. In the rhesus and other blood group systems the Basques contrast markedly with their neighbours. The Basques are characterised by a high O gene and an unusually low B gene frequency, Rh-negative frequency is high (thirty per cent) with cDe frequency reaching fifty to sixty per cent.

This difference in the rhesus system is particularly important as indicative of a long period of separation of these populations enabling a different polymorphism for the rhesus system to build up. The phenomenon of Rh incompatibility means that selective forces are in operation to maintain the polymorphism at its distinctive level.

The hunters and food gatherers of mesolithic Europe disappeared gradually as the neolithic farming 'revolution' took its course, moving in from the Middle East over the period of 6,000 BP to 4,000 BP. Yet these last hunting peoples left a documentary record of the final phases of their lives in their cave art, which reflects not merely the daily activities, but 'the ideology and organisation of peoples dedicated to the hunting of large animals'. Pericot contends that the Spanish-French cave art (along with the archaeological and occupation remains) provides an unbroken record that runs from the Upper Palaeolithic to the Neolithic itself.

Apart from the magical, totemistic or initiatory significance of many of the scenes (whatever the real purpose of painting them may have been), the cave art illustrates a way of life in essentials similar to that of still existing simple communities as well as those of palaeolithic times.

The hunt was carried on either by individual hunters, by small groups or large groups surrounding the animals and driving them towards places from which they could not escape, like the cliffs near the rock shelters, or into stockades. The scenes of archers are very vivid. We see them in many positions, shooting at adult deer and their young in frescoes like those of Arana and Valltora. We have some of the most vivid scenes in the small groups, especially the hunt of the boar (Val del Charco, Gasulla) with its appearance of flying, reflecting the fine skill as hunters possessed by those men to whom it was a ques-

51 Rock paintings: (A) 'Goddess' of an agrarian cult? The horns
seem to be supporting a cornfield, Auanrhet, Tassili, north Africa
(after Lhote); (B) archers fighting, Morella la Vella, Castellon,
eastern Spain (Bandi, after Benitez); (C) harpooning fish,
Kenegha Poort, Griqualand East, South Africa (Willcox); (D)
Warriors with European axes, Oenpelli, northern Australia
(Mountford)

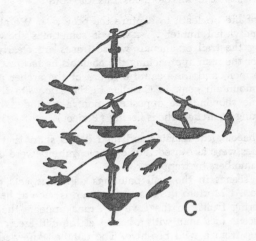

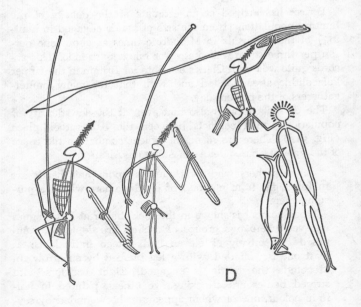

tion of life or death to capture the prey . . . We also see
the individual hunter . . . who is sometimes shown following the trail of animals whose traces are clearly seen
. . . or the man approaching the chamois he has just killed
in Tormon, and the beautiful figure of the archer aiming
at a mountain goat, in Gasulla. In the same site there is
a scene showing the opposite action, a wounded bovine
attacking an archer who is fleeing (Pericot).

The archaeological remains and food debris show that other
techniques were also used. For example, rabbits were caught
in large numbers by trapping.

Many scenes in the wall paintings depict aspects of the
daily life. At Mortero in Alocan a woman is seen at her task
of gathering fruits. In the cave at Arana appears the well-
known scene of a man with a basket at the cliff-face collecting honey from a wild bee-hive. The detailed knowledge of
their environment is indicated by the representation of insects, birds and plants.

Pericot has arrived at an estimate of the density of the
hunting population (from the size of bands engaged in hunting) of the Peninsula in Mesolithic times as about one person per three square kilometres or one square mile. This accords quite well with Clark's estimate for Britain in the Upper
Palaeolithic already cited and with that for many hunter-
gatherers of the present day.

The cave art records also that even at this low density of
population armed conflicts between the bands took place
(Fig. 51b). There are scenes of violent combat on the frieze
of the Val del Charco del Agua Anerga in Alcanez.

Seven archers who wear plumes upon their heads are
in full flight from a group of eight archers who are pursuing them.

Open combat is shown in the rock shelter at Les Dogues
in Aves where two groups of archers are deployed, composed respectively of eleven and sixteen individuals: at
least one is wounded, with a leg pierced by an arrow. In
Menetada the battle is engaged. Eight warriors with
striped bodies are attacking five others, painted in uniform colour, one of whom appears to be wounded by sev-

eral arrows. Lesser scenes of battle may be seen in Alpera and Alacon (Pericot).

Finally the rock art records the advent of the agriculturalist. In the cave of Letresor (Velez Blanu) is a painting of a masked man carrying a sickle in each hand.

(ii) Middle East and Asia

The mesolithic societies of supreme inportance for the history of mankind were those where the practices of agriculture—grain cultivation and animal herding—were first instituted. At a number of sites in the Middle East and Near East (western Asia) the first crucial steps in plant and animal domestication were taken at about 10,000 BP. Quite independently the same discoveries were made in Meso-America, but perhaps some 2,000 years later.

One of the best known of the Middle East groups who helped to inaugurate the new economy were the Natufians of Palestine. The archaeological remains testify clearly to their transition from the hunting and gathering to an agricultural economy and from a wandering to a settled existence.

The Natufians of Mt Carmel lived in rock shelters and on adjoining hillside terraces, subsisting mainly on the local game (gazelle particularly) and also by fishing; but they had begun to reap the wild emmer wheat; for this purpose, in their microlithic equipment they possessed flint sickle blades which show the 'corn-gloss' along their edges from cutting cereal grasses. They also used picks primarily for turning the soil and their cup-like stone mortars have been worn down by grain-grinding. They probably planted the grain, early strains of barley and wheat, with the help of a weighted digging stick. Hunting continued, as testified by food remains and by the arrowheads and crescents for tipping reed arrows.

The Natufian transitional culture extended into Egypt, Syria and Lebanon; its final stages are not readily separated from the earliest pre-pottery phase of the Neolithic such as the first permanent settlement at Jericho about 10,000 BP where a population of about 2,000 were housed in an area of ten acres.

The Natufians were physically no different from peoples living today in the area or in the Mediterranean generally. Their skeletons show they were lightly built, of short to medium stature, with longish heads and narrow faces (Ferenbach). Then, as now, they were of less rugged build than their mesolithic contemporaries in Scandinavia, who were also like the present inhabitants, of heavier build than the first farmers of the Middle East (Broshe and Jorgensen). At a number of other sites in southwestern Asia, such as at Zarzi and Jarmo in Iraq, and Alikosh (Khuzistan) in Iran, the transition from hunting to domestication of animals and plants has also been identified. No doubt the pre-agricultural peoples of these localities were representative of hunting bands over the whole area between the Mediterranean to the west, the Caspian Sea to the east and the Persian Gulf to the south. Here their main food sources were onagers and gazelle on the plains and flat-bottomed valleys, sheep in the hills, goats on the craggy mountain ridges and cattle and deer in the forests (F. Hole). Noteworthy is the fact that the people at Alikosh in an area rich in diverse game could be settled into permanent villages; this seems to have been an immediate prelude to animal domestication.

Mesolithic remains extend into the central Asian region (Uzbekistan) and mesolithic industries have been traced in Inner and Outer Mongolia dating from about 8,000 BP. The most important site is at Ikherging, Inner Mongolia, but of the people themselves we know little.

In the dry lands of western and central Asia—Iran and Iraq and surrounding areas—the climatic conditions favoured the adoption of pastoralism, with greater or lesser degrees of nomadism. This mode of life is based on a flexible ecological balance between the grazing capacity of the land, the number of animals and of human beings. The regulation of this balance as it exists today has been elucidated for the Kurdish pastoralists (Barth).

As in Europe, nowhere in this region have any subsistence hunter groups survived to the present time, but in the Indian peninsula and in southeast Asia survivals of these early pre-agricultural stages are still to be found.

In India, while the beginnings of the Mesolithic are ill-defined, the final phases lasted till about 4,000 BP when the first settlements were made. The microlithic flint tools, many of which recall the Tardenoisian Mesolithic of Europe (Fig. 50) continued to be manufactured not merely in the Neolithic but well into historical times (J. Hawkes). The persistence of essentially Mesolithic modes of life, with evidence of its earlier profusion and variety, is an outstanding feature of central and southern India and Ceylon. There are still communities in the remoter parts of central India and of the northern, western and eastern Ghats who continue their dependence on hunting and gathering. Favourable to this have been the extensive forests and jungle which have provided a refuge for these groups.

In the Late Stone Age of India the hunter gatherers were very widespread; very many caves and rock shelters were inhabited in western central India. The tools and weapons were often of the finest workmanship; factory sites yielding waste material and tools in great abundance are known. Small parallel-sided blades are commonest and were used as knives and spokeshaves. In general, a wide range of tools including points and barbs, arrowheads and scrapers were made and a variety of materials, depending on local resources, were used—flint, quartz, quartzite and even semi-precious stones. In western central India the caves contain many well-executed paintings or drawings depicting herds of deer or antelope, and scenes of hunting and dancing.

When one considers the paintings in their context of numerous inhabited caves and rock shelters, with the extremely fine stone industry these contain, and the vast factory sites where the same industry is found, one can hardly escape the conclusion that western central India was a Late Stone Age paradise; a paradise inhabited by people who spent their time hunting, dancing and making tools and weapons of great delicacy from semi-precious stones (Allchin).

The Late Stone Age remains in caves in Ceylon offer many

parallels to those of 'mesolithic' India. The caves have yielded much occupation debris—hearths and charcoal, tools of bone and antler as well as stone. Larger implements, such as stone hammers and pounders, are present along with plentiful finely worked microliths. These very caves were known to have been occupied a century ago by bands of Veddas, who were then still hunting over large tracts in the southeast of Ceylon.

This continued occupation of the caves by food-collectors and hunters raises the question whether the modern Veddas are the direct descendants of the Late Stone Age population. The same question may properly be asked about the still existing hunter-gatherers of India. Numbered nowadays among the 'scheduled tribes', they live by collecting edible roots, tubers and honey and by trapping birds and small animals. Some of the aboriginal tribes are now only partially following this way of life and would seem to have taken up a simple horticulture comparatively recently. In this region south of the Krishna River, in the Nollaimullais Hills (Andra Pradesh) are to be found the Chenchus and Yenadis; in Kerala live the Irulas (Tamilnar), the Malapantaram (Travancore), Paliyar of Madurai District and the Kurumba, and well-sheltered in the forests the Kadars (Cochin) and Kanikkaras.

It is regrettable that so little is known biologically of these present-day Indian and Ceylonese groups (Plate 12) with their strong links with the palaeolithic past. A knowledge of their genetic constitution would surely illuminate the natural history not only of this region but of the whole area of southeast Asia, whose aboriginal populations still bear traces indicative of some general affinity. Yet, as these are small subsistence groups, endogamous to a high degree, exposed to tropical climates, to the ravages of malaria, of smallpox and other endemic diseases, one would expect them to display clear evidence of the operation of the selective and other agencies concerned in both genetic differentiation and in adaptation. A proper biological analysis would illuminate these issues and it is no substitute merely to attach to the various groups the typological tags of 'Negrito', 'partially Australoid' or 'largely Caucasoid'.

The Veddas of Ceylon have come under genetic scrutiny

more than any other of these aboriginal groups; such comparisons as can be made between them and the south Indian populations enable some important if tentative conclusions to be drawn.

The Veddas are genetically and phenotypically very largely (but not absolutely) distinct from later arrivals on the island, the Sinhalese and Tamils. On the basis of external appearance they are considered to be related to the 'Veddid' or 'Australoid' groups such as the Chenchu, Paniyan and Irulas. In simple descriptive terms they are all of small build, dark skin colour and broad-nosed. These characters mark their long adaptation to hot climates and also their resemblance to other aboriginal groups of southeast Asia. The genetic markers indicate, however, that enough time has elapsed to allow local divergence. This is of a relatively small degree amongst the Vedda communities themselves and probably are attributable to 'founder' effects. But diversity through natural selection has very probably also been at work. The very low frequency of the A genes (A_1 and A_2) combined with a rather high frequency of B is a striking feature of the blood groups of the Veddas and one in which they differ considerably from the Tamils and Sinhalese. In this they differ also from the Indian 'Veddoids'. The aboriginal Veddas probably had even less, perhaps no, A genes. It has been suggested that natural selection against smallpox may have lowered the A gene frequency (Vogel).

The Veddas are different from their present-day neighbours, but similar to the Chenchu, Pallar and other south Indian tribes, in their gamma globulin and transferrin gene pattern, and in their MNS and rhesus gene frequencies. In the latter respect, however, the Irulas diverge markedly from the Veddas. The Irulas are also divergent in possessing the lowest known frequency of the haptoglobin Hp^1 allele. Haemoglobin E is very common amongst the Veddas, as it is in their neighbours the Sinhalese and in southeast Asia generally, but it is virtually absent in south India. This is clear evidence that the modern Veddas have not escaped genetic admixture from their neighbours; it also indicates that the gene must confer some degree of 'fitness' in view of its spread and multiplication. In India haemoglobin S (sickle-cell haemoglobin) is common in many of the aboriginal tribes. Amongst the Paniyans and Irulas the frequency of the gene reaches nearly twenty per cent, and thirty per cent of people possess sickle cells. The likely explanation here, as elsewhere, is the resistance that the sickle trait confers against endemic malignant tertian malaria.

Despite the insufficiency of basic data, the picture of regional differentiation during a period such as the late mesolithic seems fairly clear. It conforms to a theme so recurrent as to constitute a universal human micro-evolutionary pattern. Superimposed on a basic similarity, dispersed subsistence groups undergo a variety of divergent changes affecting different characters, as a result of natural selection and other influences. In some of these characters local gradients will be set up through remixing; in other instances distance and other barriers introduce and maintain discontinuities. Then, with the ultimate arrival of migrants or invaders in comparatively large numbers, usually technologically more advanced and frequently urbanised in culture, further alteration in genetic constitution through hybridisation occurs. This combination of biological and historical events thus generates much heterogeneity and regional modification of pre-existing stocks. When we look at the living groups, feral or settled, in relation to these mesolithic remains we can see the results of the usual major agencies of local diversification—historical, through movement and mixing, biological through selection and adaptation. It is only in the living persons that we can establish the network of diversity as specified more precisely by differences in genetic frequencies, range of skin colour, hair form, eye and nose shape.

Over southeast Asia, Malaya, Indonesia, New Guinea, Flores, and the Philippines, this is the pattern which emerges from the archaeological evidence of the mesolithic period taken in conjunction with our knowledge of still existing hunter-gatherer groups.

Archaeological sites in some profusion are known, but actual remains of human beings are much less in evidence. It has proved very difficult to equate with confidence the mesolithic skeletal remains to the population groups of today. The same difficulties of interpretation recur in east Africa, south

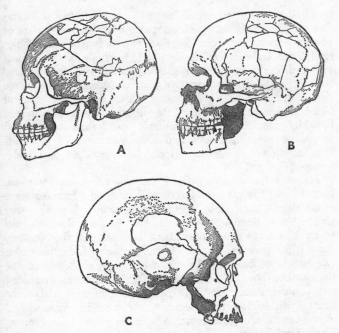

52 Mesolithic hunter-gatherers from Indonesia and New Guinea (from Jacob): (A) Liang Foge; (B) Liang Momer; (C) Papua

Africa, in China and western Europe. Mesolithic material has been designated variously as 'Melanesian' (in Malaya and Flores), or 'Negrito' (in Flores), or 'Australoid' (in Tonkin), or 'Veddoid' (in Celebes), or 'Papuan-Melanesian' (in East Java). The significant point is surely the recognition over this vast region of a substratum of populations, related to the older Wadjak variety, showing a complex differentiation of a range comparable to that recognisable today.

The mesolithic site of Gua Kepah, near Penang, consists of great mounds of the shells of edible cockles. Within the middens are grinding and pounding stones, stone axes, microliths and human skeletal remains. It has been calculated (Jacob) that the sites were occupied for rather less than one hundred years by a mesolithic group of twenty-five to thirty-five people subsisting on an adequate diet. The men were of stature between 163 cm. to 169 cm. and females about 153 cm.; there are some relatively old individuals in the burials and the longevity of about thirty years is probably greater than is usual among primitive groups (Jacob). The coarse diet is reflected in the extensive dental wear. The general belief is that these coastal Malay hunter-fishermen represent basically the 'Australo-melanesian' stock, then widespread throughout southeast Asia and the forerunners of the varieties nowadays designated as negrito, australoid and melanesian (Fig. 52).

A most interesting group of Mesolithic specimens are those from Flores; they illustrate very well how some features seem to be 'negrito' and some 'australo-melanesian'. Thus the very short stature, prognathism, gracile limb bones and some other features of a specimen from Liang Toge suggest the Negrito; there is, however, an absence of the pedomorphic appearance (i.e. a lack of frontal and parietal bulging), no depression of the nasal bridge and the shape of orbit, nasal orifice and skull and other features are more reminiscent of Melanesians or Australoids. In fact this specimen is not really pygmoid but of a short stature quite common in many present-day groups. The material from the other caves may be interpreted in the same way but local differences are always in evidence.

In some of the mesolithic remains observers have insisted on the presence of an admixture of 'mongoloid' elements (largely on the basis of certain dental features). The Mesolithic in this region is in many places penetrated by neolithic elements; the coming of cultivators in relatively great numbers and genetically quite distinct from long-established hunter aborigines is only to be expected.

How then can we interpret the evolutionary history of groups 'classified' in Malaya as Negrito, Senoi and aboriginal Malay, in New Guinea as Papuan-Negrito and Australo-Melanesian, and what are the relations of the various negrito or veddoid hunter groups to one another and to the cultivators? These groups have much in common with their mesolithic hunter forebears. They are in general short-statured, of light body build and broad-nosed. They are all dark skinned.

These features must be regarded as indicating their long adaptation to hot climates and the successful spread of related groups over a wide area, mostly jungle but also along coast lines. But there is some variability in the expression of these characters and there is clear evidence of divergence in many other features. Hair form has been taken to be a distinguishing feature of some significance; but as between the Negritos of north Malaya and the Senoi (the Semai and Temer) to the immediate south and west, there is in fact a gradation in hair form (cf. Polunin). About twenty-five per cent of the Negritos are reported as having 'frizzy' hair, the majority, about seventy per cent, as having curls (loose or deep) and a few have straight hair. This, as well as the skin colour, broad nose and short stature, is indicative of some affiliation with the Senoi, who are demarcated sharply by their much more settled mode of existence. Amongst the Senoi the hair is said never to be frizzy, but wavy (seventy-three per cent) and straight. Whilst they are similar in some genetic respects (e.g. the MNS, Lutheran, secretor systems, absence of Diego factor), the affiliation must be judged as quite a distant one. Amongst the Senoi the B gene is quite common, the R_0 chromosome absent, whereas amongst Negritos the A gene is frequent, B low and R_0 present in twenty-seven per cent.

Superimposed on a general morphological similarity there is clearly a complex pattern of divergence amongst the present-day hunter-gatherers of India, Ceylon, Malaya, Melanesia and Australia and the first and still surviving simple cultivators, Veddids, Senoi and others. With more information we should probably find within the undoubted local diversity a series of affiliated sub-groupings. Thus the R_0 chromosome is absent in the south Indians—Chenchu, Kannikan, Irulas and Pallars as well as Veddas. It is absent in some but not all Melanesian or Australian groups. The affiliation between Melanesians and Australians is revealed by their possession of N gene in greater frequency than M gene (seventy-five per cent vs twenty-five per cent) whereas the reverse is true for Malayan Negritos. Melanesians and Australians also have in common the Gc allele called Gc Aborigine. In New Guinea this mutant has been found in both highland and lowland groups.

Related to the Semang (Malacca) and the Aeta (Philippines, Plate 13) the Andamanese and Nicobarese represent the survivors of a network of peoples and cultures widely diffused by ocean-going canoes like those of the Onges (Cipriani).

Like the Aeta and Semang, the Onges possess a variety of food-getting and hunting implements. These include a digging stick and a hatchet for gathering edible roots and tubers, but the main weapons are the palaeolithic throwing stick, and the hunting and fishing arrows shot from a well-made bow. The wild boar is hunted and secured by the arrow harpoon and despatched with a spear. The introduction of dogs about a hundred years ago has much increased their hunting efficacy. For fishing there is a fishing arrow or harpoon as well as nets. The canoes from which these harpoons are used are identical with those in Oceania and even north Queensland. The art of fire-making was unknown; burning logs were carried about on their journeys.

The Andaman Islanders, like the Semang or Aeta in their jungle homes, appear as highly self-sufficient communities, and very ready to defend their territory from outsiders. But amongst themselves Cipriani never saw any disputes over territory or hunting rights; the three peoples—the Onges, Jarawas and Sentinellese—possess a similar language but isolation has made pronunciation sufficiently different to render communication between them difficult if not impossible. Nevertheless these peoples have been subject to outside influences from time to time. Their use of nets, pottery and dogs are the result of such contacts.

The exploitation of their environment by the Andamanese is impressive. In their continual search for food the Onges have acquired a detailed botanical and zoological knowledge, not only of food sources but also of material for basket making, and for temporary and permanent shelters.

Of their genetic constitution we possess very inadequate information. The Onges certainly resemble the Malayan Semang in their relatively high A gene and low B gene frequency; but the Nicobarese possess a fairly high B gene frequency. This and some physical features appear to justify the belief that they are now a rather mixed group, the original 'negrito' element overlaid by 'mongoloid' infiltration.

In the Indo-Malaysian-Melanesian region, where the aborigine hunter groups like their mesolithic counterparts are short-statured, the question of the existence of a widespread 'pygmy' race has been a long-standing issue. Of course when Aeta or Semang, Papuan, Onges or Darwin aborigines are compared with European, East African or many other populations the disparity in stature is obvious enough. But to use this as evidence of a world-wide pygmy race is to fall into crude typological error. The fact is that all 'pygmy' groups represent local modifications in physique and other characters in relation to their immediate neighbours. In stature the 'pygmy' groups reach the lower levels of the ranges of the peoples nearby. Thus in many Indonesian populations the height is below 140 cm. and as low as 135 cm. (e.g. Nias). More important is the finding that blood group frequencies are in the main similar to those of neighbouring groups. This is the case in Papua as in the Congo, or in the Kalahari. Adaptation to particular habitats under the influence of isolation and natural selection, apart from random effects, is clearly the key to an understanding of this local modification which may take the form of 'pygmisation'.

(iii) *Australia and Tasmania*

When and how the first human inhabitants of Australia crossed from the islands in the north remain unsettled questions. If it took place before the end of the Pleistocene, 15 to 20,000 years BP, the crossing could have been made over dry land from Indonesia. Human occupancy of this dating is claimed on archaeological, but not osteological, evidence from the site at Kenniff near Charlesville in Queensland. Not all Australian anthropologists subscribe to this conclusion, for the oldest dated material definitely associated with human remains is only 10,000 years BP by radiocarbon dating, the next oldest 8,000 years. Unfortunately the dating of the Talgai and Keilor skulls, probably the two earliest so far discovered, is uncertain. Abbie believes that the crossing was not achieved till after the ending of the Ice Age and therefore was made as a sea-voyage from western Indonesia, perhaps Java, in the direct route of the northwest monsoon, to a landing on the northwest corner of Australia.

Links between the earlier populations of Indonesia and Australia are provided by the Javanese solo and Wadjak specimens, which certainly resemble present-day aboriginal skulls. The similarity of Wadjak to the Keilor skull (Plate 14) is evident. The oldest Australian specimens (Talgai, Keilor, Mossgiel, Cohuna, Tartanga) and Aitape (New Guinea) have much in common. They are described as massive and rugged to a degree which is still found in modern specimens. At the same time the variability is such that both primitive and modern traits co-exist. Talgai and Mossgiel possess nuchal bones nearly as prominent as those of Solo man, but in Keilor and Cohuna they are not so pronounced; flattening or retreat of the frontal bone in Cohuna, Talgai and Mossgiel contrasts with the roundedness of Keilor and Tartanga (and Wadjak also). Talgai shows a marked prognathism, the others are orthognathic. MacIntosh sums up 'the mark of ancient Java is on all of them, but that can be seen in modern aboriginal crania too . . .'

The peopling of Australia (and Tasmania) from the north presents very much the same kind of problem as that of the New World from Asia. Here also there are two schools of thought. One sees the present aborigines as the product of several distinct waves of migration by quite small bands; in the other view the total occupation was based on a single small breeding group, probably of a relatively recent arrival date, producing a continent-wide homogeneity despite the subsequent isolation of tribal breeding units and an exposure to a wide range of contrasting environments.

The debate centres on the interpretation of the diversity displayed both by the skeletal remains and by the modern aboriginal populations. Is it the result of the hybridisation, in various proportions, of three different stocks coming in at different times? Or is it the outcome of the usual agencies of local differentiation, random genotype sampling and selection acting on a single expanding ancestral group?

The archaeological evidence supports the general biological picture of Australian origins from the islands to the north, the links still visible despite a wide area of diffusion over the continent, and extending probably into Tasmania. At the same time there were regional and local developments in technology in response to the diversity of habitats and the sparseness of occupation over so large a territory (Plate 15).

The first Australians brought with them a hunting, gathering and fishing economy (including the domesticated dog) similar to that prevailing at the very end of Palaeolithic of the Old World. The archaeological record of the first stages remains unclear, but it seems that a culture quite comparable to the Mesolithic, with microlithic industries as a notable ingredient, came in to overlay the older palaeolithic industries of large chopping tools, hammerstones and uniface worked pebbles. These early phases possess some clear affinities with Tasmania (Cooper).

Between about 5,000 and 6,000 BP, small finely worked artefacts became widely distributed and persistent. In many areas these were typical microliths used probably for tipping and barbing spears (but not arrows, since the bow seems never to have existed in Australia). The microliths provide definite links with extra-Australian cultures, in Indonesia and further north.

Also at about this time a distinctive item, the superbly shaped and trimmed leaf-shaped, uniface point (the *pirri*), was brought to a high degree of perfection specially in southern Australia; this too has affinities with the uniface points of Indonesia. Although the pirri persisted for many thousands of years, the quality of craftsmanship was not sustained. It continued in use as a functional spearhead into modern times.

Another implement dating from about 6,000 BP and a notable invention of the aborigines themselves was the adze-stone (stone chisel or 'tula'). The artefact was fixed in resin on a strong wooden holder. It was well suited both for rough shaping or hollowing (by a two-handed chopping motion) and for delicate woodworking, engraving and shaping. This tool found widespread use and similar artefacts occur in Tasmania. Yet another wood engraving burin-like tool was made by mounting the incisor of a 'possum, wallaby or kangaroo, in gum on a wooden holder or spear-thrower. This device was widely employed; in some areas, notably in central Australia, both the tula and the 'possum's incisor were in use. The 'possum incisor performed the services of the European burin. It was the tool for incising patterns on stone (as well as wood), for example, the designs on stone jurunga.

A tool of great utility which also persisted into modern times is the hafted edge-ground axe.

> With its help (the aboriginal) ascends trees; . . . cuts open limbs of trees to get opossums out of the hollows; . . . to take out honey or grubs or the eggs of insects; cuts off sheets of bark for his mia-mia or for canoes; cuts down trees and shapes the wood into shields or clubs or spears; cuts to pieces the larger animals of the chase . . . strikes off flakes for inserting in the heads of spears . . . (Brough Smyth 1878).

The development of this tool 'from a ground-edge uniface pebble, or from a pebble or lump of stone flaked to shape, to the pecked . . . and polished implement' . . . all form part of similar advances that took place progressively in Oceania (McCarthy 1966). This technique of grinding represents the closest approach to the 'Neolithic' in Australia. The date when it diffused into the continent has not been finally established.

Despite the cultural and palaeontological evidence of derivation from islands to the north, the exact affinities cannot be determined with finality at the present day. The homelands of the original Melanesian migrants have very largely been occupied by peoples different in many respects, so that the ancestral groups have become partially hybridised; and at the same time a marked degree of differentiation has overtaken the continent-wide occupants of Australia even if they originated from a single small immigrant band.

In a very general way the aborigines of today may be said to resemble physically the pre-Dravidians of India and their Ceylonese offshoots. The connection is supported by similarity of hair form, by palm and fingerprints (a high frequency of whorls) and a high frequency of hairy pinna, but the sero-genetic relationships are not particularly close. Amongst the south Indo-Ceylonese aboriginal collector groups and simple cultivators, the Veddas, Irulas, Yanadis, and Chenchu, the gene frequency of the blood group B is now high, as is usual throughout the whole of the Indian-southeast Asian region. It is also high amongst the Malayan Senoi, though it was once probably much lower, as indicated by the Paniyans, Kanikkars, Kurumbas, the Andaman and Semang Negritos as well as Melanesians generally. Since the B gene is practically absent in Australia, the aborigines have remained close to the Semang and Melanesians and close to the Semang in the Rh system and to the Melanesians in the M-N system—though the S allele is absent in Australia and reaches low values in New Guinea and Malaya. The very high N gene frequency and the Gc^{Ab} gene are common to Australia, New Guinea, Melanesia and Micronesia. In New Guinea selection for malarial resistance has evidently favoured the presence of haemoglobin variants and the gene for G6PD deficiency.

The irregular distribution of blood group genes in New Guinea today allows the possibility of the peopling of Australia from New Guinea by a group of migrants characterised by its own peculiar genetic make-up through chance selection. It is more difficult to believe that the 'founder' or other chance agencies operated on three different waves of immigrants so that each stock lacked at least A$_2$, B, S, rh, rh″, Fy^b, K, Lu^a—a strong argument (Simmonds) against the tri-hybrid theory of Birdsell.

The genetic distribution pattern of today in Australia is one of wide areas of genetic similarity or of gradients; but there are also some instances of sharp discontinuities between geographically close groups. While there is also an overriding general similarity of body, physique, facial form, hair form and other morphological traits, the extent of regional variation in these traits should not be underestimated. The combination of general similarity with local differentiation in some characters mirrors the pattern of cultural and technological adjustment to the continent as already described. The aboriginal languages too are split into a multiplicity of dialects while retaining an underlying similarity.

The morphology (Plate 16) of the indigenes is quite well known for most parts of Australia. The predominant physique is linear, with slender trunk, narrow shoulders and hips, long slender limbs, hands and feet. The head shape is mostly long. Relative to total height the trunk (sitting height) is shorter and the lower limbs longer than in Europeans. The range of physical type or somatotypes, as is the case universally among all pre-urbanised groups, is relatively small. The physique as a whole and its proportions are in their linearity quite in accordance with what one would expect (from the so-called Bergmann-Allen rules) for people derived from and living in a predominantly hot environment. There is in fact a detectable accentuation of the linearity and an increase in the height : weight ratio in the hotter areas. As among warm climate peoples generally the subcutaneous fat layer as measured by skinfold is thin and body hair sparse. Similar somatotypes could no doubt be easily found in other arid hot regions (e.g. Sudan) and in a minority in many other parts of the world. Such comparisons remain to be documented. Like active hunters and simple agriculturalists elsewhere (e.g. in east Africa or Amazonia), the muscularity especially of the shoulder girdle is well developed.

In one area, north Queensland, the average body size is significantly reduced but there is really nothing to support the view that these folk represent a 'pygmoid Tasmanoid' pocket; individuals of similar stature can be found in other groups, e.g. in central Australia. These so-called 'Barreans' of north Queensland in their blood group frequencies and in hair form and skin colour merge with the neighbouring rather taller people.

Throughout Australia the facial and cranial morphology, the broad cheek bones, broad noses, wide mouths (the lips are not particularly thick), pronounced brow-ridges, the straight to curly, but never woolly or frizzy, hair form—all these present a general homogeneity. Hair colour is generally dark brown to black, but there is much regional variation in the occurrence amongst children of blondness on the scalp and of the primary down on the trunk and limbs. Blondness reaches a high frequency in central Australia (Birdsell) and in general the hair colour darkens with age. The skin colour is by no means accurately known. The exposed skin areas are of course dark, but covered areas (the axillary area) are said by Abbie to be quite light. Yet Walsh's reflectance values for subjects in the Darwin region show the axillary skin colour to be darker than that of New Guinea natives and darker than that of Bushmen or Hottentots. The spectro-photometric method needs to be extensively used, in this as in so many other regions, if the true facts of human skin colour variation and its relation to ultra-violet intensity are to be properly established.

The aboriginals of today provide a picture of contrasting adaptive modes of life. Much of the land may well have been grass and tree-covered to a far greater extent when the first immigrants arrived; their occupancy extended and intensified the desert areas. With the arrival of Europeans many of the tribal groups were forced into these more inhospitable areas. From a population estimated at about 300,000, the full-blooded indigenes dwindled to some 40,000 persons (1960), distributed in a variety of habitats and living by a variety of economies. There are the fishing peoples on the coasts and river outlets, fishermen-hunters of the inland river systems, and hunter-collectors of forest and plain. Perhaps some 4,000 still live a nomadic existence on the arid steppes, the spinifex deserts of the interior and northwest, in the subtropical northern lands of Arnhem land and along the Gulf of Carpentaria. The remainder are mostly in mission stations, government settlements, sheep and cattle farms. In or near the towns there is now a large hybrid population, some the result of admixture with Europeans, others with people from the islands to the north. There are now large contrasts in genetic constitution, physique, development, nutritional standards, medical condition, in demography as well as in physiological adjustments to those varying ways of life.

Some few groups of the Australian indigene illustrate even nowadays the ability of man in a hunting-gathering economy to survive by reliance as much on his biological adaptability as on his technological equipment. The ecological challenge is as sharp as any that faced pre-neolithic man—an uncertain food supply demanding patient hunting and collecting, aided only by the dog and requiring a high degree of physical fitness; the menace of overpopulation; the great aridity; the extremes of environmental temperature—below freezing point in the night time during winter, over 100°F during daytime in the summer, with solar and strong ultra-violet radiation added.

In central Australia the requirements for nutrients and calories have to be met by an intimate knowledge of the food animals and plants, since nothing edible can be ignored. In the desert eighty per cent of the diet is made up of plant foods supplemented with lizards, snakes and rats. In other areas it may be predominantly fish with birds' eggs, edible plants, honey and insects. In some tribes moths may be eaten, or araucaria pine seeds as in the Binya Mountains. Small scale food preservation is practised, for example drying of fish or kangaroo meat. Food preparation includes roasting and baking. The sharing of food follows strict rules and has been amply documented. Unfortunately the quantitative analysis of the diet, of its fluctuation, its relation to energy requirements and population stability, has not been the subject of ecological study. But the overriding importance of water supply to group survival has been clearly established. Birdsell has demonstrated a quantitative relationship between the population size and density on the one hand and the annual rainfall on the other. The aborigines' detailed ecological knowledge includes minute description and identification both of food sources and water supplies. Indeed one test of manhood is the ability to give a complete recital of the location of all these supplies. The danger from loss of water by evaporation was well appreciated, and water holes were covered up with stones and slabs to shelter them against the sun.

While the carrying capacity in the arid regions is basically determined by the rainfall, the actual maintenance of the populations within an optimal limit would appear to require a number of social control measures. Until the era of white settlement a balance must have existed between population and resources (Strehlen). There were prohibitions on overusing water, regulations governing the killing of game, and indeed a strong emotional concern for the conservation of the animals and birds of the bush. Concomitant with environmental control there had to be reproductive controls since natural increase, despite high death rates would, here as elsewhere, have outrun available resources. Such controls included regulation of marriage dates and choices and the prohibition on intercourse at particular times. Infanticide undoubtedly was practised; lacking animals yielding milk, infants had to be breast fed till at least the age of two and in a dry season till as late as four years. There was thus an obvious limit on the number of small children who could be fed and carried about during the long wanderings in search of food and water.

Biological adaptation of central Australian aborigines is to be seen in their adjustments to extremes of cold and heat. Of the physical fitness of the aborigines as assessed by tests of working capacity, respiratory and cardiovascular function, not very much is known. 'At the time of the coming of the white man they appear to have been good physical specimens, with sound dentition and a remarkable freedom from disease' (Macpherson). Many today show themselves capable of extreme physical endurance. The rise of blood pressure or of blood cholesterol with age, so characteristic of urbanised communities, is much less marked in those groups where contact with Europeans has remained relatively slight. But dental deterioration is now widespread, though still not so serious as in urbanised Europeans.

Today the aboriginal population finds itself in a new peculiar ecological situation which is largely one of dependence on, rather than integration with, European civilisation. The effect of the new environmental and genetic situation is to bring about increasingly a whole series of biological changes to which Abbie has drawn attention; a rising immunity response to many imported diseases; a rise in mean blood pressure and with it of blood cholesterols and phospholipids; a change in the menstrual pattern towards a younger age of onset; a fading of skin pigment and some susceptibility to sunburn; obvious dental deterioration, and the possibility of preserving (under western medical care) undesirable genetic recessives and mutants in subsequent generations.

Unlike the Australians, the Tasmanian hunter-gatherers have failed to survive into the twentieth century. The extinction of the last remnant in the nineteenth century was recorded, but the first stages of the human occupation of Tasmania are shrouded in uncertainty as archaeological enquiry has so far been inadequate in technique and intensity. It seems likely (Macintosh and Barker) that a fifty miles wide land corridor from Wilson's promontory to northeast Tasmania existed before 12,000 years BP. As man may quite possibly have occupied Australia before 16,000 years BP, colonisation of Tasmania from an Australian source, followed by isolation by a rise of sea level, seems the best hypothesis. There remains the need to test this hypothesis on securely dated early material.

That the Tasmanians were allied to the Australian aborigines is evidenced by the craniological data, but there are a number of consistent differences (Macintosh and Barker). This evidence is not, however, sufficient to support alternative theories of Tasmanian origins, namely that they were quite separate from Australians (and were Oceanic, Asiatic, Negritos or Melanesians, or hybrids of these stocks with Australian. The probable existence of a land bridge points to the usual process of movement, spread and local differentiation, as across the Bering Straits or into Australia itself. The archaeological evidence seems quite clear. 'On the evidence of stone implements alone, it could be proposed that the Tasmanians arrived on their island from Victoria, at a time before the diffusion of edge-grinding ideas . . .' (Mulvaney). Subsequent reverse hybridisation of these people with Australian groups cannot be ruled out. Such hybridisation could of course have affected the genetic pool of some mainland aboriginals. Birdsell believes that the first Tasmanians and their contemporary Australian neighbours belonged to the same stock but the stock itself was quite different from later incoming groups, and both the extinct Tasmanians and the present south Australians underwent the same kind of hybridisation with the incoming negrito Murryan. But this theory, resting as it does on the peopling of Australia by a number of different strains, remains controversial.

Inexact descriptions of the physical appearance of the Tasmanians have given rise to conflicting theories as to their origins. In their dark skin colour, short stature and facial features they were apparently not distinct from their neighbours, the southern Australian aborigines. It is because the hair, in contrast to the straight or wavy hair of the aborigines, has variously been described as woolly or spiral that they have been accorded a negroid or 'negrito' ancestry; but the hair has also been described as curly. We have already seen that among Malay indigenes a range of hair form from straight to curly can be found. Indeed the so called pepper-corn hair of Africa when grown long becomes 'woolly'. One must take leave to doubt that this criterion of hair form should be used as ground for excluding the Tasmanians from the affinity which, on a number of counts, they bore to their northern neighbours.

Like the Australian aborigines, the Tasmanians possessed only rudimentary protection against cold and heat and in their near naked condition must have relied greatly on their biological adaptiveness.

All observers are impressed by the simplicity of the recent Tasmanian material culture. 'They lacked the skills of hafting and grinding and . . . therefore microlithic, pirrian and other mainland types were not produced . . . the boomerang, shield and spear-thrower were absent, their watercraft rudimentary . . . their flimsy encampments not even enlivened by the presence of the dingo' (Mulvaney). All this stands in contrast to the older industries, which included a variety of superbly finished microlithic and other implements.

The impoverishment of their material existence points to a vulnerability of the Tasmanians to the stresses of contact with the European, even greater than that of most Australian aboriginals. Their depopulation and final extinction was the outcome of disease, malnutrition and physical destruction. They rank with the 'classical' neanderthal hunting groups, most of whom were apparently destroyed rather than absorbed by peoples of different genetic make-up and cultural achievement.

(iv) *Africa*

Throughout Africa the mesolithic stage of hunting and gathering was successfully adapted to the demands of a great range of habitats, lake sides, open savannah, scrub, woodland, forests and inhospitable arid regions.

Beginning about 6–5,000 years BP, mesolithic cultures

gradually came into being throughout north, east, central, and south Africa. As in Europe and elsewhere, links with the final phases of the preceding Palaeolithic cultures can clearly be traced, though biological continuity rests on sparse skeletal remains. In north Africa the last phases of the post-glacial Oranian and the Caspian merge into true microlithic cultures. The skeletal remains of the people, the 'Mechta-type', who were responsible for the post-glacial cultures, are essentially similar to the modern Mediterranean.

The art (and the associated archaeology) preserved in caves on both sides of the Mediterranean, in the Sahara, in east, south and southwest Africa, carry the record of the vanishing palaeolithic and mesolithic life on from the pre-neolithic period to modern times. As in Spain the cave art records also the coming of agriculture. In the Tassili Saharan Neolithic, industries with pottery occur in rock shelters containing paintings of cattle scenes dated by radiocarbon to 8000 BP; in the later Bushman's art the paintings depict hunting and other activities comparable to the practice of the last surviving hunter-gatherers of the Kalahari desert and show also the coming of cattle-keepers.

The Hadza of Tanzania, the Congo pygmies, the Kalahari and Okavango Bushmen and the landless Bergdama of S.W. Africa (Plate 17) are the present-day reminders of the time, probably a mere 8 or 7,000 years ago, when all of Africa south of the Sahara was still peopled by a network of hunting and collecting peoples. The archaeological evidence is replete with remains of Hottentot and other negroid peoples at a pre-agricultural stage living alongside the encroaching pastoralists and horticulturalists.

From the sixth to the third millennium BC the material culture of the southern Sahara, from Mauritania in the west to the Nile at Khartoum, is that of a way of life based on hunting and fishing. The Makalian (first post-Pleistocene) wet phase enabled hunters and fishers to populate the Sahara to an extent greater than previously (or at the present time), by movement both from the Mediterranean littoral southwards and from the savannah of west and central Africa northwards. The presence of bone harpoons, fish-hooks, and bifacially worked stone projectile points 'implies a reasonably well-watered and bush-covered terrain very different from the desert conditions of today' (J. D. Clark) round the pans and river courses of such sites as Asselar, Tamaya, Mellet, Early Khartoum and several central Saharan sites. Here were the communities who were soon to adopt agricultural practices and who were to transmit their knowledge to the sub-Saharan populations when the post-Makalian dry phase enforced a movement southwards from the desert about 2500 BC.

The few known representatives of the late palaeolithic peoples, such as Asselar man, attest to their probable biological continuity into the mesolithic population of this Saharan and sub-Saharan region. Such continuity is clear in east Africa where, as in north Africa, the Kenya Capsian culture (and the Gamble's Cave people who practised it) gave way to a true microlithic culture—the Elmenteitan, practised by physically similar people.

Over central Africa and to the south, microlithic elements spread widely, largely in a number of cultures which still retained links with earlier stages. In central Africa the industries are clearly related to the major ecosystems; the true microlithic Wilton spread over the open parkland and scrub, the Smithfield (a non-microlithic culture) into dry river valleys, and a forest culture (Nachikufan) developed about 6,000 BP. In the latter the equipment included advanced arrow heads, polished axes and other woodworking equipment. Likewise in South Africa the less advanced Smithfield persisted alongside the Wilton. The latter began about 6,000 BP and continued to be practised by south African food-gathering cave-dwellers until relatively recent times. The earliest Smithfield was associated with proto-Bush skeletal remains at the Matjes River Caves of Cape Province. The related Wilton Keursboom people were living at the same site a thousand or so years later.

At the beginning of the present era the distribution pattern appears to have been that of mesolithic food-producing peoples spread over parts of the woodland savannah and peripheral forest zones of west and central Africa; these were negroid peoples akin to the present west African stock. The southern and the drier parts of eastern Africa carried stock-raising communities of diverse 'mesolithic' origins—as now, these were the so-called proto-Hamitic negroids with Mediterranean affinities. Further south some of the pastoralists would have belonged to the so-called Bush-Boskop stock, or more precisely they were ancestral Hottentots. The Bantu-speaking agriculturalists of southern and eastern Africa were later immigrants who, in their movements to the southeast absorbed a good deal of the pre-existing Hottentot communities, genetically, culturally and linguistically. But for a long time from the present era onwards, side by side with the Iron Age immigrants, autochthonous hunter-gatherers remained, some allied to west African negro stock (e.g. the Hadza of Tanzania), some becoming the distinctive forest pygmies, some of Bush-Boskop Khoisan-speaking lineage, differentiating as Bushmen hunter-gatherers. Amongst the latter some continued to speak Hottentot languages, others evolved their own Bushmen languages.

As living examples of environmental adaptation by hunters and gatherers in Africa the Kalahari Bushmen, the Congo pygmies (Plate 17) and the Hadza illustrate many of the factors involved in the survival of small groups. Like the last hunters, gatherers and fishers of the Indian subcontinent, southeast Asia and Australia, those of Africa are now to be found largely in fringe or refuge areas and islands. On modern genetic evidence, the relationship of the primitive survivals to the more advanced pastoralists and agriculturalists cannot be doubted and the claims of typologists of a high degree of subspeciation cannot be sustained. At the same time the African evidence illustrates how ecological differences can bring about important degrees of differentiation, for example in the populations of the Congo or the Kalahari.

The pygmy morphology is consistent with the hypothesis of the long-term action of selective forces linked with the wet equatorial forest (Hiernaux). Thus the stature, the nasal index, the facial index and cephalic index of the Mbuti pygmies are in clear contrast with those of peoples in the savannah and arid zones. All four characters vary concordantly with increasing humidity. In their ABO blood groups the Ituri pygmies stand out quite clearly from their neighbours in the dry areas (Tutsi), the savannah (Mutu) and forest fringes (Twe). In morphology the Jwa peoples are intermediate between pygmies and the Bantu and are sometimes called 'pygmoids' on this account. But their intermediate characters are more likely a reflection of the intermediate situation of their habitat, since in the ABO and MNS systems they differ from both Bantu and pygmies. Yet all these groups show their general negroid affiliation in the high prevalence of the R_0 chromosome, the Hp^1 allele, and the marked predominance of whorls over loops in the dermatoglyphics. The pygmy and the settled peoples alike show the selective influence of malaria on the maintenance of a high sickling percentage. The frequency of the Hb^s gene shows a correlation of -0.73 with altitude in the Kwanda-Burundi-Kivu areas (Livingstone) probably through differences in malarial infestation. Despite the elevation of Bushmen and Hottentots to members of a special human race (indeed subspecies) by Coon, the facts are perfectly clear. The affinities of the Khoisan peoples are undeniably with African groups generally as is evidenced by the high frequency of the R_0 chromosome, the ratio of A_1 to A_2, and the presence of Henshaw and other 'African' genes. The extent of the negroid affinities is shown in Table 11.

Bushmen and Hottentots are correctly grouped together as varieties of a modified negroid population that once occupied the major part of southern Africa. This conclusion is supported by the similarities of their language, and confirmed by resemblances in body physique, facial features, skin colour, and certain of the serological characters (Table 11).

The Hottentots diverged when they adopted a pastoral, cattle and goat-keeping economy little different from that practised by so many other African peoples further north from neolithic times onwards. The Bushmen remained as hunters and collectors. In due course through selective and other agencies they altered physically to some extent from the Hottentots, who meanwhile experienced in the eastern and southeastern region of South Africa close contact with and displacement by incoming Bantu-speaking pastoralists. The arrival of Europeans in the Cape displaced all the Khoisan-speakers to the northwest into Namaqualand and

Table 11.   Bush, Hottentot and Bantu Comparisons

Serological Characters

	Bush	Hottentot	Bantu
cDe% frequency	84	76	71–60
CDe frequency	14	17	7–14
cDE frequency	2	7	7–1
Cde frequency	0	0	3–2
cde (Rh-ve) frequency	0	0	13–23
M:N	60:40	73:27	58:42
S:s	S > s	S > s	S > s
SM:SN	SM > SN	SM > SN	SM > SN
V + % frequency	5	9	(5)
Js + frequency	5	7	(5)
Diego frequency	0	0	0
Hb-sickling	absent	absent	absent
A1:A2	$A_1 > A_2$	$A_1 > A_2$	$A_1 > A_2$
pA % frequency	20	27	15–25
qB % frequency	2	23	15–20
rO % frequency	78	50	70–55
$Hp^1:Hp^2$ frequency	0·29:0·71	0·51:0·49	0·53:0·47

Morphological Characters

	Bush	Hottentot	Bantu
Skin colour % reflectance (red filter)	45	45	35
Eye colour	dark	dark	dark
Hair colour	black	black	black
Hair form	coiled (tufted)	coiled (tufted) woolly	woolly
Body hair	very sparse	very sparse	sparse
Median eye fold	+	+	?
Ear lobe, 'bushman'	+ +	+	?
Lips	'negroid'	'negroid'	'negroid'
Fingerprints: %			
Whorls	16–35	19	24
Loops	60–58	76	65
Arches	24–7	5	11
Cummin's Index	9–12	11:4	11

the Kalahari. The Kalahari Bushmen now show some genetic results of their isolation (Table 11). The frequency of the B gene is much lower than that of Hottentots, the haptoglobin values are different; the physique is more 'gracile' and there is less prognathism. In some characters, for example in hair form and facial features, there is a strong gradient or cline running from Bushmen to Hottentots and from them to the neighbouring Bantu. In body size, while some Bushmen are of dwarf stature, there is considerable overlap with Hottentots. As in the Congo a gradient of selection seems to have been established. Bushmen along the Okavango river also show the results of later hybridisation with southward moving darker Bantu peoples in Angola.

The Khoisan peoples are thus the result of a pre-neolithic differentiation within the general African or negroid stock leading to a lightening of skin colour, a modification of hair shape (woolly rather than frizzy), a selection for smaller body physique and steatopygia. The earlier Khoisan populations can with some confidence be equated with the Bush-Boskop remains identified from a wide area of South Africa: Cape Flats, Matjes River, Skildergat, Zitzikama, Ingwavuma, etc.

(v) *America*

The peopling of the New World by migratory expansion over the Bering Strait during Wisconsin time is nowadays believed to have occupied not only a longer period (from as far back as 30,000 years BP till 11,000 years BP or so) but also a much wider area of crossing. The origins of the Bering Sea Mongoloids and of the American Indians are bound up with the geological fact that the eastern Aleutian Islands were once part of the Bering land bridge. The living Aleuts are very likely the direct descendants of some of the original Bering 'bridge' inhabitants. The ancestral Amerindians or Palaeo-Indians, with their land-based economy, could have crossed often, following big game without coming into contact with the sea-orientated New World Mongoloids, the Eskimos and Aleuts (Laughlin). Before the Bering platform was inundated a whole network of 'contiguous isolates' probably stretched from Hokkaido to what is now Umnak Island. This ancestral network would have included the Eskimo and Aleut, the Chukchi, Koryak and Kamchadal and possibly the Yupik-speaking Eskimos of Siberia and St Lawrence Island, who may have withdrawn into their present isolation as the platform was inundated. This view of the Bering land bridge as an enormous continental area extending 1,500 kms southwards from the Arctic Ocean to the present eastern Aleutians means that populations of the southern coastal area, expanding and moving slowly eastward and southward,

53 Contacts between Eurasia and the North American continent: Bering Straits

over many generations occupied ecological conditions quite different from those of the interior. This enlarged perspective of time and territory explains the varying degrees of resemblance between Asiatic Mongoloids and American aborigines, closest to the Eskimo and Aleuts (who with the Chukchi and Koryak make up one biologically closely related group), less with the Western Indians of North America and still less with the Amerindians to the south.

In the far east of Asia a mesolithic cultural stratum can be identified in Outer Mongolia and in Siberia. The latter is of special significance because of affinities with the Cape Denbigh complex at sites on the north Bering Sea coast. This culture, while reminiscent of the Upper Palaeolithic, contains true microliths. It is characterised by large numbers of micro-blades, burins and small bifacially retouched blades for insertion in the sides of harpoon heads, medium sized bifaced points and knifeblades. 'The Denbigh has many features in common with early Eskimo cultures, and it seems reasonably certain that this and related mesolithic cultures discovered in Arctic regions from Alaska to Greenland provided the basis for the cultural tradition of the Eskimo' (J. Hawkes).

Since their migration from Siberia to Alaska the Eskimo-Aleut peoples have established themselves in a variety of habitats, ranging from the harsh and poorly lighted terrain of the polar regions to the more moderate marine environments of the Aleutian Islands. They have been able to occupy the entire coast of northern North America from Alaska to the northeastern coast of Canada and the entire coast of Greenland. The ecological success of these simple food-gathering communities rests on an impressive series of physiological and cultural adaptations. At the same time the demands of these difficult habitats, as well as the small size and dispersion of the groups, have brought about a measure of micro-evolutionary change in their genetic constitution and morphology. This differentiation is mirrored in the divergence of the Eskimo languages, not only from the Siberian and American Indian languages, but even between the Eskimo and Aleutian languages themselves.

The subarctic ecosystem of the Aleutians was an unusually favourable one in its abundance of fish (e.g. cod and halibut), sea-mammals (e.g. the sea-otter), birds, molluscs and edible algae, all easily accessible to the Kayak hunters. The absence of winter ice greatly eased the exploitation of this rich littoral sea. In some places the complex configuration of the coastline led to the trapping of driftwood, dead whales and sea-lions and facilitated the killing of otters. From their earliest occupancy onwards the technology of the Aleuts richly illustrates the exploitation of the manifold resources of their environment. Thus, as Laughlin has found at the Chaluka site, the earliest palaeo-Aleuts used various kinds of harpoons and spearheads, fish hooks and weights for fish lines; adze bits and whale-bone wedges were evidence of wood-working. The harpoon heads, carved and incised with great artistry, are fluted and slotted to receive straight-based bifacial stone points. And these have been found embedded in sea-lion bones. There are also bird spears, root diggers, stone knives, and flaking tools. The oval houses had ribs and mandibles of whales for rafters, and stone lamps were used. So effective was this assemblage that during 4,000 years of occupancy the artefacts are modified only in detail. These favourable conditions, not surprisingly, meant that the Aleutians had a much longer life-span than that of the Eskimos living in the harsher arctic environment, where infant mortality was high and age at death was rarely as much as forty-five or fifty-five years.

The material culture of present-day (and recent) Eskimo and Aleuts has often been described on account of its extraordinary ingenuity and efficiency for adaptation to cold. The ordinary clothing includes undergarments, pants, boots, mittens, and parka with ruff. Where hunting is done from kayaks, the clothing is made of waterproof materials, such as the oesophagus of hair seal or sea-lion and the intestines of various mammals, such as whales, walrus, or seals. Parkas made of the skins of birds—cormorants, puffins, and auklets in particular—are used in all areas. Insulating materials such as dried grass and caribou skin are worn inside boots.

Glare from water, ice, or snow is minimized by the use of slit goggles or visors. In the Aleutian Islands and in southern Greenland, kayakers habitually wore visors or shades for protection against spray and glare. Eskimos who use sleds wear slit goggles instead of visors.

The biological adaptations of the Eskimos still remain incompletely understood. One would suppose, as Laughlin says, that selection for cold-adapted individuals has probably been extensive in the southern area, where there is greatest use of the sea. Heat loss is so greatly accelerated in cold water that a victim who has been immersed for a few minutes often cannot be saved even by rapid rewarming techniques. Ability to withstand wet cold for even a few additional minutes can make all the difference, as it may mean rescue by another hunter. On land, by contrast, a fully clothed person can survive many days of extreme cold. No studies on the heritability of resistance to cold have been made. Yet in the compactness of the body, and the short legs relative to the trunk, the Eskimo conforms with the Bergman-Allen rule (Roberts). It has been postulated speculatively that the flatness of the mongoloid face is advantageous in resisting cold. The narrowness of the nasal aperture would appear to counteract the extreme dryness and coldness of the inspired air (Plate 18).

Thermo-regulation in the Eskimo is characterised by a basal metabolism that is higher than European clinical standards for normal metabolism. Eskimos, clothed as they are, maintain their warmth even while lying on the winter ice, hunting seal. Blood flow to the hands and legs is greater when the limbs are cooled in water than it is in normal white controls. The perception of pain resulting from cold appears to be less acute in both children and adults than it is in other races, and the Eskimos have higher finger temperatures during cooling in cold air (Fig. 43).

When fully clothed, the Eskimo reproduces a microclimate that is essentially tropical; if he works hard he sweats easily.

The Eskimo-Aleut stock is characterised by a large cranium, a large flat face, a broad mandible with unusually broad ascending ramus (broader than in neanderthal men), and a medium to narrow nose. Whereas blood group B is absent in American Indians it is always present in the Eskimos and Aleuts, who also share a similar rhesus gene complex.

Within the Eskimo-Aleut stock such factors as isolation, smallness of the breeding unit, and migration into new terrain, have led to a degree of local micro-evolution and geographical variation.

Thus earlier Aleuts and Eskimos had relatively narrower heads (cephalic index less than seventy-five per cent); today these Kodiak islanders possess on average a cephalic index as high as eighty-six per cent with this value decreasing to the west and to the north. The total body height varies, the coastal peoples being shorter than those of the interior. Blood group B is dispersed along a gradient, being rare (two per cent) among the highly isolated Polar Eskimos, more frequent along the west coast of Greenland and reaching higher values among the Angmagssalik Eskimos of the southeast. The migration by the Eskimos in two directions, from a single point of entry round the coasts of Greenland, brought about a marked difference in the terminal isolates, as Laughlin and Jørgensen showed in a study of the skulls.

An interesting cline characterises the frequencies of the MNS blood group system. Chown and Lewis found the occurrence of type MS higher in the Copper Eskimos of the central Canadian Arctic and lower as one proceeds to the southeast. Significantly, where the Eskimos approach the Indians geographically they become genetically more dissimilar from them. The genetic differences of the Eskimo-Aleut stock from the Amerindians' include also a low haptoglobin type 1–1, a high percentage of non-tasters of phenylthiocarbamide, and low rates of excretion of β-amino-isobutyric acid.

There was ample space in the interior of the original Bering land bridge for small groups of hunters in bands of fifty or one hundred, constituting a total population at any one time of only a few hundred, to move about in pursuit of game without intruding upon each other. The interior landscape was evidently a low rolling plain, for the most part devoid of relief, studded with bogs and swamps, frozen much of the time, and lacking in trees or even many bushes. Grass-eating herbivores may have been present in fair numbers. The human adaptation to this region must surely have been that of big-game hunters, living by means of scavenging dead mammoths and such bovids as caribou, bison and muskox, and by hunting live animals. The big-game hunting tradition was well developed at an early date in the New World, as is evidenced by the Folsom and Clovis cultures of ten to twelve thousand years ago (Laughlin).

Contemporary interior hunters, such as various Athabascan Indian groups of Alaska, are characteristically partitioned into small bands often numbering fewer than fifty persons, and there are great distances between bands. The camps must be moved annually or sometimes frequently in the course of a single year in order to intercept game. Every few years the people must concentrate in a totally different area, or at least one that partially overlaps the previously hunted area; thus the total exploited area is very large. An extremely important consequence is that when such hunting bands migrate, they pick up the entire camp—tents, utensils, and people—and move, leaving no one behind and little evidence of their occupation.

The occupancy of the Americas as a result of a long drawn out migration implies that present-day American Indian populations are the product of multiple factors. Although they do not go back to a 'single' origin, this is not to say that the present populations represent a succession of physically quite distinctive waves of migration.

Migration by small hunting-gathering groups and later by simple horticulturalists is in reality a slow process of outward diffusion with retention of some genetic continuity; at the same time, local differentiation proceeds through the usual agencies of mutation, drift, partial isolation and selective adaptation, counteracted by hybridisation. This is the pattern for much of America, as it is over great areas of Europe, Africa, Asia and Australia.

The oldest known skeletal remains of American Indians, though by no means as old as some of the claimed archaeological datings, go back some 15,000 years and they closely resemble those of more recent Indians (Newman) (Plate 19).

The evidence for an underlying genetic continuity amongst American Indians is clear enough from our knowledge of their present-day genetic constitution. In part this shows merely that the present population of sixteen millions could well have arisen from an initial group (or succession of similar groups) of only 500 or so. Of course for a long time the original hunting bands would have been small and dispersed; but here again, as in the whole history of human evolution, isolation was never so complete as to prevent genetic interchange. The genetic characteristics of American Indian populations are sufficiently similar to one another and different from those of other continental groups to permit (as a first approximation) of their description as a 'distinct' sub-group of the human species. The distinctive genetic features which provide this 'profile' are presented in Table 12 (see also Table 7).

Closer analysis of genetic affinities reveals that over larger

Table 12.   Some distinctive genetic features of the American Indian

ABO system:	high frequency of I^o
MN system:	high frequency of I^M
Rh system:	the frequency of R_2 is higher than anywhere else in the world; r and R_o low or absent
Kell system:	K may have been absent in pre-Columbian Indians
Duffy system:	high frequency of Fy^a
Diego system:	high frequency of Di^a
Lewis system:	almost all populations show Le(a —) only
Lutheran system:	almost all populations show Lu (a —) only
Haemoglobin types:	abnormal types very rare or absent
Colour blindness:	low frequency of defectives

areas the genetic continuity takes the modified form of gradients or clines. Thus the frequency of the gene for blood group A decreases from north to south, that for the allele for the Diego factor and the M gene increases from north to south. Detailed comparisons of particular traits reveal much local variation. The factors making for local diversity between small nomadic groups and complicating or obscuring affinities have been shown by the studies of Neel and Salzano, Diaz Ungria and others to involve the action of differential fertility, 'drift', random gene extinction by isolation and the 'founder' effect.

In those New World areas characterised by morphological continuity trends in body size seem to follow Bergman's rule (Newman). The tall present-day Indians in areas of colder climates evolved from shorter-statured ancestors, whereas the shorter Indians in warmer areas had taller ancestral populations. 'Within a time-span of over 5,000 years the Indians of the eastern United States increased by an average of four to five centimetres. In the Pueblo area of the southwest and the lower Sacramento valley mean stature decreased by two to six centimetres, and similarly in Middle America'.

The Indians of the New World are remarkable in that within a period of no more than 15–20,000 years at the palaeolithic or mesolithic level of culture almost every imaginable habitat was successfully exploited, ranging from Arctic conditions of the Yukon, the northwest fishing coasts and rivers and the great plains to tropical Meso-America and the Caribbean, the Amazon jungles and Patagonian cold wet terrains. Further exploitation of these and additional habitats, notably the high uplands, required the cultural advance to agriculture.

Until the mid-nineteenth century, the Shoshonean bands of the Great Basin of the American West followed a way of life broadly similar to that of the peoples of Meso-America who in 5000 BC were the first to domesticate maize. As hunters and collectors they possessed a simple social organisation with very low population densities. Shuard has shown that each band followed a short seasonal round which passed through a whole series of micro-environments, from the lowest salt flats up to the pinos forest.

The era of food production

At about the time when the outward movement of the hunter-gatherer bands intensified at the periphery, the palaeo-mesolithic way of life began to draw to a close in the long occupied regions of the Near and Middle East. The cultivation of a few domesticated plants, wheat and barley, first gradually and then entirely supplanted the wild foods of the hunting-gathering life. Concurrently with this gradual but inexorable agricultural 'revolution' there came into being by 8,000 BP a new kind of environment in the form of farming settlements and villages. This new urban environment would in due course exert its own effects on the biological properties of its inhabitants.

The supersession of the hunting-gathering way of life now began to spread outwards from its original foci in the Near and Middle East; about 6,000 years BP the farming 'revolution' was repeated in the New World in Meso-America; it overtook the peripheral areas of east Asia about 5,000 years BP and southern Africa about 4,000 years BP. Even in our age of space exploration this process is still going on as the few remnants of food collecting bands and simple fishing communities of Africa, Australia, Malaysia and New Guinea are absorbed into the modern food producing industrial world. In 1966 the last Bantu-speaking hunting tribe of Africa—the Hadza of Tanzania—became a settled horticultural community.

The cultivation of cereals, declared Tylor, was 'the great

moving power of civilisation'. Wherever it was introduced it led to revolutionary alterations in the whole way of life, and in many parts of the world it stimulated a continuous and progressive sequence of cultural change. As Childe says, these cultural developments based on exotic cereals and exotic sheep, represent stages of rural adaptation to particular environments, some of limited, others of improvable or even of unlimited agricultural potential. The outcome, in terms of productivity, technology, settlement size and density, or in socio-political structure, from the very beginnings of the Neolithic, whether in the Middle East, central or northeastern Europe, Meso-America, sub-Saharan Africa, or the loess of northern China, has depended to a marked degree on the intrinsic agricultural fertility of the soil. As the major unit of production, agriculture was not to be displaced until the industrial revolution.

The introduction of farming seems everywhere to have been a slow process and the conditions of life remained in many respects similar to those of the pre-agricultural era. Reliance on the newly discovered emmer or barley was by no means total and food gathering and hunting went on. The groups remained small, self-sufficient and in many places semi-nomadic. But important differences soon showed themselves. The greater security of food supply ensured by even the partial inclusion of the new crops in the dietary enabled the neolithic groups to multiply more quickly than in the hunting era. A new pattern of co-operative work was required for house-building, for clearing scrub and woodland, for sowing and reaping the plots. A new appreciation of the environment was called for. There had to be an understanding of the soil, the water supply, the rainfall, the properties of food plants and the needs and behaviour of domesticable animals.

The mainstay of these more highly organised communities was of course the cereal plant. The remarkable variety of cereals brought into cultivation have in common a wide tolerance to climatic extremes—like man himself. Wheat and barley are the cereals of the European Neolithic; by selecting appropriate strains, man was able to expand cultivation over a wide area. Rye and oats were much later additions, probably of the early Iron Age. Rice cultivation spread outwards either from India or south China in the second millennium BC. Millet, also Chinese in origin, can withstand considerable seasonal variation, especially in rainfall. Millet became the traditional crop of Africa south of the Sahara. Maize is the New World cereal.

Emmer, barley, goats and sheep flourished in the wild state in many places in Syria, north Persia and even near the Taurus mountains. It is not surprising therefore that at a number of sites in the eastern Mediterranean and southwest Asia the beginnings of farming can be detected superimposed on an essentially mesolithic way of life (microliths, bone-worked equipment, absence of pottery). This new way of securing food was introduced with varying degrees of success into regions very different and remote from the homelands of the original cereal plants. The culture complex which developed in association with plant and animal cultivation was very varied in population density, in settlement patterns, in dietaries, work routine, and exposure to disease. The Neolithic brought with it new biological stresses and compensatory biological effects.

The dominant influence shaping the whole culture complex of the cultivator can be traced to one major factor—the natural fertility of the soil (Meggers). In Europe, Asia, Africa and America this prime ecological factor can be seen to bring about roughly similar grades of cultural development.

In a few restricted areas, the alluvial deposits of the river valleys provided by far the most favourable conditions for agricultural exploitation. Year after year new soil is laid down by the natural irrigation of the flood water; the same patches can be successfully worked, permanent settlements can be established and the complex organisation necessary for clearing the swamps and keeping the channels clear, as well as for actual cultivation, can be developed. Populations can be maintained at densities ten or more times greater than in the hunter economy. As men begin to live together continually in crowded dwellings, medical hazards appear on a new scale of intensity—infectious airborne and waterborne diseases, pollution of water channels, infestation with malaria, hookworm and bilharzia. The monotonous high carbohydrate, low protein diet carry the dangers of vitamin and amino-acid deficiency. Despite the high death rate at all ages, population numbers were maintained by a high birth rate, as was essential for the requirements of intensive agricultural manual work. In the river systems of Egypt, Sumer, India and China the new ecology of the neolithic and urban 'revolution' put the large and growing populations to severe medical, climatic and physical stress. Nevertheless, underpinned by the relative secureness of the food production, and as bronze and then iron tools were introduced, urbanisation and with it diversity of labour, trade, and notably, record keeping, all were developed in these riverine civilisations within a few thousand years after the inception of agriculture.

By contrast were the developments on those soils of limited fertility. On these the neolithic hoe or garden culture sprang up. On this land the yield declines after a couple of seasons and new plots have to be cleared and cultivated afresh. This 'shifting' agriculture was inaugurated in the temperate forest zones of Europe; and here it was supplemented by the keeping of domestic cattle and pigs and some hunting. Where the 'slash-and-burn' mode was adopted the settlements remained small and scattered. But these same soils possessed enough potential to enable them to be exploited much more intensely with the introduction of bronze tools. Relatively high crop returns could be maintained by the introduction of the plough as long as soil exhaustion was avoided by the new techniques of rotation, fallow and fertilisation. Fertility was ensured by grazing the sheep on the fallow and stubble. Animal manure and compost provided adequate return of fertility to the soil. As in the easier conditions of the alluvial valleys, man established a closed ecological cycle. Productivity increased noticeably; population density rose and villages grew in size (as reflected in the size of the iron age cemeteries). Trade and warfare were now part of the way of life and most villages were well fortified. All these changes were magnified when cheap iron tools replaced bronze. Cultivation became more intensive, the exploitation of the land still more efficient.

In northwest Europe, the Mediterranean shores, Asian grasslands and Andean uplands, in Africa, as the soil becomes more suited to easy grazing and less suitable for plough culti-

vation, mixed husbandry gives way to stock-raising and pastoralism. Aridity favours the herdsman as does the loss of
the original fertile soil cover. Ecological factors clearly dictate
the shift to stock-keeping and in different areas to the particular type of herding with sheep, cattle, horses, asses, camels
or goats.

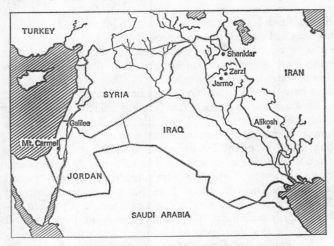

54 Middle and Near East: archaeological sites

(i) *The Middle and Near East; The Mediterranean*

At a number of sites in southwestern Asia, such as those at
Zarzi, Jarmo and Shanidar in Iraq, Alikosh (Khuzistan) in
Iran, and on Mount Carmel the transition from hunting and
gathering to domestication of animals has been detected and
documented. No doubt these incipient agriculturalists were
drawn from the hunting bands who roamed over the area
between the Mediterranean on the west, the Caspian sea on
the east and the Persian Gulf to the south. Here 'onagers and
gazelles on the plains and flat-bottomed valleys, sheep in the
rolling hills, goats on the craggy mountain ridges and cattle
and deer in the forests, were their main food sources'
(Hole). Noteworthy it is that the people at Alikosh in an

area rich in diverse game could be settled in permanent villages—this seems to have been an immediate prelude to domestication. Even more interesting are the Natufian sites on Mount Carmel and Shanider in Iraq. At both places, about 8,000 BP, the mesolithic economy had been broadened by cultivation of cereals and the intensive exploitation of local herds of gazelle, goats and wild sheep. As evidence of crop cultivation there are the well-known sickles made of flint blades fixed by gum into a grooved bone, as well as stone mortars and pestles. In two places at least—Jericho and Jarmo —the new food resources were secured on such a scale that quite soon at Jericho fairly large settled villages were established, within strong defensive walls. The economy was not fully neolithic; there was no pottery or weaving.

By about 9,000 BP neolithic farming villages were well in evidence at sites in Egypt and the Middle East. Once the new food producing economy was well established its adoption by many mesolithic hunters and fishers was rapid. The shore of the lake that once filled the Fayum depression was 'quite abruptly . . . fringed with a chain of hamlets devoted to farming. The Nile valley from the first cataract down to Cairo is quickly lined with a chain of flourishing peasant villages, all seeming to start about the same time and all developing steadily down to 3000 BC [5000 BP]' (Childe).

The Middle and Near Eastern peoples responsible for the first ventures in farming, for example the Natufians, were closely aligned in their physical make-up to other neolithic groups in the Mediterranean and to the pre-dynastic Egyptians. There is little doubt that they form the major component of the general population of Mediterranean peoples of today. These farming peoples (perhaps for nutritional reasons) were of smaller and slighter build (the Natufians averaged 5′ 3″ for men, 5′ 0″ for women) than people of the same region living in earlier mesolithic and palaeolithic times. They were less rugged in such features as the eyebrow, occipital and other bony ridges of the skull, and their cranial capacity was somewhat smaller. In these respects they offer some contrast to their still mesolithic contemporaries of Europe. They had 'diminished to a sort of standard Mediterranean form of more recent times' (Howells). It seems a reasonable explanation that these are concomitants of the more settled life, the predominantly cereal diet and the warmer climates as compared to the strenuous hunting life, the meat diet and the cooler climate of the pre-neolithic northern Eurasian peoples. Indeed when farming spread into northern Europe it demanded a high level of physical fitness, and a strong physique for forest clearing; as mixed farming was practised the diet remained high in protein. To this day a morphological gradient of body height and body weight remains in evidence from north to south.

The migratory and expansive character of early farming must have imposed a much greater degree of uniformity of physical and genetic characters over a wider area than could have existed before. The archaeological record strongly suggests that the Neolithic was brought to nearly all of the circum-Mediterranean area by actual immigrants. From Syria and Cicilia, as the pottery indicates, there was an early diffusion of peasant communities by sea, setting up their hamlets and villages, some of substantial size, at many landfalls along the coasts and islands of the Mediterranean. In Crete, southeast Sicily, Apulia, Malta, and southern Greece, successive waves brought a high degree of genetic as well as cultural unity to the region. The overall genetic homogeneity finds clear expression at the present time in the gene frequencies of the ABO blood group system. The values given in Table 13 reveal a similarity from one end of the Mediterranean to the other and on both shores.

Table 13. ABO frequencies in the Mediterranean (from Mourant, Kopec and Sobzcak)

	p	q	r
Greece (mainland)	25	10	65
Crete	24	10	66
Yugoslavia (Rijeka)	24	11	65
Albania	25	12	63
South Italy	22	9	69
Naples	23	9	68
Sicily	23	10	67
France (Var)	27	7	66
South Spain	24	11	65
South Portugal	27	7	66
Algiers	24	13	63
Morocco (Marrakesh)	21	12	67
Tunis	26	9	65

This homogeneity may of course reflect the existence of a pre-neolithic uniformity in the area, but it is also consistent with the archaeological evidence of a widespread colonization from the Neolithic onwards.

Widely diffused throughout the Mediterranean is the condition called Mediterranean anaemia or beta-thalassaemia. The anaemia is caused by a genetically determined block in the formation of normal haemoglobin in the red cell. In the homozygous state it is very serious and often lethal, yet the frequency of heterozygote carriers is such as to allow the gene to reach high values. Its persistence must presumably be due to some selective advantage favouring the heterozygote. This advantage may lie in resistance to malaria. There is good evidence that the frequency is high where malignant tertian malaria was endemic until quite recently. This correlation has been well demonstrated in Sardinia. The wide dispersion of the gene must represent in part the results of migration.

In the Mediterranean region of neolithic expansion we must refer again to the existence of the major discontinuity presented by the people of the Basque-speaking area. These populations, despite the incursions of neolithic and later colonizers along the Mediterranean coasts and inland, have maintained clear differences in sero-genetic and morphological features. The Basque area is a region of conspicuously high O and low B gene frequency. The rhesus-negative frequency of the Basques is about thirty per cent, so that the cde frequency is between fifty per cent and sixty per cent. The peoples outside the Basque-speaking area are predominantly Rh-positive with much lower cde frequencies. The fact that the Basques have retained a strong measure of genetic distinctiveness testifies to the existence of barriers to gene flow which still persist into the modern era. In the case of the Basques, language, geography, and culture have, no doubt, served as effective barriers.

(ii) Continental Europe

Another major early diffusion of neolithic culture into western Europe was along the Danube as far west as Belgium.

'The loess lands north and west of the Danube were first occupied by a Neolithic population whose whole culture down
to the finest details remains identical from Hungary to north
Germany and from Galicia to Belgium . . . perhaps the most
classically neolithic culture in the ancient world' (Hawkes).
The mesolithic populations were apparently very sparse, detectable only in the forest fringing the loess to the west and
north. The burials reveal a long-headed neolithic 'mediterranean' physical type over this wide peasant area.

Yet another important cultural movement was that associated with the spread of megalithic architecture. The building
of these stone tombs was not a feature of the first neolithic
cultures, but by about 3000 BC the megalithic monuments
had become the most remarkable characteristic of the neolithic of western and north Europe. Childe writes:

> It must have taken a considerable force to build such
> burial places and in fact some contain as many as two hun-
> dred skeletons. The growth of the population must then
> have been rapid . . . The multiplication implied by the
> tombs must have resulted from the fecundity of a few im-
> migrant families (since they were apparently seafarers)
> and that of the elder hunters who had joined with these
> in exploiting the agricultural resources of the virgin north.

The broad picture of the neolithic 'colonization' of Europe
invites a simple model of the basic genetic pattern which
would have been established by the dominance of incoming
originally Mediterranean peoples over local mesolithic
groups. We should expect genetic gradients to be set up corresponding to the general pathways of neolithic advance. For
such an underlying pattern to persist to the present time, it
is necessary to suppose that the neolithic peasantry established a hold so strong that the subsequent technological advances of the bronze and iron ages on the whole consolidated
this neolithic pattern of settlement. It would follow also that
many of the migrations of peoples in European history took
place for the most part to a relatively limited or localised
extent.

This highly simplified hypothesis is offered in default of

any other at present available. The geographical distribution of the ABO gene system is in accord with this simple interpretation. Along the Danubian neolithic pathway the gradients are surprisingly regular. The moderately high B and low O gradually move into a low B and a high O frequency.

Table 14. Danubian pathway

	p	q	r
Carpathians	33	15	51
Bulgaria	33	13	54
South Hungary	31	14	54
Moravia	28	14	57
South Austria	29	11	61
East Germany	28	12	60
South Germany	28	8	64
North Germany	27	9	65
Belgium	23	6	71
West Germany	24	5	71
Holland; North France	25	5	70

The Iberian-megalithic coastal pathway carries by no means as clear a genetic gradient; it is as if the culture itself was diffused by small numbers and adopted by local inhabitants. Britain and northern France seem to be much more part of an extension of the Danubian gene gradient with high values of blood group O in Scotland and Ireland.

The persistence of the underlying geographical genetic distribution is attested also by the strong indications of a south to north gradient of increasing tallness, larger body size and larger percentage of colour blindness.

There is certainly another major but historically much later movement from east to west across Europe setting up a corresponding gradient in the ABO system and merging with the early southeast to northwest gradient. This takes the form of a gradient in B gene frequency from high values in the east to low values in the west.

As always these broad tendencies are interrupted by local factors of all kinds. Local barriers to genetic flow operate to this day in many small communities. These may be geographical as in the Alps, Caucasus, islands of the Mediterranean or of the North Sea. They may be economic and cultural, such as have maintained the Lapps as a fairly distinctive component of the Scandinavian peninsula.

(iii) *Africa*

Cereal cultivation was first adopted in Africa probably early in the fifth millennium BC. The staples cultivated in the lower Nile at this time were barley and emmer. This was a time when a great area of the Sahara was well-watered and bush-covered and could be exploited by the incoming horticultural-ists. In this, the Makalian wet phase, the first cultivators arose from mesolithic groups who spread from the savannah of west and central Africa northwards, making their settlements round the pans and water courses at such sites as Asselar, Taferjit, Tamaya Mellet, Guezzan, Koureunkorale and Khar-toum. The skeletal remains from these places show close re-semblances to modern peoples of west Africa and the Sudan.

The later dry phase (the post-Makalian) forced cereal crop cultivation to spread further south and after the third millen-nium it was progressively taken up by sub-Saharan popula-tions. As elsewhere these early stages were really stages of partial cultivation in which hunting, fishing and collecting remained important. Later developments in this region were based partly on the acquired knowledge of millet (this prob-ably from an Ethiopian locus) and partly on the local domes-tication of such crops as yams, oil plants, fluted pumpkins, pulses and bananas. The first sites over this vast area were on watersides and on the fringes of forests. After 1000 BC full food-producing communities were established on these forest margins and in the savannah. These neolithic communities were technically well equipped to deal with their habitats—they possessed wood-working tools, the axe and the adze, as well as the hoe. As everywhere the factor of soil fertility operated to determine the limit of exploitation, population densities and cultural complexity. Wheat and barley could not spread widely because of the unsuitability of the tropical savannah in the absence of irrigation. Shifting agriculture developed widely as the necessary adaptation to the proper-ties of the savannah and bushland. Sorghum and eleusine (varieties of millet) provided the basis for the successful spread of cultivation from the zone between Nigeria and western Ethiopia into eastern, central and southern Africa.

The east African neolithic cultures and the rock art of the time provide evidence of the adoption of pastoralism by about 1000 BC. This diffusion of cattle-keeping to east Africa proceeded from its main origin in south Arabia, via the Sudan or Nubia and the Horn of Africa. In this area the first cattle-owning groups were predominantly of Mediterranean stock. Migration of cattle owners took place down the high ridge country on either side of the rift valley, presumably a tsetse free route. The movement in due course enveloped Negro-Bantu peoples and further south almost certainly provided the source for the stock-raising culture of the Hottentot-Khoisan peoples (sometimes referred to at this stage as Bush-Boskop).

These movements brought Negro-Bantu and Khoisan stock-owners in close contact, reducing the territory available to the latter and greatly restricting the food-collecting areas of the Bushmen-Khoisan bands. These great southern movements in Africa afford some of the clearest instances of gene cline formation and hybridisation. In suitable conditions of isolation local differentiation of the surviving palaeolithic groups—forest pygmies, desert Bushmen—continued, as we have seen.

Thus from the very beginnings of agriculture the ethno-economic pattern was set. The food-producers in the savannah and peripheral forest areas of west and east Africa, with their axe and hoe cultures, were negroid peoples; whereas the first stock-raising communities of east Africa and Nubia had close cultural ties and genetic links with Mediterranean-Caucasoid peoples. Even in the late Palaeolithic, judged by skeletal remains, the whole region to the west of the Horn of Africa was an area of Afro-Mediterranean differentiation. Genetic data from the modern populations show this to have been of some complexity involving both hybridisation and selection. There is a strong and regular ABO gradient from the Egyptian, Ethiopian and Sudan regions into east Africa, showing a steady fall in the A gene and B gene frequencies and rise in the O gene frequencies. How far it represents an interpenetration of contiguous populations as a stabilised gene flow is not easy to say.

Africa has furnished a number of striking instances of the

operation of natural selection; there is good evidence for the
selective action of hot humid and hot dry climates, of ultra-
violet radiation and of disease, particularly malaria, as well
as the influence of other (and complicating) agencies such
as hybridisation, cline formation and chance effects. Phenotypic adaptation and modification in physiological response
to heat and nutritional status have also been clearly established in a number of investigations.

In the Sudan–east African region where the sub-Saharan
merges into the equatorial zone, the influence of climate as a
selective agent seems particularly clear. The striking 'nilotic'
body build of such peoples as the Shilluk and the Dinka
(Plate 20) of the southern Sudan has often been commented
on. These tribes lived strongly contrasting lives—the Shilluk
predominantly agricultural and sedentary along the rivers,
the Dinka pastoral (with a little subsistence farming) and
migratory in the dry season. The Shilluk diet is the lower in
protein, higher in carbohydrates, but neither group is under-
nourished. Despite differences in way of life they possess in
common the attenuated long-limbed 'ectomorphic' physique,
fairly muscular but with low subcutaneous fat.

Roberts, who has made a thorough comparison of the
body build with that of other populations, has argued co-
gently that the 'nilotic' physique is not to be attributed to
undernourishment (which can of course cause an appearance
of ectomorphy) but is to be seen as an advantageous modification to local climatic conditions. The Shilluk and Dinka
are genetically very similar on the basis of comprehensive
blood grouping and haemoglobin characterisation (Roberts).
Despite their present-day economic and cultural divergence
they obviously share a long, presumably pre-neolithic period
of adaptive exposure to the rigours of the heat and aridity of
the region. The relatively low body weight, low subcutaneous fat, marked ectomorphy and linear build are (or were)
in varying degree widespread in other regions of this zone
across sub-Saharan Africa.

Hiernaux has made a most illuminating analysis for peoples of the Congo. In the Kwanda–Burundi–Kivu, the three
endogamous groups—the Tutsi, Hutu and Twa differ in their
social structure and way of life, yet they speak the same

language. They also differ considerably in physique, as they do from the Hutu pygmies. The Tutsi have a much higher ectomorphy score than the Hutu but are not nutritionally inferior to them. They are more linear, taller with narrow shoulders, lower in relative weight and limb circumferences. As these groups now live in close proximity, these differences must be genetic and indeed in blood group characters the two groups are clearly not related. In fact the Tutsi are biologically very similar to some of the ethnic groups of west Africa like the Sarakole who live in the dry and hot Sahel. This strongly suggests that the Tutsi physique evolved in a hot dry condition. The groups in the Congo region make up in their morphology a cline which extends from wet to arid zones, as shown in the following table:

Table 15.

	Stature (cm) (mean values from Hiernaux)	Nasal Index	Facial Index	Cephalic Index
Mbutu Pygmies	144	103·8	78·3	77·0
Wet forest dwellers	164	94·0	81·9	76·1
Savannah dwellers	169	85·9	85·8	75·3
Arid zone	171	85·0	89·7	74·8
Tutsi	176	69·4	92·8	74·4

Another group showing a fairly high degree of ectomorphy, particularly in the limbs (but less than that of the Tutsi) are the Kikuyu of Kenya (Danby). The fact that they live in an equatorial climate considerably modified by altitude may explain why they are not more ectomorphic. It is also possible that they represent a mixture of peoples in this area.

The sickle cell trait in the Congo region varies greatly—from one per cent in the Tutsi to thirty-six per cent in the Humu and Mvuba who live at the foot of the Ruwenzori Mountains. The Hb^s gene frequency correlates with altitude and there is a negative correlation of altitude with malarial infection. This finding (by Hiernaux) is consistent with the hypothesis that malaria has a strong selective influence on Hb^s frequency; this is strengthened by the geographical distribution in Africa, as shown in the map.

Many comparisons of agricultural communities living on contrasted diets (e.g. Kikuyu and Masai in east Africa or

Sikhs and Madrassi in India, or coastal and inland Brazilian Indians) present difficulties of interpretation since the groups are also genetically different and differences in physique, as we have just seen, can have a strong genetic determination. Among the Tutsi Hiernaux found two groups genetically similar who presented a marked contrast in ecological conditions. Those living above an altitude of 1,900m were better fed and suffered much less malarial infection than those below this level. Not surprisingly the former were heavier and more muscular. The noteworthy element in Hiernaux's study was that those characters which differed greatly between the groups (weight, thigh girth, calf girth, upper arm girth, chest depth and breadth) are largely those which twin studies have shown to have a low heritability component and therefore susceptible to nutritional and other environmental factors. In features with a high heritability the difference between the groups was not so marked.

Perhaps the outstanding fact in the anthropology of southern Africa was the occupation at one time of practically the whole region south of the Zambesi and Okavango Rivers by peoples speaking the distinctive click Khoisan languages, and possessing lighter skin colour than the peoples further north. The skeletal remains (of so-called Bush-Boskop stock) are in keeping with the modern biological evidence that these are peoples related to Africans generally but who have undergone some degree of local differentiation, presumably through natural selection. In many 'African' blood group characters the Khoisan Bushmen and Hottentots as we have seen (Table 12) are clearly related to their Bantu-speaking neighbours. The divergence has affected not only the skin colour but the bodily physique, the hair form and some of the blood group systems. In some respects the pastoral Hottentots and the food gathering Bushmen have undergone a further divergence from each other (Table 12).

The consequence of the movement of both Bantu-speaking peoples and of Europeans into southern Africa has been a widespread degree of hybridisation with the Hottentot-Khoisan peoples. The more gradual interpenetration with Bantu has brought about some striking genetic and morphological gradients. For example along the east coast an ABO

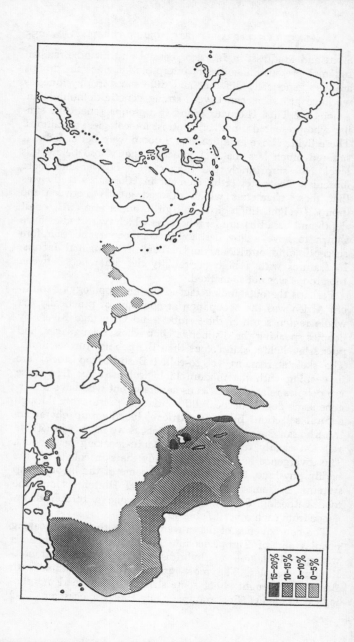

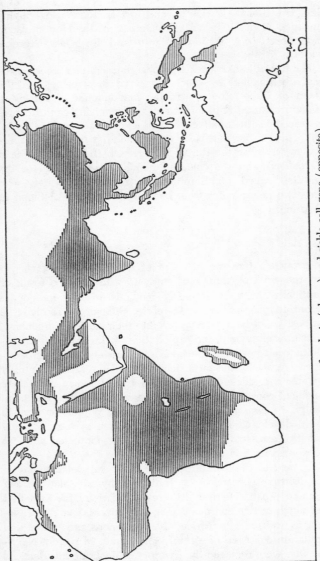

55 Frequency of malaria (above) and sickle cell gene (opposite)

cline is evident with low A and low B frequencies moving into high A and B values characteristic of the Hottentots. In some areas (e.g. Caprivi) Bantu and Bush admixture is evident.

The hybridisation with European farmers and stock-raisers was accompanied by much territorial displacement of the mixed or Cape-coloured groups. The amount of European admixture varied in different areas. This mixing can of course be traced in the usual gene markers and skin colour variation. There is one particular gene which has spread in a spectacular way from the European source, both in the European (Afrikaner) and the coloured population—the gene for the condition called porphyrinuria, in which individuals who carry two genes suffer from haemolysis and loss of blood in the urine.

(iv) *Asia*

As elsewhere the establishment of neolithic farming was in part the work of immigrant cultivators, in part the result of adoption of new food-getting methods by the indigenous mesolithic peoples. It is, therefore, difficult to resolve the composition of later populations into their earlier components. In Asia as elsewhere, the exploitation of the land and the resultant ecological balance takes on a variety of forms determined largely by the intrinsic fertility of the soil, availability of water and efficiency of crop and animal management. The ecological consequences range from self-sufficient rural community, pastoral or horticultural, of small population size, to highly developed irrigation and plantation systems, leading in many cases to the over-exploited over-populated areas so widespread in Asia today.

The arrival of neolithic culture has been documented at many sites in central Asia, India, southwest Asia, the Far East and Japan. There is little real support for the idea that over much of this enormous area, and into Malaya and Indonesia as well as into Africa, the indigenous pre-agricultural population consisted of a thinly-spread race of pygmy Negritoes who were replaced by a variety of neolithic invaders. As we have seen, the surviving Negritoes of today—many of whom have become cultivators—on genetical grounds are not closely related to African peoples. It is by no means certain that their dark skin is genetically or even phenotypically comparable with that of Congolese or West Africans, for example.

Over much of India, Burma, Assam and Malaysia agriculturalists still practise the 'slash and burn' method of crop cultivation. No doubt both the mode of cultivation and the agriculturalists themselves go back in an unbroken line to the neolithic populations, either immigrant or autochthonous, with roots in the preceding mesolithic era. An illuminating illustration of the complexity of this kind of historical situation is that provided by Formosa (Chen Kang Chai). The present population is, of course, predominantly Chinese whose migration from the east coast of Fukien and Kwangtung Provinces went on steadily from about AD 200 onwards. Culturally distinct from them are some eight tribal groups of simple cultivators mostly in the mountain regions, with one group living on a strip of land on the east coast. The differences in blood groups and morphological characters between these groups are clearly determined by geographical and social isolation. Chance effects, such as 'drift' or 'founder bottleneck', may have been at work. At the same time some of the local groups differ also in characters which represent genetic infiltration from the still earlier populations. These divergences both of genetic traits and features such as broad nose, short wide face, broad hand, point to aboriginal groups comparable to Negritoes of the present time.

In some areas differentiation may well owe more to the impact of immigration by a number of distinctive groups than to purely local factors. To cite a well-analysed instance, this seems to be the case on the island of Bougaineville where Nekabesuab-speakers arrived when non-Melanesians (Papuans) were already present, some of these immigrants arriving as late as the mid-nineteenth century. The original population was a single negrito population, but the immigrant waves have produced a high degree of heterogeneity which is now closely related to linguistic deviations (Howell).

Leaving aside the much later immigration of the last 1,000

years or so, Malaya presents a picture of several major stocks distinguishable as early occupants and intruders. The early occupants are represented by Negritoes (allied to those in the Philippines and Andaman Islands), some still living as nomadic hunter-gatherers, some as semi-settled primitive agriculturalists. Early intruders were the simple agricultural Senoi and proto-Malays. The latter possess a general similarity to Mongoloids in blood group gene markers (e.g. high incidence of B, CDe, absence of A2 and cde, and low N and S). The inter-group variation between all the small subsistence units is, however, complex. Some gradation between Negrito and Senoi, and Senoi and proto-Malay, points to hybridisation. At the same time neighbouring villages are often quite diverse genetically, indicating the operation of drift and founder effects as new settlements were created and old ones disappeared. The situation seems similar to the fission-fusion process operating amongst the simple agriculturalists of Xavante Indians in Brazil (Neel and Salzano) (Plate 21).

Thus, the reasons for local diversity amongst agriculturalists, as with hunter-gatherers, may be very different in different circumstances and the operation of 'historical' causes (e.g. migration, hybridisation, splitting) as distinct from 'biological' factors (notably selection or differential mating systems) very difficult to unravel.

The functional and ecological characteristics of cultivators in their great variety of Asian habitats show some interesting adaptive features. Adaptations to the hot climate are to be seen in body size, skin colour and in physiological regulatory processes. The conditions in which agricultural work has to be carried out in the equatorial and monsoon lands of southeast Asia and the jungle areas of India and Malaysia, with air temperatures constantly over 90°F, high humidity, low air movement and strong solar radiation, all impose a severe heat load for many months of the year. Without the physiological adjustments of the heat regulatory processes in the circulatory and other bodily systems there could be no survival for the many millions who now live in these regions. These adjustments are, in fact, so efficient that these Asian warm climate dwellers develop a high degree of acclimatisation. This enables them to keep their internal and skin temperatures from rising unduly in spite of hard work. To do this they sweat more readily as they can dissipate much more heat by evaporation than the unacclimatised person. At the same time the stress on the circulation is lessened; work capacity is maintained and discomfort lessened. The main features of the acclimatisation process can be acquired by active men of all 'racial' groups. These features are equally demonstrable in Indians at the end of the hot season (Fox *et al.*) and in Europeans (naval ratings) who have experienced a hot season in Singapore (Hellon *et al.*).

It has been claimed for people indigenous to these hot regions (and also for Africans) that their heat responses are more efficient than those of newcomers even when the latter are well acclimatised. In particular, the sweat production is said to be more economical—there is less 'drippage' and a more even coverage of the skin. Some data from Singapore seem to support this contention, but the explanation may lie in the smaller body size and relatively greater skin surface area of the indigenous people.

The smaller body weight and slighter physique of tropical Indians, Burmese, Malaysians or Indonesians compared to their more northerly neighbours accords with the Bergmann-Allen ecological rules (Fig. 45). The selective advantages of body size may have arisen in relation to both the needs for heat loss and for survival during food shortage. A mechanism for the operation of selection in favour of genetically determined small body size may be postulated in the differential survival of genotypically undersized mothers who produce offspring more efficiently (that is, with less maternal mortality) than the mothers whose poor bony development, through undernourishment, leads to difficult labour and higher maternal and infant mortality (p. 161).

Any understanding of the state of fitness—physical, developmental, medical or nutritional—of the peoples of Asia requires above all an appreciation of the ecological situations presented by the contrasting modes of food producing. These range from the slash and burn shifting cultivation of small self-sufficient villages (still very widespread) to the intensive rice production on which populations at high densities depend. In India, for example, they include those communities which have achieved a conservation of soil fertility through a peculiar accretion of the wastes and excrement of the village population—human and animal—in the fields close to the village, fields which are intensively cultivated and highly productive.

In the past, contemporaneous with the Roman Empire at its zenith, India attained a highly successful agriculture through a well developed irrigation system. Yet over great areas of India land usage is today completely unbalanced in relation to the population. The maintenance of an over-population of cattle by an over-population of human beings is patently self-destructive. Religious tabus ensure that all cattle are allowed to grow up and multiply, not so much for their milk yield, which is poor, but for their dung which provides a major and easy source of fuel. But this use of cattle is self-defeating as it means a continuous loss of fertility—not only because there is so much manure lost to the soil, but the soil itself is so impoverished as to produce sparse grazing. Both the tree and grass cover are further despoilt by the un-restricted movement of the cattle, sheep, goats and buffalo, so that wind erosion cannot be checked.

The impoverishment of agricultural resources, the lack of adequate calories and protein, brings not only periodic famine but all the classical syndromes of protein, calcium and vitamin deficiency. Yet the high population densities are maintained by high birth rates, despite (or because of) the short ex-pectation of life.

A number of surveys have been made of the food intake and nutrient content of the diets of various states in India. Most of these studies have been confined to families in a low income group, consisting of agricultural labourers, small agri-culturists, petty tradesmen and industrial labourers, who form the majority of the population of India. These surveys have shown that the bulk of the diet of Indians is formed by cereals, which provide seventy to ninety per cent of the total calories. The consumption of protective foods, like pulses, vegetables, fruits, meat and milk is very low. This is because they are in short supply and are expensive for ordinary men to buy. Although food habits differ somewhat from region to region, the general food pattern is quite the same.

The calorie requirement of an adult Indian man has been placed at 2,400–3,900 kcal per day and of an adult woman at 2,000–2,700 kcal per day. The average Indian, however, is not able to get the required number of calories. In Bihar, Madras, Assam, Kerala and Maharashtra, the calorie content of the food is well below these standards; many people are living in a semi-starved condition. The quantity of animal food and total protein in the diet is exceedingly low throughout. The best diet seems to be in Punjab and Delhi, where the daily calorie intake is about 3,300 kcal and the total protein varies from 91 to 119 g per day.

The comparison of the heights of the people of different states in India reveals that there is a gradual decline in stature as one proceeds from Punjab to Madras. While there are differences in both genetic and environmental factors, the predominant reason for these variations appears to be differences in nutrition. The average height of the residents of Punjab and Delhi, according to Majumdar is 168.4 cm, as compared to 163.74 cm of people from Madras and Kerala.

To ensure a satisfactory standard of living, health and nutrition, the ecological balance in India requires a stabilisation of population growth combined with a major restoration of soil fertility, its conservation and further improvement.

(v) *America*

In Meso-America, where farming first began in the New World, the change from subsistence on wild foods to full dependence on cultivated foods was probably even more gradual than it had been in the Old World. Evidence from the Tehuacan Valley of southern Pueblo, Mexico, shows that, prior to 6500 BC, the inhabitants of the valley lived more as collectors of seasonally gathered wild plant foods than as 'big game hunters'. With the adoption of simple maize cultivation after 5000 BC, these people became rather more sedentary; but part-time nomadism for extensive plant collecting and hunting, particularly in the dry season, continued for a long time, probably as late as the Christian era. By then fully sedentary village cultures had come into existence in other parts of Meso-America. The gradual spread of maize cultivation is

attested by finds in west-central New Mexico dating from
about 4000 BC and at other sites in the southwest about 2000
BC. After this, the agricultural economies in this area were
firmly sustained on the production of corn, beans and squash.

It is a safe generalisation (Meggers) that as agriculture
diffused over the continent, culture in each area was elabo-
rated to the limit determined by the environmental and soil
potential and having attained that level, remained relatively
stationary.

In the tropical forest and selva, because of the strictly
limited soil fertility, cultivation was necessarily of the shifting slash-and-burn variety, supplemented by hunting, fishing
and gathering. Unlike the case with the early Danubian,
small potential existed for improvement and intensification
of food production. When the natural vegetation cycle is
broken by clearing, planting and harvesting, the soil, poor
to begin with, is exposed fully to the detrimental effects of
the clearance; it is quickly extracted of plant nutrients and
the addition of fertilizers is not feasible at this primitive stage.
Large concentrations of population cannot be supported and
the settlements are semi-permanent. The low agricultural
potential places a definite limit on technological and culture
development, which stabilises at a simple level. The agricultural limitations of the tropical forest are such that 'advanced
culture traits did not diffuse into it from adjacent regions of
higher cultures and advanced cultures could not colonise
the tropical forest and maintain their culture.'

Where soil conditions permitted, as in the circum-
Caribbean area and the Peruvian coastal valleys, intensive
agriculture succeeded the single slash-and-burn horticulture,
with a corresponding improvement in the abundance and
stability of food supply. This permitted the establishment of
good-sized permanent communities. In the Andean culture
area the highest development was achieved.

Large irrigation works increased cultivatable land in the
valleys on the coast, and terracing with fertilisation was
employed in the highlands . . . The surpluses of one year
or area were stored for distribution in time of need. These
methods were so productive (and distribution so efficient)

that many thousands of commoners could be levied for non-agricultural activities—for military service or on public works (Meggers).

The consequences on the biological constitution of the semi-nomadic simple agricultural way of life has been explored amongst the Xavante (Plate 21) and some of their neighbours by Neel and Salzano. Their findings would appear to have a widespread application to human communities at this simple cultural level: for they emphasise yet again the world-wide co-existence of genetic continuity with some genetic diversity.

At any specific moment in time, a Xavante village may appear highly endogamous. Periodically, however, as the tensions inherent in the social relationships of strong males accumulate, the village, already split into two or more factions, undergoes a physical fission. The smaller product of this fission, numbering some forty to sixty persons, may take any one of four courses, namely, join another village (often at a considerable distance); form a new village; rejoin the original village after a period of 'cooling off'; or, if it wanders so far from other villages that cultural exchange is minimal, conceivably become the nucleus for a new tribe. These fissions—as might be expected—are along kinship lines, leading to a highly non-random sampling of the gene pool. The term *fission-fusion* has been applied to these events.

Perhaps the most important consequence of this sequence of events is that the phase of 'fission' provides the conditions in which new combinations of gene frequencies will be put to the test. In so far as these are successful, they can achieve a wider distribution when 'fusion' of population sub-units occurs. This is very much the situation which Sewell Wright argued as most compatible with effective evolutionary change.

Another consequence is that at any time the small local residential groups, of which the tribe is composed, will very likely not be in genetic equilibrium. Mean gene frequency differences between tribal units though related by descent, will in some cases be due to chance and in others to selective differentials. The operation of selection will be complex; it must to a large degree be concerned with restoring genetic equilibria.

The evidence suggests that fertility differentials have far more genetic significance for the Xavantes than is true for civilised man today. The position of chief or head of clan is not inherited but won on the basis of a combination of attributes (prowess in hunting and war, oratory, skill in wrestling, etc.). The greater fertility of these leaders (assuming this to be a rather general pattern) must result in a proportionally greater genetic contribution from the more gifted individuals.

The outcome of this complex temporal and spatial situation appears quite simply in the striking differences in frequencies of many gene markers between different Xavante villages.

These fission-fusion events are without doubt a very widespread feature; they are favoured by the conditions of early agriculture as well as hunting and gathering. These modes of existence demand the frequent movement of family groups or villages and the occupation of new sites, with the consequent breaking up of groups and the formation of new units. These new units will, in due course, intermarry and even fuse. Thus a high degree of heterogeneity in the gene pattern amongst the sub-units of a tribe is almost always the general rule, even when some characters are more uniformly distributed or conform to well-defined clines.

'Micro-evolution' comparable to that found in the Xavante villages obtains in other South American aboriginal tribes, among the western Apache of Arizona, the Navajo Indians of the southwestern United States, the Caingang Indians of southern Brazil, the Pemon Indians of southeastern Venezuela, the Tzotzil of southern Mexico and the eastern Algonkians of Canada; also among the relatively undisturbed Yanomama of the Upper Orinoco region of Venezuela. Evidence of similar differences between villages has been encountered, as we have seen, in tribal ethnic groups, of other continents as, for example, within the sub-divisions of the Malayan aborigines and Melanesian linguistic groups.

The operation of 'chance' or 'drift' factors in bringing about a degree of local micro-evolution in earlier times has been detected among southwestern Amerindian communities, on the evidence of skeletal remains dating back to about AD 1000 (Hulse and Bennett).

One of the striking findings on these simple agriculturalists exemplified by the Xavante, is the extraordinary contrast between the high standard of physical fitness and stamina of the young Xavante and his later health and life expectation. The relative absence of people over forty years of age is probably due to a high accident death rate among the males; although there is little evidence of cardiovascular disease, and blood pressure levels are low, while dental caries and peridontal disease largely absent, the older men and women of the community are for the most part in poor physical condition. The exact reasons for the rapid decline remain obscure.

One may suppose that the manifold stresses and hardships of this existence can be fully tolerated only when strength and stamina are at their peak and by those who have shown their superiority by surviving the hazards of childhood.

CHAPTER 6

TOWARDS A WORLD ECOLOGY

This account of the natural history of mankind has taken us to the point where mankind (or rather a fraction of it) has left the natural world of hunting, fishing and food collecting to enter the era of food production and a settled existence. This is the most momentous event in the history of genus *Homo*, when man is no longer so completely at the mercy of the vagaries and stresses of his habitat but begins to exert some degree of deliberate control over the conditions of his existence.

To reach this new phase of ecological control, the genus *Homo*, as we have seen, passed through two major stages of animal evolution. The first stage comprised the establishment of the genus *Homo* itself, characterised by those basic and peculiar properties already described in detail—the fully erect bipedal posture and locomotion, the high manipulative ability, acuity of vision and of colour perception, the capacity for learning, conceptualising and memorising—all based on a concomitant advance, expansion and elaboration of the neurological system. All these properties contribute to impart the hallmark of the genus—an all round biological adaptability. As we have seen, this is matched by the flexibility of physiological and metabolic responses permitting adjustment to a wide range of climates, activities and diets. These basic 'species' properties which make for 'homeostatic' adjustment are, as we shall see, those that man utilises in his present-day phase of bio-engineering and medical control.

The second stage was concerned essentially with the diffusion of the genus on a world-wide scale. While this was based on and made possible by species adaptability and to a growing extent by technological progress, it also entailed some degree of genetic differentiation in response to selection and other agencies acting in ways particular to local conditions. The effect of this was to bring in to being new variants of basic species characters and new patterns of inter and intra population variation. Variation is itself a fundamental species property, since it represents the genetic reserve available to the species or population. It makes possible a new range of genotypes, as may be required for survival should circumstances change, or to fit the different niches offered by increasingly complex habitats. We assume that these modifications must have emerged and become established by virtue of their survival value and the increased fitness they gave to their possessors. Some evidence of this we have seen in the variations in skin colour, nose shape and bodily physique all of which bear some functional relationship to climatic factors; and there are also examples of genetic variants which provide some degree of resistance to disease. Unfortunately the number of instances where the selective value of genetic polymorphisms or other character variants are known with any degree of plausibility remains very few. Only to a small extent can we explain human diversity in Darwinian terms. Indeed Darwin himself doubted whether human differences were accountable by natural selection. In the *Descent of Man* he wrote

As far as we are enabled to judge, although always liable to err on this head, none of the differences between the races of man are of any direct or special service to him . . . man resembles those forms which have remained extremely variable, owing, as it seems, to such variations being of an indifferent nature, and to their having thus escaped the action of natural selection.

In fact Darwin thought that sexual selection was the more likely agency, though he did not 'intend to assert that sexual selection will account for all the differences between the races'. The modern view is that for man as for all species natural selection remains the most likely agency of differentiation.

Despite the existence of geographical clines, of variations related to climate or disease, it has repeatedly been the case that populations differing conspicuously in one or several bodily features have been able to exploit successfully the same geographical region. This is true for example of the diverse population groups in the Congo, in southwest Africa, the Malayan archipelago or the Indian subcontinent at the present time; though by far the most spectacular examples are provided by the spread of European communities into Australia, Africa and America, of Japanese and Chinese into the Pacific and America, of Indians into Africa, Asia and Europe, and of Africans into America. Technological as well as all-round biological adaptiveness has easily compensated for the lack of any advantage that indigenous genotypes might confer.

The biological significance of diversity as a mechanism for species survival has decreased progressively as science and technology began to master both interacting components of the ecosystem—the organism as well as the environment. The understanding of the organism has progressed so far that even pathological deviations from the normal genetic range can be remedied or at least mitigated. Individuals carrying manifestly disadvantageous or deleterious genotypes can be medically treated or given conditions which nullify the ill effects of their disorder. Examples where therapy is successful and in which the genetic element is important include myopia, diabetes mellitus, phenylketonuria and rhesus incompatability. In the pre-technological age, individuals born with defects such as cleft palate or valvular abnormalities of the heart would not have long survived. Thus modern societies can tolerate an increase in the 'load' of deleterious genes (and of course some of these are carried in a masked condition by every normal individual).

It is therefore not surprising that in modern conditions of the controlled environment the variant expression of normal bodily characters is of decreasing significance. If American Negroes tended to suffer more frostbite in the Korean war than Europeans, if Europeans are more prone to malaria or to heart-disorders than indigenous tropical peoples, if white South Africans or Australians contract rodent ulcer to a greater extent than the darker native inhabitants, or if island peoples are known to be more susceptible to poliomyelitis or measles—the outcome nowadays is not (or need not be) left to the operation of natural selection.

In the modern era biological control seeks to establish the 'optimum' conditions in which homeostatic adjustments are easily made and 'stress' stimuli greatly reduced if not abolished. The 'optimum' environmental range, as we have noted, is biologically very similar for mankind as a whole. In supplying this environment the bio-engineer can either ignore the population variations or make allowances for them.

We can exemplify this by looking at some of the environmental stresses peculiar to the modern era—the stresses of deep mining, of modern steel-making, of nuclear engineering, of polar and high mountain exploration, of military operations, air travel, space travel and deep sea exploration. They all present challenges to the human organism which the age old physiological endowment cannot now meet adequately. We now use our biological understanding in a different way—in the way in fact pioneered by the Eskimos. The Eskimos have learnt not to depend to any great extent on physiological acclimatisation to cold. They are the great pioneers of micro-climatological bio-engineering. The Eskimo clothing, including gloves and headwear, as we have noted, has remarkable properties of waterproofing, of resistance to compression and of thermal insulation, which is seldom equalled even by the assemblies of modern explorers. What the Eskimo is doing is to re-create the climate of early pleistocene times. And this is the principle which we have now adopted universally in physiological bio-engineering. In many kinds of situations we tend not to worry so much about the range of innate physiological adaptability but rather to try to reproduce, inside the protective shell, a micro-climate of desirable levels of oxygen, carbon dioxide, atmospheric pressure, temperature and humidity.

Whether it is in relation to heat or cold, diving or altitude, the endeavour is to reproduce what are essentially the optimum tropical conditions. Take the Ama as an example. In many parts of Japan these remarkable women divers are moving away from reliance on their physiological attributes. They have developed their own one-piece diving suits; and their underwater goggles are very ingeniously constructed, with a counter-pressure system which prevents them from pushing the eyeball back at depth. Plate 22 shows the change from the simple physiological condition to sophisticated bio-engineering.

Another example concerns protection against high radiant heat. In spite of the extraordinary efficiency of physiological heat tolerance described earlier on, there are a number of situations in the modern world where this adaptability is simply not good enough. Take for example the repairs that have to be done in an open-hearth furnace in a modern steel works. To carry these out one needs a bio-engineering solution for coping with temperatures which are as high as 200°C and with quite hard work for two hours or so. This depends on using a permeable suit from which the air leaves at the temperature of the suit's outer surface, about 120°C, a temperature rise of 100°C compared to skin temperature. A counter-flow heat exchange system (called dynamic insulation) is in fact set up in the permeable suit material.

In modern high-flying aircraft the physiological shell has to be of still greater complexity, for now abnormal pressures on the body have to be counteracted and oxygen has to be supplied at correct tension. The oxygen helmet with speaking attachments has become a highly sophisticated piece of microclimate. For supersonic flights, suits are also cooled by means of turbine coolers and blowers and there are permeable suits operating on the 'dynamic' principle.

In contrast to the basic species properties of all-round adaptability, the polytypic population variation may justifiably be regarded on biological grounds as of secondary importance in the present phase of man's natural history. Nevertheless these 'secondary' characters have held and continue to exercise a political influence out of all proportion to their biological significance. Throughout recorded history, men have classified themselves and others into groups using as distinguishing markers some of the obvious differences which exist between population groups. This is the activity of race classification and the criteria used are 'racial characters'. In the light of the biological significance that we can attach to human diversity, what is the true nature of the 'race concept'? We must examine both the process of classification and the 'taxonomic' criteria employed.

The evolutionary account we have presented here has furnished ample grounds for the long-established and continuing unity of mankind and the complete absence of evidence of regional separation. Nevertheless, a long-standing belief has it that with the geographical spread of *Homo sapiens*, mankind became divided into a small number of 'primary' continental races—Caucasoid, Mongoloid, Negroid and Australoid—and that present-day variation could be attributed to migration and inter-mixture between these primary 'races'. Leaving aside for a moment the effects of mixture, is it feasible or even informative to allocate every population group or every individual to these categories? To do this we need to know what criteria to adopt.

The simplest (in the popular mind anyway) of such criteria is difference in skin colour, so that mankind seems divisible into white, black, yellow and brown categories. We have in previous pages presented sufficient evidence to show how misleading or superficial this is in fact. In Africa south of the Sahara, there are populations as light as Mediterranean Caucasoids and as dark as Indian Caucasoids. The Australoids have a similarly wide range if Melanesians and Australian aborigines are included in one category, and many Mongoloid populations are as dark or darker than Khoisan or Mediterranean peoples. Thus this classification on the colour criterion is seen to be artificial, arbitrary and basically non-scientific since it ignores the fact that skin colour (like most other variations) will depend on factors not restricted to the presumed 'racial' area. We have seen that many bodily characters, including the racial criteria of hair form, hair colour and head shape, have a graded geographical distribution and these gradients or clines are of varying extensions for different characters. The geographical variation in one character thus shows little concordance with that in another. The geographic distinction of blood group B is totally different from that of skin colour variation and both these from abnormal haemoglobin E.

Thus if the primary races are defined in terms of a cluster of characters instead of a single feature, the classification may be improved in descriptive value but loses much of its applicability; many, if not most, populations will fall outside rather than inside the grouping. The concordance of characters in Africa is such that in some regions populations tend to be characterised by dark skin, flat wide noses, woolly hair, prognathous jaws and a high-frequency of the cDe chromosome. But in fact this category will only apply to a proportion of African groups—in many the hair will not be woolly, or the skin dark, the jaw prognathous or even the nose flat or wide. Similarly a concordance between light skin colour, blond hair, blue eyes, and longheadedness may be detected in northern Europe, but it is very far from proving a specification for Caucasoids as a whole.

There is in fact only one sense in which the 'race' concept possesses scientific validity. Whenever we can recognise distinct breeding populations, we find that they possess to a greater or lesser degree differing gene pools. The causes for this have already been discussed and illustrated, with particular reference to small human communities at both the gathering and cultivating stages of organisation. The most likely cause of this genetic differentiation is generally held today to be natural selection—despite Charles Darwin's doubts. As mentioned in preceding pages, many factors in the environment could have operated in this way. Concordance of distinguishing characters in some regions could have been the result of a number of characters being selected together by a single factor, or by a group of environmental factors with a similar geographical distribution. Other factors, as we have noted, also played a part in bringing about diversity—those arising from fluctuations in numbers (drift, p. 186), or from the formation of new groups by an unrepresentative breakaway sample (founder effect, p. 187) while intermixing between populations has produced varying effects. Simple crossing between neighbouring populations would affect all characters and lead to a clear pattern of resemblance. But in many cases hybridisation would have produced a more complex picture if the incoming groups were of distant invaders or migrants and some of the characters underwent selective modification more quickly than others. In fact we must recognise that there has never been anything fixed about population micro-evolution. 'Races', however defined, have evolved and will evolve by isolation, by mixture and by selection and differential breeding.

The popular recognition of race differences has arisen not from an appreciation of the fact that *Homo sapiens* constitutes a reticulum or continuum, but merely from a crude comparison between the observer's and distant groups. It is easy to understand why the more distant populations must necessarily tend to be dissimilar. Gene flow between them is much less likely than between nearby groups and very different selection pressures will be acting upon them.

It is seldom if ever possible to disentangle conflicts involving different 'racial' groups from the simultaneous operation of cultural, religious, social or economic factors. Indeed the major wars that have beset mankind have, in the main, been between groups or nations of ostensibly similar racial composition. The notion of superiority of one racial group over another cannot be justified by biologists.

The variation presented by the human species must be seen for what it is, a reservoir of genetic variation from which characteristics suited to a wide range of conditions, social as well as physical, can be produced. Indeed if we accept for the moment the highly simplified view that a Negroid race spread over Africa, a Caucasoid over Eurasia, the Mediterranean and southwestern Asia, a Mongoloid throughout eastern Asia and into America, and an Australoid throughout southeast Asia and into the Malayan archipelago and Australia, we can see that each carried the genetic potential for coping with an enormous variety of habitats and developing a variety of cultures. But these subdivisions were not established from pure or homogeneous races. The combination of genetic differentiation and environmental modification necessary for this widespread colonisation produced a varied population complex in each region. Purity of race is impossible for the survival of a population network, as it is for smaller groups. It will be recalled that the variation within populations is of the same order as between them and often greater (Table 10, p. 183).

The modern era has been characterised as the era of scientific control of the entire world ecosystem in the interests of mankind. This is, of course, still very far from being the case. Even in the most technologically advanced societies where spectacular medical, hygienic, scientific and engineering achievements abound, standards of living are very uneven and the balance between population numbers and resources and services are only precariously being maintained.

If the industrialized societies have removed many of the basic causes of age-old insecurity from large concentrations of population this has, nevertheless, been accomplished by the appearance of new stresses and these, in turn, have to be overcome. Many of the communicable diseases are now both preventable and curable and have become rare; yet new medical hazards, or old hazards in greater frequency, have emerged in the conditions of modern western civilization. In some instances this has been paradoxically the direct result of improvement in environmental conditions and of greater affluence and increased longevity. Problems of biological adjustment will always remain, although their character will alter.

One aspect of mankind's present-day biological situation is clearly illustrated by the disease patterns prevailing on a world scale. Using information compiled by the World Health Organization in 1967, a striking contrast in disease profiles emerges between the less developed and the technologically advanced regions. Table 16 lists the health problems that were ranked at that date as of pressing concern by a substantial number of governments in each region. It is evident that the difference in disease patterns reflects on the one hand the relative lack of environmental control in the countries still very much in the traditional agricultural and pre-industrial stage; and on the other that the disorders characteristic of the urbanised and industrialised areas arise paradoxically from their technological superiority. The less developed countries suffer from the basic environmental deficiencies of polluted and insufficient drinking water, insanitary housing, inadequate arrangements for waste disposal, easily contaminated food, as well as lack of protein and essential nutrients. The death toll remains higher in early life. In the developed sector, these environmental deficiencies exist to a very limited extent;

Table 16.   Major diseases in 1967 (from WHO Bulletin) (an abbreviated and simplified list)

Developing Regions	'Westernised' Regions
Africa, Central and South America, Caribbean Southeast Asia (India, Burma, Ceylon, Indonesia) Western Pacific	Europe Canada, USA Japan Australia New Zealand
Malaria	Cancer
Tuberculosis	Heart diseases
Diarrhoeas	Degenerative arterial diseases
Dysenteries	Accidents
Smallpox	Mental diseases
Leprosy	Alcoholism
Malnutrition	Venereal disease
Venereal disease	Respiratory virus diseases
Trachoma	Dental ill-health

medical, nursing and sanitary care is highly developed, the dietary intake is adequate and for some groups excessive. These countries have as their problem diseases associated with obesity, with ageing, with the stresses associated with urban concentration and the motorised way of life. New menaces threaten as the soil, the water and air suffers contamination by an increasing number of industrial and agricultural pollutants. Intermediate between the less developed and the westernised region are the countries of South America and the eastern Mediterranean.

The great medical advances of the last few decades have, of course, brought about the present-day world population problem. But for the industrialised countries with their low birth rate and small family size and their increasing productivity and output, this is not so great a problem of ecological unbalance as it is in the pre-industrialised world. Amongst these the mortality has been falling steadily but the birth rate remains high because of the continuing dependence on human muscle power and the still low life expectancy. In their different ways, the contrasting phases of human development since the neolithic 'revolution' reveal the difficulties of establishing ecological equilibria. First came the relatively static balance of pre-industrial times, with moderate increases in population and standards of living; now we have the more dynamic equilibrium of the present day, characterized by large population increase and rising expectation of material comforts and amenities of all kinds. Wars of the past and the dangerous tensions of the present reflect to a large extent the complex rivalries engendered in the struggle to attain these ecological equilibria. Just as the human species is biologically one, an interconnected network, so is its ecology. The problems of today are those of a world ecology.

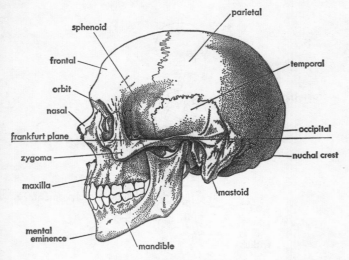

56 Human skull—side view

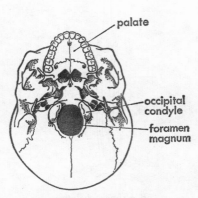

57 Basal view of human skull

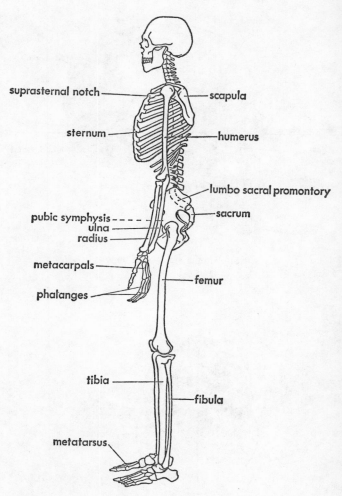

suprasternal notch

scapula

sternum

humerus

lumbo sacral promontory

sacrum

pubic symphysis

ulna

radius

metacarpals

phalanges

femur

tibia

fibula

metatarsus

58 Human skeleton

GLOSSARY

(Note: for skull and skeletal features see figures 56–58)

ALBINISM—condition in which little or no melanin is produced, with the skin and hair very pale and the eyes pink; an inherited homozygous recessive condition

ALKAPTONURIA—condition in which alkapton (homogentisic acid) is present in the urine, causing it to darken; an inherited homozygous recessive condition

ALLELE—alternative form of a gene at the same locus in one of a pair of chromosomes

APOCRINE GLAND—a kind of sweat gland

ASSOCIATION AREAS—parts of the cerebral cortex; their functions are concerned with the interrelation of activities of the sensory and motor projection areas

AXILLARY—armpit region

BASAL GANGLIA—(basal nuclei) part of the fore-brain, having motor functions

BERGMAN-ALLEN RULES—in a given species mammals living in colder places tend to have greater body bulk and shorter extremities than those living in warmer regions

BETZ CELLS—giant cells in motor area of the cortex

CALVARIUM—skull excluding the bones of the face and mandible (see Fig 56)

CAPITATE—one of the small wrist (carpal) bones

CARBON 14 DATING—determination of the age of a specimen by measurement of the amount of the radioactive isotope of carbon (C 14) present in it

CENOZOIC—the geological era beginning about 75 million years ago covering the Quaternary (Pleistocene and recent) and the preceding Tertiary period from Palaeocene onwards

CAROTENE—yellow unsaturated hydrocarbon present in carrots and butter; converted into vitamin A in the animal organism

CINGULUM—ridge of enamel around the base of the crown of a tooth

CLADOGENESIS—evolutionary development by branching from a common stock

COCHLEA—spiral cavity of internal ear containing the auditory receptor cells

DECIDUOUS (TEETH)—the milk teeth, lost before maturity

DEME—a relatively isolated population group

DENTATE GYRUS—one of two curved strips of cortex comprising the hippocampal formation of the brain

DIASTEMA—space between two teeth, usually between the upper incisor and canine

DOMINANT GENE—gene (or allele) which expresses itself in both the heterozygous and homozygous condition

ECCRINE GLANDS—sweat glands distributed all over the skin

ECTOMORPHY—one of Sheldon's three components of bodily physique making up the somatotype (see also ENDOMORPHY and MESOMORPHY); linear or thin component with little muscle or fat

ELECTROPHORESIS—technique used to separate mixtures of similar compounds based on differential migration rates of charged particles in solution in an electric field

ENDOMORPHY—one of Sheldon's three components of bodily physique making up the somatotype (see also ECTOMORPHY and MESOMORPHY); essentially the fat component

EPIPHYSIS—the region at the end of a long bone where growth takes place

EPIDERMIS—the superficial layer of stratified epithelium which with the connective tissue layer—the dermis—on which it rests, makes up the skin

EXOGAMY—matings outside a social group

FACIAL INDEX—length of face from root of nose (nasion) to the lowest point of the chin expressed as a percentage of the greatest breadth across the cheek bones

FOVEA—shallow pit in the retina of the eye

G–6PDD—glucose–6 phosphate dehydrogenase deficiency; an inherited anomaly of the red cells causing favism, a haemolytic condition

GALACTOSSAEMIA—hereditary disease in which galactose accumulates in the blood and is excreted in the urine

GAMETE—sperm cell or ovum

GENE POOL—the total of genes in a breeding population

GENIAL TUBERCLES—(see SUPERIOR GENIAL TUBERCLES)

GENOCLINE—gradient in gene frequency between two geographically separated populations interconnected by a series of intermediate populations

GENERALISED—retention of ancestral characters with little or no modification or specialisation

GENOTYPE—the genetic composition of an organism; genetic basis for particular characters

HAIRY PINNA—an inherited condition causing a prominent growth of strong hairs within the ear

HARDY-WEINBERG LAW—expression of the proportions of various genotypes in a stable population

HELIX—outer edge of the ear

HETEROSIS—hybrid vigour; increased reproductive advantage displayed by offspring of matings of individuals from two genetically different groups; an exaggeration of the size of certain dimensions of the crossbreeds compared to that of both parental groups

HETEROZYGOUS—having two different alleles at corresponding loci on a pair of homologous chromosomes

HOMOZYGOUS—having the identical allele at corresponding loci on a pair of homologous chromosomes

HYLOBATINATE—gibbon-like (from Hylobatinae, sub-family of the Pongidae)

IMMUNO-CHEMICAL—relating to the chemical properties of antigens and antibodies

INTERNAL CAROTID ARTERIES—the two great arteries in the head going to the brain

LATERAL GENICULATE BODY—cellular structure of visual centre in the thalamic region of the brain

LEVALLOISIAN—technique of striking flakes from a prepared core used in Palaeolithic industries

LOESS—the deposit of rock dust carried by wind from exposed glacial moraines

LOCUS—place on a chromosome occupied by a single gene

MACULA LUTEA—area of acute vision on retina of eye around fovea q.v.

MELANIN—dark pigment granules present in skin and hair

MESOMORPHY—one of Sheldon's three components making up the somatype (see also ECTOMORPHY and ENDOMORPHY). Component in which muscle and bone predominates

MESOZOIC ERA—the fourth of the five geological periods, preceding the cenozoic. The mesozoic—the Age of Reptiles with the dinosaurs predominant—saw the beginning of the mammals

MOUSTERIAN—Palaeolithic flake industry of Europe and western Asia associated with Neanderthal Man

MULTIFACTORIAL INHERITANCE—inheritance based on genes with a cumulative effect (polygenes) causing quantitative variation

MUTATION—a heritable, spontaneous, random change in the chemical composition of a gene

NASAL INDEX—percentage ratio of breadth to height of the nose

NASAL TURBINATES—small bones in the nasal cavity carrying receptors for smell

NEURONE—nerve cell and its processes

OPPOSABILITY of thumb (or big toe)—ability to bring the thumb across the palm and to place the pulp of the thumb directly against the pulp surfaces of one or more of the other digits

ORTHOGRADE—standing and moving in upright position

PANMIXIS—a random breeding population

PEDOMORPHISM—retention of infantile characters in the adult form

PHENOCLINE—gradient in character variation produced by genocline q.v.

PHENOCOPY—mimic of genetic effects caused by environmental conditions

PHENOTYPE—observed expression of the genetic composition of an organism

PHENYLKETONURIA—inherited inability to metabolise the amino acid phenylalanine, leading to impaired mental function

PHYLETIC—evolution by succession whereby one species evolves out of another

PHYLOGENETIC—evolutionary sequence of species; origin and evolution of higher categories

PLASMODIA—*Plasmodium falciparum,* a parasite causing tertian malaria

POLYGENES—genes whose individual effects are small but which act cumulatively in the determination of a single character

POLYMORPHISM—genetic variation; occurrence in the same locality of two or more discontinuous forms of a trait; balanced polymorphism—maintenance of more than one allele at a specific locus as a result of an equilibrium between opposed selective forces

POLYTYPIC—a species having two or more genetically distinct races or subspecies

PRONOGRADE—standing and moving on all four limbs

PROTOCONID—lateral cusp on trigonid (anterior portion of lower molar)

RECESSIVE—gene or allele which is expressed only in the homozygous condition

RETINITIS PIGMENTOSA—condition in which pigment migrates into the retina, causing night blindness and gradual contraction of the field of vision

RHESUS INCOMPATIBILITY—destruction of foetal red cells by antibodies produced by a rhesus negative mother in response to antigens the foetus has inherited from a rhesus positive father, which may result in haemolytic disease of the newborn

RHINENCEPHALON—region of brain concerned with smell

SECTORIAL—cutting and shearing teeth, the incisors and canines

SEX-LINKED INHERITANCE—trait passed on by alleles located on a sex-determining chromosome

SEXUAL DIMORPHISM—different traits exhibited by males and females of the same species

SIMIAN SHELF—internal bony buttress reinforcing the centre of the lower jaw (symphysis) in apes

SHELDONIAN—describing the somatotypes distinguished by W. H. Sheldon (see ECTOMORPHY, ENDOMORPHY, MESOMORPHY)

SPATULATE—broad or spreading incisor teeth

STEATOPYGIA—accumulation of fat on buttocks and thighs, characteristic of Bush, Hottentot and Andamanese women

STRATUM CORNEUM—the horny outermost stratum of the epidermis

SUPERIOR GENIAL TUBERCULES—(mental spines) small, irregular elevations on the internal surface of the mandible at the chin region

SUPRAORBITAL TORUS—bony ridge above the eye sockets; brow ridge

TALONID—posterior projection on lower molars bearing cusps

TERTIARY—see CENOZOIC

TAURODONTISM—fusion of the roots of the molars, resulting in a large pulp cavity

TAXON—category in a classificatory scheme; group of organisms recognised as a unit

THALAMUS—central mass of grey matter in the brain, concerned with sorting incoming impulses and relaying them to the cortex

VISUAL AREAS—part of the occipital cortex of the brain

WHORL—one of the three main dermatoglyph or finger-print types (the others being arch and loop) in which the ridges surround a central core

WISCONSIN TIME—the Wisconsin glaciation of America corresponding to the Würm or last glaciation of the Pleistocene of Europe

ZYGOMATIC—a paired bone which forms part of the lower and outer borders of the orbit or eye socket

ZYGOTE—fertilized ovum; also individual that results after differentiation of the fertilized ovum

BIBLIOGRAPHY

ABBIE, A.A. (1963) Origin and antiquity of Australian aborigines, *Centenary of the opening of the Tasmanian Museum and Art Gallery Building*, Hobart

ALLISON, A.C. (1957) Malaria in carriers of the sickle-cell trait and in newborn children, *Exp. Parasitol.* 6: 418–447

ALLCHIN, BRIDGET (1963) Indian stone age sequence, *J. Roy. Anthrop. Inst.* 93: 210–234

ANDREW, R. (1963) Trends apparent in the evolution of vocalisation in the Old World monkeys and apes. In *The Primates:* Symposia of the Zoological Society of London 10: 89–102

BAINBRIDGE, D.R. and ROBERTS, D.F. (1966) Dysplasia in nilotic physique, *Human biol.* 38: 251–278

BARNICOT, N.A. (1959) *Climatic factors in the evolution of human populations.* Cold Spring Harbor Symposia on Quantitative Biology, XXXIV: 115–129

BARNICOT, N.A. (1964) Taxonomy and variation in modern man, in *The concept of race* (ed. Ashley Montague) IX. New York and London, Free Press of Glencoe

BARTH, F. (1964) Competition and symbiosis in northeast Baluchistan, *Folk*, København 6: 15–22

BARTHOLOMEW, G.A. and BIRDSELL, J.B. (1953) Ecology and the protohominids, *Amer. Anthrop.* 55: 481–498

BENNETT, K.A. and HULSE, F.S. (1966) Microevolution at Mesa Verde, *36th Congr. Internat. de Americanistas*, 2: 369–376

BERRY, R.J. (1967) Genetical changes in mice and men, *Eug. Rev.* 59: 2, 78–96

BIEGERT, J. (1963) Evaluation of characteristics of the skull, hands and feet for private taxonomy, in *Classification and human evolution* (S.L. Washburn, Ed.), 116–145, Viking Fund Publications Anthrop. 37, Chicago, Aldine Publishing Co.

BIRDSELL, J.B. (1953) Some environmental and cultural factors influencing the structuring of Australian aboriginal populations, *Amer. Naturalist.* 87: 171

BONIN, A. (1937) Brain weight and body weight of mammals, *J. gen. Psychol.* 16: 379

BOYCE, A.J., KÜCHEMANN, C.F. and HARRISON, G.A. (1967) Neighbourhood knowledge and the distribution of marriage distances, *Ann. Hum. Genet.* 30: 335

BRANDTNER, E.J. *et al.* (1961) Upper palaeolithic archaeology, *Current Anthrop.* 2: 5, 427–454

BRAIN, C.K. (1967) The Transvaal Museum's fossil project at Swartkrans, *S. Afr. J. Sci.* 63: 2, 378–384

BRÖSTE, K. and JØRGENSEN, J.P. (1956) *Prehistoric man in Denmark.* E. Munksgaard, Copenhagen. 2 vols

BRUCE-CHWATT, L.J. (1965) Paleogenesis and paleo-epidemiology of primate malaria, *Bull. Wod Hlth Organ.* 32: 363–387

BRUCE-CHWATT, L.J. (1968) Malaria zoonosis in relation to malaria eradication, *Trop. geogr. med.* 20: 1, 50–87

BUCY, P.C. (1944) *The precentral motor cortex* 1st ed. University of Illinois: Champaign

CAMPBELL, B. (1962) The systematics of man, *Nature*, 194: 225–232

CAMPBELL, B.G. (1965) The nomenclature of the hominidae, including a definitive list of hominid taxa, *Roy. Anthrop. Inst. Occasional Paper No. 22*

CARPENTER, C.R. (1940) A field study in Siam of the behaviour and social relations of the gibbon (Hylobates lar), *Comp. Psychol. Monogr.* 16: 5

CARR-SAUNDERS, A.M. (1922) *The population problem.* Oxford Univ. Press

CHANCE, M.R.A. and MEAD, A.P. (1953) *Social behaviour and primate evolution.* Symposium No. 7, Soc, Exptl. Biol.

CHEN KANG CHAI (1967) *Taiwan aborigines.* Harvard Univ. Press

CHILDE, V. GORDON (1936) *Man makes himself.* Watts: London

CHOWN, B. and LEWIS, M. (1959) The blood group genes of the copper Eskimo, *Am. J. phys. Anthrop.* 17: 13–18

CIPRIANI, L. (1966) *The Andamanese Islanders.* London, Weidenfeld and Nicolson

CLARKE, J.G.D. (1947) *Archaeology and society.* 2nd ed. London, Methuen

CLARK, J. DESMOND (1962) The spread of food production in Sub-Saharan Africa, *J. afr. Hist.* 3: 211–218

COBB, S. (1968) In Penfield, W., *Proc. Roy. Soc. Med.* 61: 831–840

COOPER, H.M. (1961) Archaeological stone implements along the lower River Wakefield, south Australia, *Trans. Roy. Soc. S. Aust.* 84: 105–118

COLLINS, K.J. and WEINER, J.S. (1964) The effect of heat acclimatisation on the activity and number of sweat glands: a study on Indians and Europeans, *J. Physiol.* 177: 16–17P

COON, CARLETON, S. (1963) *The origin of races.* Jonathan Cape: London (originally published New York, Knopf, 1962)

CRAWFORD, M.P. (1937) The co-operative solving problems by young chimpanzees, *Comp. psychol. Monogr.* 14: 2

CROOK, J.H. (1966) Co-operation in primates, *Eug. Rev.* 58: 63–70

CROOK, J.H. and GARTLAN, J.S. (1966) Evolution of primate societies, *Nature.* (London) 210: 1200–1203

CRUZ-COKE, R., CRISTOFFANINI, A.P., ASPILLAGA, M. and BIAN-

CANI, F. (1966) Evolutionary forces in human populations in an environmental gradient in Arica, Chile, *Hum. Biol.* 38: 421–438

DANBY, P.M. (1953) A study of the physique of native East Africans, *J. Roy. Anthrop. Inst.* 83: 194–214

DART, R.A. (1925) *Australopithecus africanus,* the man-ape of South Africa, *Nature.* 115: 195–199

DART, R.A. (1959) *Adventures with the missing link.* London, Hamish Hamilton

DARWIN, C. (1934) *The expression of the emotions in man and animals.* Thinkers Library edition. London, C.A. Watts and Co.

DARWIN, C. (1871) *The descent of man.* Reprinted 1930: London, C.A. Watts and Co.

DEVORE, I. and WASHBURN, S.L. (1963) Baboon ecology and human evolution: African ecology and human evolution, *Viking Fund Publications in Anthropology* 35: 335–367

DUNN, L.D., LEVENE, H. and McCONNEL, R.B. (1956) Effects of natural selection on human genotypes, *Ann. N.Y. Acad. Sci.* 65: 1

FERENBACH, D. (1959) Les restes humains epipaleolithiques de la grotte de Taforalt (maroc oriental), *Comptes-rendus Hebdom. de Sciences de l'Acad. de Sci. Paris* 248: 3465–7

FERENBACH, D. (1960) Les hommes du Mesolithique d'Afrique du Nord et le probleme des isolats, *Boletin da sociedade Portugesa de sciencias naturais* 8: 1–16

FOX, R. (1967) In the beginning: aspects of hominid behavioural evolution, *Man* 2: 415–433

GILL, E.D. (1966) Fossil finds—provenance and age of the keilor cranium: oldest human skeletal remains in Australia, *Current Anthrop.* 7: 581

GOLDING, W. (1955) *The Inheritors.* London, Faber and Faber

GOODALL, JANE (1963) *Feeding behaviour of wild chimpanzees:* In *The Primates* Symposia of the Zoological Society, London, 10

GOODMAN, M. (1963) Serological analysis of the systematics of recent hominoids, *Hum. Biol.* 35: 377

GREGORY, W.K. (1922) *The origin and evolution of the human dentition.* Baltimore, Williams and Wilkins

GROVES, C.P. (1967) Ecology and taxonomy of the gorilla, *Nature.* 213: 890–893

HARLOW, H.F. (1958) The evolution of learning. In *Behaviour and evolution* (A. Roe and A.A. Simpson, Ed.) 269–290. New Haven, Yale University Press

HARRISON, G. AINSWORTH (1967) The biological structure of human populations, *Proc. R. Anthrop. Inst.* Curl Lecture, 29

HARRISON, G. AINSWORTH (1966) Human evolution and ecology, *Proc. Internat. Congr. Hum. Genet.* 351–360, (Ed. J.F. Crow and J.V. Neel) Baltimore, Johns Hopkins Press

HARRISON, G. AINSWORTH (1965) The concept of race, *Race* vi: 288–297

HARRISON, G. AINSWORTH, WEINER, J.S., BARNICOT, N.A. and

TANNER, J.M. (1964) *Human Biology. An introduction to human evolution, variation and growth.* Oxford Univ. Press

HAWKES, JACQUETTA and WOOLLEY, L. (1963) *Prehistory and the beginning of civilization.* History of Mankind: I. London, Allen and Unwin

HAYES, K.J. and HAYES, C. (1954) The cultural capacity of the chimpanzee, *Hum. Biol.* 26: 288–303

HEBB, D.O. and THOMPSON, W.R. (1964) The social significance of animal studies, *Handbook of Social Psychology,* 15: 532–561. Cambridge, Mass., Addison-Wesley

HELLON, R.F., JONES, R.M., MACPHERSON, R.K. and WEINER, J.S. (1956) Natural and artificial acclimatisation to hot environments, *J. Physiol.* 132: 559

HIERNAUX, J. (1966) Peoples of Africa from 22°N to the Equator. In the *Biology of Human Adaptability* (Ed. P.T. Baker and J.S. Weiner) Oxford, Clarendon Press

HIERNAUX, J. (1966) Human biological diversity in Central Africa, *Man* 1: 287–306

HOLE, F. (1962) Archaeological survey and excavation in Iran 1961, *Science* 137: 524–526

HOWELLS, W. (1967) *Mankind in the making.* London, Penguin Books

HURZELER, J. (1958) Oreopithecus bambolii, *Verlo Nat. Ges.* 69: 1–48

HUTCHINSON, J. (1966–67) Land and human populations, *Brit. Ass. adv. Sci.*

HUXLEY, J.H. (1942) *Evolution: the modern synthesis.* London, George Allen and Unwin

HUXLEY, T.H. (1863) *Evidence as to man's place in nature.* London, Williams and Norgate

JACOB, TEUKU (1967) *Some problems pertaining to the racial history of the Indonesian region.* Utrecht, Drukkerij Neerlandia

JEPSON, G.L. Selection, orthogenesis and the fossil record, *Proc. Amer. Phil. Soc.* 93: 479–500

JERISON, H.L. (1963) Interpreting evolution of the brain, *Hum. Biol.* 35: 263

JONES, F. WOOD (1948) *Hallmarks of humanity.* London, Balliere Tindall and Cox

KEITH, A. (1925) *The antiquity of man.* London, Williams and Norgate

KELEMAN, G. (1948) The anatomical basis of phonation in the chimpanzee, *J. Morphol.* 82: 229–256

KIMURA, M. and CROW, J.F. (1963) The measurement of effective population number, *Evolution:* 17: 279–288

KÖHLER, W. (1931) *The mentality of apes.* 3rd ed. New York, Harcourt Brace and Co

KOENIGSWALD, G.H.R. VON (1958) Der solo-mensch von Java: ein tropischer Neanderthaler, in *Hundert Jahre Neanderthaler* (G.H.R. von Koenigswald, ed.), Utrecht, Kemink en Zoon

KORTLAND, T.A. and KOOJJ, M. (1963) *Protohominid behaviour in primates.* In 'The Primates' Symposia of the Zool. Soc. London, 10: 61–88

KRUT, L.H. and SINGER, R. (1963) Steatopygia: the fatty acid composition of subcutaneous adipose tissue in the Hottentot, *Amer. J. Phys. Anthrop.* (N.S.) 21: 181–187

KÜCHEMANN, C.F., BOYCE, A.J. and HARRISON, G.A. (1967) A demographic and genetic study of a group of Oxfordshire villages, *Hum. Biol.* 39: 251–276

KURTEN, B. (1966) Holarctic land connexions in the early tertiary, *Commentationes Biologicae* (Societas Scientiarum Fennica) 29: 1–5

KURTEN, B. (1960) Chronology and faunal evolution of the earlier European glaciations, *Comment. Biol.* Helsingfors 21: 1–62

LAUGHLIN, W.S. (1967) *Human migration and permanent occupation in the Bering Sea area.* Rep. from The Bering Land Bridge, 23: 410–450. Stanford, Cal., Stanford University Press

LAUGHLIN, W.S. (1963) Eskimos and aleuts: their origins and evolution, *Science.* 142: 633–645

LEAKEY, L.S.B. (1968) Upper miocene primates from Kenya, *Nature.* 218: 527–528

LEAKEY, L.S.B. (1968) Lower dentition of *Kenyapithecus africanus, Nature.* 217: 827–830

LEBLANC, J. (1966) Adaptive mechanisms in humans, *Ann. N.Y. Acad. Sci.* 134: 721–732

LE GROS CLARK, W.E. (1959) *The antecedents of man.* Edinburgh University Press

LE GROS CLARK, W.E. (1959) The crucial evidence for human evolution, *Proc. Amer. Phil. Soc.* 103: 159–72 (Penrose Memorial Lecture)

LEWIS, G.E. (1934) Preliminary notices of new man-like apes from India, *Amer. J. Sci.* 27: 161–179

LIVINGSTONE, F.B. (1958) Anthropological implications of sickle cell gene distribution in West Africa, *Am. Anthrop.* 60: 533

McCARTHY, F.D. (1965) Archaeological and material equipment, in *Aboriginal Man in Australia* (R.M. and G.H. Berndt ed.) London, Angus and Robertson

MACINTOSH, N.W.G. (1965) *Aboriginal man in Australia* (Ed. R.M. and G.H. Berndt) (the physical aspect of man in Australia). London, Angus and Robertson

MACPHERSON, R.K. (1966) Physiological adaptation, fitness and nutrition in the peoples of Australian and New Guinea regions. In *The Biology of Human Adaptability.* (P.T. Baker and J.S. Weiner Ed.) Oxford, Clarendon Press

MAJUMDAR, D.N. (1961) *Races and cultures of India.* Bombay, Asia Publishing House

MALHOTRA, M.S. (1966) Peoples of India including primitive tribes. In *The Biology of Human Adaptability* (P.T. Baker and J.S. Weiner Ed.). Oxford, Clarendon Press

MATHER, K. (1965) Medicine and natural selection in man. In *Biological Aspects of Social Problems* (J.E. Meade and A.S. Parkes Ed.) 114–134. Edinburgh, Oliver and Boyd, Ltd.

MAYBURY-LEWIS, D. (1965) *The savage and the innocent.* London, Evans Bros

MEGGERS, BETTY S. (1954) Environmental limitations on the development of culture, *Amer. Anthrop.* 56: 801–824

MORANT, G.M. (1927) Studies of palaeolithic man II. A biometric study of neanderthaloid skulls and their relationships to modern racial types, *Ann. Eug.* 2: 318

MOURANT, A.E., KOPEC, A.C., and DOMANIEWSKA-SOBZCAK, K. (1958) *The ABO blood groups: comprehensive tables and maps of world distribution.* Oxford, Blackwell Sci. Publ.

MOVIUS, H.J. Jr. Radiocarbon dates and upper paleolithic archaeology in central and western Europe, *Current Anthrop.* 1: 355–391

MULVANEY, D.J. (1961) The stone age of Australia, *Proc. Prehist. Soc.* 27: 56–107

NAPIER, J.R. (1967) Evolutionary aspects of primate locomotion, *Amer. J. Phys. Anthrop.* 27: 333–342

NAPIER, J.R. and NAPIER, P.H. (1967) *A handbook of living primates.* London and New York, Academic Press

NAPIER, J.R. (1962) The evolution of the hand, *Sci. Amer.* 217: 56–60

NAPIER, J.R. (1962) Monkeys and their habitats, *New Sci.* 295: 88–92

NAPIER, J.R. and WEINER, J.S. (1962) Olduvai gorge and human origins, *Antiquity* 36: 41–57

NEEL, J.V., SALZANO, F.M., JUNQUEIRA, P.C., KEITER, F. and MAYBURY-LEWIS, D. (1964) Studies on the Xavante Indians of the Brazilian Mato Grosso, *Hum. Genet.* 16: 52–140

NEWMAN, MARSHALL T. (1953) The application of ecological rules to the racial anthropology of the aboriginal new world, *Amer. Anthrop.* 55: 311–327

OAKLEY, K.P. (1964) *Frameworks for dating fossil man.* London, Weidenfeld and Nicolson

OAKLEY, K.P. (1959) *Tools makyth man,* Smithsonian report 1958, 4367: 431–445

OAKLEY, K.P. (1955) Fire as palaeolithic tool and weapon, *Proc. Prehist. Soc.* 21: 36–48

OLIVER, D.L. and HOWELLS, W.W. (1960) Bougainville populations studied by generalized distance *Ext. des Actes du VIe Congres Internat. des Sciences Anthrop. et Ethnol.* 1: 497–502. Paros

PENROSE, L.D. (1961) Genetics of growth and development of the foetus. In *Recent Advances in Human Genetics* (L. Penrose, Ed.), 56: London, Churchill

PERICOT, L. (1962) Social life of Spanish palaeolithic hunters as shown by Levantine art, in *Social life of early man* (S.L. Wilkins, ed.), 194–213, London, Methuen

PICKFORD, R.W. (1963) Natural selection and colour blindness, *Eug. Rev.* 55: 97–102

POLUNIN, I. (1953) The medical history of Malayan aborigines, *Med. J. Malaya.* 8: 55–174

POLYAK, S. (1957) *The vertebrate visual system.* Chicago, University of Chicago Press

POST, R.H. (1962) Population differences in red and green colour vision deficiency, *Eug. Quart.* 9: 131–146

RENSCH, B. (1959) *Evolution above the species level.* London, Methuen

REYNOLDS, V. (1965) *Budongo, an African forest and its chimpanzees,* Garden City, New York, Natural History Press

ROBERTS, D.F. (1953) Body weight, race and climate, *Amer. J. Phys. Anthrop.* (N.S.) 11: 533–558

ROBERTS, D.F. (1962) Serology and the history of northern nilotes, *J. Afr. Hist.* 3: 301–305

ROBERTS, D.F. and BAINBRIDGE, D.R. (1963) Nilotic physique, *Amer. J. Phys. Anthrop.* (N.S.) 21: 341–370

ROBINSON, J.T. Telanthropus and its phylogenetic significance, *Amer. J. Phys. Anthrop.* (N.S.) 11: 445–501

ROBINSON, J.T. (1964) Some critical phases in the evolution of man, *S. Afr. Archael. Bull.* 19: 3–12

SCHALLER, A.B. (1963) *The mountain gorilla.* Chicago, University of Chicago Press

SCHREIDER, E. (1950) Geographical distribution of the body weight/body surface ratio, *Nature.* 165: 286

SCHULTZ, A.H. (1949) Ontogenetic specialisations of man, *Arch. Julius Klaus-Stiftung.* 24: 197–216. Reprinted 1949 *Yearbook of Physical Anthropology,* 200

SCHULTZ, A.H. (1950) The physical distinctions of man, *Amer. Phil. Soc.* 94: 428–494

SHARIFF, G.A. (1953) Cell counts in the primate cerebral cortex, *J. Comp. Neurol.* 98: 381–400

SIMMONS, R.T., GRAYDON, J.J., GAJDUSEK, D.C. and BROWN, P. (1965) Blood group genetic variations in natives of the Caroline Islands and other parts of Micronesia, *Oceania.* 36: 132–7, Sydney, Australia

SIMMONS, R.T., GAJDUSEK, D.C. and NICHOLSON, M.K. Blood group genetic variations in inhabitants of West New Guinea, with a map of the villages and linguistic groups of south west New Guinea, *Amer. J. Phys. Anthrop.* (N.S.) 27: 277–302

SIMONS, E.L. (1960) New fossil primates: a review of the past decade, *Amer. Sci.* 48: 179–192

SIMONS, E.L. (1960) Apidium and Oreopithecus, *Nature,* Lond. 186: 824–826

SIMONS, E.L. (1963) A critical reappraisal of tertiary primates, *Evol. and Genet. Biol. of Primates,* 1: 65–129, New York, Academic Press

SIMONS, E.L. (1963) Some fallacies in the studies of hominid Phylogeny, *Science.* 141: 879–889

SIMONS, E.L. (1964) On the mandible of Ramapithecus, *Proc. Nat. Acad. Sci.* 51: 528–535

SIMONS, E.L. and PILBEAM, D.R. (1965) Some problems of hominid classification, *Amer. Sci.* 53: 237–259

SIMONS, E.L. and PILBEAM, D.R. (1965) Preliminary revision of the dryopithecinae (pongidae, anthropoidea), *Folia primat.* 3: 81–521. Basel, New York S. Karger

SIMPSON, A.A. (1947) Holarctic mammalian faunas and continental relationships during the Cenozoic, *Bull. Geol. Sci. Amer.* 58: 613–688

SIMPSON, A.A. (1950) *The meaning of evolution.* London, Oxford University Press

SMITH, A. ELLIOT (1927) *Essays on the evolution of man.* London, Oxford University Press

SMYTH, BROUGH R. (1878) *The aborigines of Victoria.* 2 vols. London

STRAUS, W.L. Jr. (1962) Fossil evidence of the evolution of the erect bipedal posture, *Clin Orthopaedics:* 25: 9–19

STRAUS, W.L. Jr. (1963) The classification of Oreopithecus, *Classification and human evolution* 146–177. Chicago, Aldine Publishing Company

STRETHLOW, J.A.H. (1965) Culture, social structure and environment in aboriginal central Australia. In *Aboriginal man in Australia* (R.M. and C.H. Berndt ed.) Sydney, Angus and Robertson

STRYDOM, N.B. and WYNDHAM, C.H. (1963) Natural state of heat acclimatisation of different ethnic groups, *Fed. Proc.* 22: 801–809

THOMA, A. (1966) L'occipital de l'homme Mindelien de Vertesszöllös, *L'Anthrop.* 70: 495–534

THOMSON, M.L. (1951) Dyshidrosis produced by general and regional ultraviolet radiation in man, *J. Physiol.* 112: 22

TINSDALE, N.B. Distribution of Australian aboriginal tribes: a field survey, *Trans. Roy. Soc. S. Aust.* 64: 140–231

TOBIAS, P.V. (1963) Cranial capacity of Zinjanthropus and other Australopithecines, *Nature, Lond.* 197: 743–746

TOBIAS, P.V. and VON KOENIGSWALD, G.H.R. A comparison between the Olduvai hominines and those of Java and some implications for hominid phylogeny, *Nature, Lond.* 204: 515–518

TOBIAS, P.V. *Australopithecus, homo habilis,* tool-using and tool-making, *S. Afr. Arch. Bull.* 20: 4, 167–192

TOBIAS, P.V. (1965) Early man in East Africa, *Science.* 149: 22–33

TOBIAS, P.V. (1966) The distinctiveness of *H. habilis, Nature,* 209: 953

TREGEAR, T.T. (1966) *Physical functions of skin.* London, Academic Press

TURNBULL, C.M. (1965) *Wayward servants.* London, Eyre and Spottiswoode

TUTTLE, R.H. and ROGERS, C.M. (1966) Genetic and selective

factors in reduction of the hallux in *Pongo pygameus*, *Amer. J. Phys. Anthrop.* (N.S.) 24: 191–198

TUTTLE, R.H. (1967) Knuckle-walking and the evolution of hominoid hands, *Amer. J. Phys. Anthrop.* (N.S.) 26: 171–206

TYLOR, E.B. (1903) *Primitive culture* 4th ed. London, John Murray

VALLOIS, H.V. The social life of early man: the evidence of skeletons, in *Social life of early man* (S.L. Washburn, Ed.) 214–235. London, Methuen

VALLOIS, H.V. (1958) La grotte de fontechevade: anthropologie, *Arch. Inst. Palaéont. Hum. Mem.* 29, pt. 2

VEVERS, A.M. and WEINER, J.S. (1963) Use of a tool by a captive Capuchin monkey, *Symp. Zool. Soc. Lond.* 10: 115

VOGEL, F.D., PETTENKOFER, H.J. and HEMBOLD, W. (1960) Ueber die populations-genetic der ABO-blutgruppen, *Acta Genetica.* 10: 247–294

WALSH, R.J. (1963) Variations of melanin pigmentation of the skin in some Asian and Pacific peoples, *J. Roy. Anthrop. Inst.* 93: 126–133

WALTER, H. and NEMESKERI, J. (1967) Demographical and serogenetical studies on the population of Bodrogköz (N.E. Hungary), *Hum. Biol.* 39: 224–240

WASHBURN, S.L. (1967) Behaviour and the origin of man, *Proc. R. Anthrop. Inst.* (Huxley Lecture) 21

WASHBURN, S.L. and AVIS, VIRGINIA (1958) *Behaviour and evolution* (Anne Roe and G. G. Simpson Ed.) 19: 421–436. New Haven, Yale University Press

WASHBURN, S.L. (1959) Speculations on the inter-relations of the history of tools and biological evolution, *Hum. Biol.* 31: 21–31

WASHBURN, S.L. (1963) Classification and human evolution, *Viking Fund Publications in Anthropology* 37

WEIDENREICH, F. (1943) The skull of *Sinanthropus Pekinensis*, *Geol. Survey of China*, New Series D, 10, whole Series 127

WEINER, J.S. (1958) The dawn of mind. *The concise encyclopaedia of world history*, p. 13–23. London, Hutchinson

WEINER, J.S. (1964) The biology of social man, *J. Roy. Anthrop. Inst.* 94: 230–240

WEINER, J.S. and CAMPBELL, B.A. (1964) The taxonomic status of the Swanscombe skull, in *The Swanscombe skull* (C.D. Ovey, ed.), 175–210. London, Royal Anthropological Institute

WEINER, J.S. (1966) Man's physiological conquest of the environment, *Proc. R. Inst. Gt. Britain.* 41: 310–324

WEINER, J.S. (1966–1967) Aspects of adaptation, *The Advancement of Science.* 23: 1–9

WEINSTEIN, E.D., NEEL, J.V. and SALZABO, F.M. (1967) Further studies on the Xavante Indians: VI. the physical status of the Xavantes of Simões Lopes, *Amer. J. Hum. Genet.* 19: 532–542

WORLD HEALTH ORGANISATION (1968) The world health situation: major problems, *WHO Chronicle.* 22: 11–15

WRIGHT, S. (1938) Size of population and breeding structure in relation to evolution, *Science.* 87: 430

WRIGHT, S. (1938) Breeding structure of populations in relation to speciation, *Amer. Natur.* 74: 232–248

WYNDHAM, C.H. and MORRISON, J.F. (1958) Adjustment to cold of bushmen in the Kalahari desert, *J. App. Phys.* 13: 219–225

WYNDHAM, C.H. (1965) The adaptation of some of the different ethnic groups in southern Africa to heat, cold and exercise, *S. Afr. J. Sci.* 61: 11–29

WYNDHAM, C.H., STRYDOM, N.B., MORRISON, J.F., WILLIAMS, C.G., BREDELL, G.A.G. and HEYNS, A. (1966) The capacity for endurance effort of Bantu males from different tribes, *S. Afr. J. Sci.* 62: 259–263

ZEUNER, F.E. (1959) *Dating the past* 4th ed., 516, London, Methuen

ZEUNER, F.E. *The Pleistocene Period,* 2nd ed. London, Hutchinson

ZIEGLER, A.C. (1964) Brachiating adaptations of chimpanzee upper limb musculature, *Am. J. Phys. Anthrop.* 22: 15–32

ZUCKERMAN, S. (1932) *Social life of monkeys and apes.* London, Kegan Paul

ZUCKERMAN, S. (1933) Sinanthropus and other fossil men, *Eug. Rev.* 24: 273

Zoological Society of London Symposia No. 10 (1963) *The Primates*

INDEX